Risk and the control of technology

**Public policies for
road traffic safety in Britain
and the United States**

For Val

Risk and the control of technology

**Public policies for
road traffic safety in Britain
and the United States**

Alan Irwin

Manchester University Press

© A. Irwin, 1985

First published by
Manchester University Press
Oxford Road, Manchester M13 9PL, UK
and 51 Washington Street, Dover
New Hampshire 03820, USA

British Library cataloguing in publication data
Irwin, Alan
   Risk and the control of technology.
   1. Traffic safety—Government policy—
   Great Britain   2. Traffic safety—
   Government policy—United States
   I. Title
   363.1'2575'0941   HE5614.5.G7

Library of Congress Cataloging in Publication Data
Irwin, Alan
   Risk and the control of technology.
   Includes index.
   1. Traffic safety—Government policy—United States.
  2. Traffic safety—Government policy—Great Britain.
  I. Title.
  HE5614.2.179 1985   363.1'25561'0941   84–17153

  ISBN 0–7190–1723–8 *cased*

Photoset by
Northern Phototypesetting Co., Bolton
Printed in Great Britain by
Butler & Tanner Ltd, Frome and London

Contents

Preface

The focus of this book is on public policies for the control of technological hazards. With the increased specialisation (and fragmentation) of studies in 'science, technology and society', reference to this subject area may immediately categorise the book as being relevant solely to the, undoubtedly growing, number of policy makers, pressure group members, industrialists and academics specially concerned with matters of risk. However, the broader theme developed here – the need to create a social setting where both the promotion and control of technology can be organised in an effective but equitable fashion – suggests that risk studies should not be divided off from wider issues of technology policy, R and D management or technology transfer. The best regulatory policies are those where risk is not considered as an afterthought but as an integral part of the development process.

The second issue which must be raised concerns the definition of 'policy analysis'. Certainly, a considerable proportion of the following chapters is devoted to an analysis of road traffic safety decisions in Britain and the United States. It must be noted, however, that 'policy analysis' as advocated here covers both the political and economic framework in which decisions are made and the technical input to the regulatory process. Whilst there are obvious difficulties for such an approach – not least those of methodology – it was considered better to be broad-ranging in this way rather than limit the presentation to a more narrow and descriptive account of events. In matters of technology policy – as in other areas of decision-making – what is *not* under discussion is often more important than what actually is. Hence in this context, the importance of 'unravelling the choices' for technology policy. What this also suggests is that 'policy studies' can be of practical value whilst adopting a critical approach to the events and phenomena under investigation.

This book represents yet another attempt at throwing a line across the institutionalised gulf between the natural and social sciences – this time by a social scientist who has subsequently trained in science policy studies. The perils of such a venture are clear; my hope is that the failures of this assault will not discourage others from making their own attempts. In the case of technological risk, the natural and social sciences have a need to be heard for the problems belong to both technology *and* social policy.

I hesitate to confess that this book started life as a doctoral thesis for fear of losing my readership before the first chapter has even begun. However, this must be admitted so that I can gratefully acknowledge the assistance offered by Roger Williams and Ron Johnston and subsequently by Ken Green, Michael Gibbons and the staff and students of the Department of Science and Technology Policy. I would also like to record my appreciation for the help and encouragement given by Stephen Cotgrove, Peter Gloyns, Jerry Ravetz, Steve Ashton, Murray Mackay, John Adams, Brian O'Neill, Bill Haddon Jr., Mary Sayers and Judith Reppy. More generally, I would like to thank the Department of Transport, the National Highway Traffic Safety Administration, the Insurance Institute for Highway Safety, the Center for Auto Safety and the Accident Research Unit at Birmingham University. The Joint Committee of the SERC/ESRC sponsored the research in its earliest stages and I am grateful for the opportunity they provided. Gill Greensides has helped enormously – Yvonne Aspinall not only typed this manuscript in its various forms but has also been an invaluable source of spelling correction, repetitious phrase spotting and punctuation querying.

Debts become harder to acknowledge as they get closer to home. My gratitude to my family (Irwin, McCain *and* Bittlestone) is greater than they will realise. Let me add a simple note of remembrance to George William Irwin to whose love and inspiration I owe so much. As for Val, Abigail, Lauren and Benedict, publicly expressed thanks seem a very poor reward – but let me offer them anyway.

Part I

Chapter 1

Risk and the control of technology: introduction

The focus of this book is on 'technological risk' and on the ways in which national policies have been developed to cope with this category of social and technical problem. Examples of technological risk are not hard to find: they would include a range of topics from the debate about genetic manipulation to the continuing controversy surrounding nuclear power, from chemical carcinogens to river and air pollution. What unites these apparently disparate areas of concern is the notion of a threat being posed to human life and well-being as a direct consequence of developments within science and technology. This definition is less than rigorous, but it does serve to direct attention towards a type of issue that has aroused increasing public concern at least since the environmentalist movements of the mid-1960s. In this book we will consider the technical and political reactions to this concern, both generally and with regard to one specific issue – road traffic safety.

Already two main issues for investigation have been introduced. At the general level there are the problems posed by technological risk, and at a more specific focus there is road traffic safety policy. It is not by chance that these two topics have been included within one study. Although this book is certainly concerned to analyse the problems of technological risk in the broadest fashion, it will be argued that it is impossible to deal adequately with the issues involved while working only with rather nebulous abstractions such as the 'problem of risk'. However, this approach is rather different from that taken by much of the expanding academic literature in this area. My assertion is that investigations of risk, or attempts to pinpoint 'acceptable risks', which do not take care to specify particular cases and to deal with real examples, are likely to degenerate into somewhat vacuous exercises reminiscent only of the quest for the Snark in Lewis Carroll's nonsensical tale. The case for this assertion will be established in the next chapter and elaborated during those that follow it.

What, then, does this book hope to achieve with regard to the general issue of technological risk? The broad orientation will be to see these topics as an area of both technical and political debate. At first glance, many of the controversies over hazards may appear to be almost entirely technical in character. 'What is the safe level for exposure to this chemical?' 'What are the odds on a major nuclear accident occurring?' However, in practice they hinge on a variety of broader questions. How are we to balance the costs and benefits of a particular course of action? How are the inevitable technical uncertainties to be evaluated? The argument will be that unless the complexities of decision making in this area are properly understood, then policies are likely to fail in their twin objectives of protecting health and maximising social benefits. The nature of risk decisions will be explored in some depth with a special regard to one question: 'How can the adverse consequences of technological risks be controlled in a manner which is both effective and equitable?' Thus the focus is on public policies for technological risks and on the manner in which they might be improved.

For our present purposes the 'policy-making process' will be defined in a broad manner. The analytical framework, which will be outlined fully in the next chapter, will categorise four major influences within this process. First, we have the state itself – the bureaucratic arrangements for monitoring hazards and drawing up regulatory strategies. In formulating policies and giving overall direction, this heterogeneous body clearly has a vital part to play. Secondly, we have the 'outside' bodies who may seek to channel both overall policies and specific decisions according to their own wishes. Such groups may be industrially based or may claim to represent the 'public interest' in some way. Sometimes, as in the case of Members of Parliament or Congressmen, individuals may have been elected to serve this purpose or, alternatively, the organisations may have a rather less clearcut relationship to their 'constituents'. Thirdly, we have the mass of the population – a group often seen as an amorphous 'general public'. This public is of course divided according to class, locality, occupation, race, gender and a number of more particular criteria in specific situations and circumstances. The problem to which we will return in later chapters is the extent to which these 'general publics' are represented in the policy-making processes. This problem leads, of course, into a broader discussion of the desirability, and indeed viability, of increased public participation.

The fourth group with which we will be particularly concerned here consists of the technical experts of differing backgrounds and experience who find themselves involved in decision making. It is in the nature of technological risk that it involves an unavoidably scientific component. It is not surprising, therefore, to find experts being given special prominence in providing advice and assisting in the state management of hazards. However, this important status gives rise to a whole range of questions regarding the role of experts and their relationship to the political process. To what extent should we rely on their evidence when the issues involved are not simply technical but also political and economic? How should such technical evidence be taken into account when contradictory scientific reports may well exist? The consideration of technical expertise forces us to consider a fundamental question: 'When it comes to matters of technological risk, *who* should decide and *how*?' Of course, this question has a close link with the previously stated concern with the effectiveness and equity of decision making.

The basis for this overall framework for considering the role of the state, pressure groups, the general population and technical experts will be justified in greater depth in Chapter 2. It should perhaps be emphasised here, however, that the approach will not be to treat each of these as totally separate from the others. Indeed, it may well be that it is the interaction between the factors which is of the greatest significance in understanding present public policies and advocating strategies for the future. For example, how might the available technical expertise be influenced by the state and how do each of these relate to public perceptions of hazard? Questions such as these will be dealt with in relation to our specific case study by the use of a historical and comparative perspective. The evolution of road traffic safety policies in Britain and the United States will be investigated so that the development of each can be contrasted in later chapters.

If something has been said so far about the general analytical framework to be adopted in this book (and much more will be said about this in later chapters), nothing has been put forward about the issue of road traffic safety itself. Why has the control of automobile technology been selected for the present purposes? This question seems all the more important for a British audience as in that country road traffic safety has only rarely emerged as a matter of general public interest and has not been the subject of controversy or major political discussion. Indeed, it must be said immediately that this apparent apathy was an important reason for settling on this topic; for the reasons presented below, road traffic safety seems too important an issue to be so widely neglected.

First of all, we should consider the magnitude of the public health problem involved. In the United Kingdom, road traffic accidents regularly cause 7000 deaths and 355 000 injuries per year. For the USA, the figures are 55 000 deaths and 2 000 000 injuries. This represents a staggering toll of physical and psychological trauma, which is all the greater because of its disproportionate impact on younger members of the population. Despite this scale of human suffering, it has become commonplace to view road traffic accidents as an 'acceptable risk'. As Lord Rothschild expressed it in his 1978 Richard Dimbleby lecture:

Apart from those who have suffered personal tragedies, I do not believe there is a single one of you . . . who has ever lost a minute's sleep worrying about car accidents.[1]

Can the risks of road traffic accidents properly be labelled 'acceptable' in such a categorical manner – indeed can any risk ever be classified in this way? In this book, one of the major concerns will be to consider the 'taken for granted' nature of road traffic safety, with a view to unravelling the political and technical roots of this phenomenon. The investigation will be assisted by such notions as that of 'un-politics' and also by the knowledge that public perceptions of automobile hazards vary widely between the two nations included in this study.

In addition to the many questions raised by the consistent magnitude of road traffic deaths and injuries, this topic also has a certain importance because of the economic significance of the vehicle and component manufacturers. In Western capitalist nations, the motor industry has assumed enormous strategic importance in terms of the employment offered within its own premises and those of secondary suppliers, the resources which it utilises and its overall contribution to Gross National Products (GNPs). One vehicle manufacturer, General Motors, is the largest multinational corporation in the world, with 1982 sales of 60 025 600 US dollars – approximating the GNP of Switzerland for the same year. Ford Motor Company had sales in 1982 totalling 37 067 200 US dollars, and other vehicle manufacturers, such as Toyota, Peugeot–Citroen–Talbot,

Chrysler and Nissan, are corporations on a similarly large scale. The sheer size of these companies lends a greater political significance to the patterns of regulation that develop: other industrial sectors may well draw conclusions for the likely shape of future control policies in their own spheres of activity. In addition, those attempting to innovate regulatory policies with regard to road traffic safety must deal with powerful organisations rather than with large numbers of small and relatively isolated firms. Of course, the development of control strategies also cannot fail to have been affected by the recent, much-publicised, economic difficulties being faced by the motor industry as a whole.

A third reason for the choice of road traffic safety as an important issue for discussion is the social significance of the motor car in industralised and industrialising societies. The extent of vehicle ownership is often regarded as an indication of a nation's stage of 'development'. The car seems to serve as an almost unique symbol of an individual's affluence and social status. The marketing and advertising strategies of the manufacturers have encouraged this belief and stressed the psychosexual overtones of particular vehicles. The motor car has assumed an importance which appears unparalleled by any other consumer product. This importance is now also being reflected in the countries of the Third World, where vehicle populations are growing and road casualties amount in many places to a significant and growing problem for public health – especially as the major diseases are being brought under control.

One additional feature of road traffic safety which seems to suggest the need for study is the fact that there is a broad difference between the control policies developed in the United States over the last twenty years or so and those that are practised in Britain. The full scope of this difference will be a major concern of this book as the separate regulatory approaches are examined and a number of specific decisions are analysed. In seeking to interpret this distinction and to explain its origins, the broad analytical framework just described will be drawn upon. The role of each national state will be discussed and also that of research workers, pressure groups and public perceptions.

Throughout this consideration of road traffic safety policies, attention will be paid to the general theme of technological risk as well as to the specific case study. At the level of risk, the type of question outlined earlier will be posed regarding the equity and effectiveness of decision-making. However, if this approach is to demonstrate its value, then it must be applied to specific contexts. Accordingly, particular conclusions will be drawn for future regulatory activities relating to the control of automobile technology. The twofold nature of this inquiry should not be forgotten, and although it may be possible to pick out specific sections and chapters as relating to either risk or road traffic safety, the real intention is to see how each of these components can illuminate the other.

In the next chapter the issue of technological risk and its relationship to public policies will be discussed in greater detail. The various attempts to analyse this question will be examined with a view to assessing their value and to outlining the approach that will be adopted.

In Part II we will begin to explore road traffic safety as an instance of technological risk in practice. First of all (Chapter 3), there will be an analysis of the relevant technical expertise (known in this book as the 'science of road traffic safety'), paying particular regard to its internal structure and to its historical development as influenced by various external forces. The following two chapters will provide a broad overview of regulatory policies in Britain and the United States by describing the evolution of present institutional mechanisms and presenting the major characteristics of each national control system. In addition to offering an essentially descriptive account, attention will also be given to the political and technical forces that have shaped policies and so provided the framework within which specific decisions must be taken.

Part III enhances the discussion of road traffic accidents as an issue by dealing with three individual areas of debate in the United States and Britain: occupant restraint, fire hazards and windscreen safety. The aim behind these individual studies is to develop the analysis in greater detail and to investigate decision making at the more mundane and everyday level. The topics have been selected because of their intrinsic importance within the control of automobile technology and because of the array of regulatory procedures and issues for discussion that they offer. Part III then concludes the analysis of road traffic safety by developing the comparative analysis and making a number of policy recommendations based on the discussion in Parts II and III.

In Part IV we return explicitly to the theme of technological risk. How useful has this notion actually proven in the case of road traffic safety? What lessons can be learnt for dealing with hazards other than road traffic accidents and what are the most important problems that must be tackled by public policies? In particular, discussion will centre on the state management of technological risk and on the equity and effectiveness of current procedures.

Reference

1   Lord Rothschild, Risk, *Atom*, **268**, February 1979, p. 33.

Chapter 2

Control of technological risks

In the last two decades much has been written about the problems of technological risk and, more specifically, about the complexities involved in 'coping with risk' in the sense of drawing up appropriate control policies and learning how to deal with such factors as public attitudes and apparently contradictory technical expertise, and also intangibles like the notion of 'social benefit' or the value of a human life. Some of these accounts have proposed methods for dealing with uncertainties of this type, and some have served to highlight particular problems or to examine areas of decision making in the hope of assisting future deliberations. In this chapter, the recent debate about technological risk will be examined. The framework for analysis that has been adopted here will then be described and some of its more important features considered. However, before doing this, the issue of technological risk needs to be located within the more general category of which it is a part: the control of technology.

Control of technology

The concept of controlling technological (and also scientific) developments can be subdivided in a number of ways. Perhaps the most conventional of these is to separate the *production and guidance* of new technologies towards given social goals from the *regulation* of the adverse effects of innovations. A large and important literature has developed that is seeking to comprehend the complexities of the former category,[1] but the focus of this book is very much on the latter. However, before dismissing the issue of promotion, it is worth noting that the sponsorship and regulatory functions, although frequently separated in organisational practice, are clearly interconnected. There is indeed a danger that overconcentration on the former can create a situation where, in terms of its consequences, technology becomes 'out of control'. Alternatively, a strong emphasis on regulation may inhibit the production of new science and technology. This relationship has recently become especially controversial in the area of drug regulation.[2] Furthermore, one can argue that regulation and product or process development should not be separated in practice. A consideration of control policy only at the final stages of development dooms regulation to a *reactive* rather than an *integral* place in innovation. This point will be discussed later in greater detail.

Turning explicitly to the harmful effects of technological developments, David and Ruth Elliott have viewed the many ecological and environmental concerns during the 1960s and the 1970s and have argued as follows:

> If one concludes that these fears are well-founded we are left with the options of either turning back to a 'pre-industrial' society or else consciously and deliberately taking over the management of the environment, and attempting to minimize and control the effect of our technological intervention on the environment. We need therefore to think in terms of *controlling* technology.[3]

A key element within the overall case for controlling technology is the notion that societies have a choice with regard to the areas of technology that are developed and the specific directions that are followed.

> 'Technology' is not some total monolith, but rather consists of a variety of discrete, albeit closely related, technologies. Throughout history, *choices* have been made to develop certain technologies rather than others, and to direct them towards certain goals rather than others.[4]

This notion that technology is not a completely independent force which then influences social relations, but rather is itself a product of the social relations within capitalist societies, can be traced back to Marx and has been discussed by a number of contemporary Marxist writers.[5] In addition, the idea that technology is amenable to conscious human choice rather than chance makes the control of technological developments all the more worthy of our attention. Questions of social benefit and human need should no longer be seen as peripheral to the essentially autonomous growth of human skills and capabilities, but can rather form the very basis for this process. However, as Collingridge and a number of others have pointed out, there are certain problems for such a 'social control' of technology. In principle, technology is a human product which remains within the sphere of human influence, but in practice, technologies can become inflexible and resistant to correction. Such factors as lead times, institutional dogmatism, over-dependence on specific technologies, and the effects of national or international competition can all serve to reduce the possibilities for exercising 'technological choice'. As Collingridge describes the 'dilemma of control':

When change is easy, the need for it cannot be foreseen; when the need for change is apparent, change has become expensive, difficult, and time consuming.[6]

One other factor that complicates the exercise of 'technological choice' is the distribution of power within societies. Concepts such as 'social benefit' serve in many ways to conceal fundamental differences between the interests of various groups and, in addition, it can be argued that choices have indeed been made in the past – but to the advantage of specific sections of society rather than any 'common good'. The notion of 'choice' leads directly to the question of 'who makes the choice?', an issue to which we will return later.

The concept of technological risk

As previously defined, technological risks represent in different ways a direct threat to human life and well-being.[7] In addition to their consequences for mortality and morbidity, these agents also share a number of other features which make them especially problematic for modern societies. There is the fundamental uncertainty about future developments: a product or process considered innocuous at its inception may later prove to have a devastating environmental impact, as has been the case with asbestos production or the drug thalidomide. Secondly, there is the frequently irreversible nature of much of the decision making in this area: it is often impossible to repair the damage to human beings once it has been done. Thirdly, one finds a large dependence on technical expertise and relatively esoteric and inaccessible bodies of knowledge. This characteristic exists in a rather uneasy relationship with a fourth feature, the frequency with which matters of technological risk have become the subject of public concern and, in particular, demands for increased participation in decision making. This relationship will be discussed below, and will be explored more fully in the rest of this book.

In the face of complexities such as these and, above all, the need to weigh up the costs and benefits of decision making when the necessary technical evidence may well be inconclusive, a literature has developed[8] which seeks to clarify some of these difficulties, and so facilitate regulatory action in this area. Lowrance,[9] for example, has contended that the topic of risk assessment should be divided into two distinct categories. First of all, there is the *measurement of risk* – an essentially objective and scientific activity. Secondly, there is the *judgement of safety* – a normative and political activity. According to this schema, the first step in any assessment of risk is a technical estimation of the likelihood of a particular hazardous event and of the magnitude of physical consequences. This stage would also include a presentation of the technical estimation for broader (i.e. non-expert) consumption. For our present purposes, this expert-dominated phase in any risk assessment exercise can be termed 'risk analysis'.

The second stage as proposed by Lowrance involves a review of the technical evidence and also the consideration of questions of benefit as well as cost. The second stage may necessitate a discussion of value judgements and normative factors such as the monetary equivalent of a human life, or the social consequences of each possible decision. This phase can be referred to as 'risk evaluation'. In the following two sections, each of these stages will be examined with a particular view to establishing their interrelationships and areas of overlap.

Risk analysis

Lowrance has suggested that there are various sources of evidence which may be used in estimating the magnitude of a particular hazard.[10] These are: (1) traditional knowledge, (2) common sense, (3) analogy to known cases, (4) human experimentation, (5) inadvertent or occupational exposure, (6) epidemiological surveys, (7) animal testing, and (8) product performance trials. To these can be added the sophisticated risk analytical techniques, which have largely been developed in the nuclear power industry and for military purposes. These techniques can be divided into two categories: first, reliability and failure analysis and, secondly, consequence modelling.[11]

In Britain, the report submitted by the Health and Safety Executive (HSE), but prepared initially by the Safety and Reliability Directorate (SRD) of the UK Atomic Energy Authority (UKAEA), in which the risks involved in the large industrial complex at Canvey Island are analysed, has attracted particular public and expert attention.[12] Indeed, this study represents the first case in which such a major risk analysis has been made generally available in Britain. Subsequent criticism[13] of the original (1978) report has led to a new version, based on slightly revised data and operating principles, being published.[14] In the United States, the 'Rasmussen Report'[15] on nuclear power has been the subject of continued interest; in 1978 the 'Lewis Commission' revised some of its assumptions and conclusions.[16]

A number of detailed criticisms can be made of all of these risk analytical techniques: the wide margins of error which are typically involved when predicting future events and their consequences; their inability to cope satisfactorily with the effects of human error or malice; their partial reliance on such factors as 'professional judgement' or intuition; their acceptance of information from sources which may not be absolutely impartial, e.g. the industries under investigation. In many cases these criticisms are valid, and serve to point out certain fundamental weaknesses in the practice of risk analysis. In addition, there is the crucial point that such investigations may serve to mystify a concerned public and, by giving the appearance of scientific certainty to an unavoidably uncertain judgement, may hinder a full risk evaluation process. Given problems of this order, it may seem reasonable for oppositional groups to reject any risk analysis as a simple propaganda tool – especially when those groups may not have equivalent financial or technical resources and, therefore, feel incapable of producing their own analyses or more detailed critiques. However, a rejection of risk analysis on the grounds of its intrinsic uncertainties and failings would also entail the loss of the few available techniques that assist in the making of difficult decisions of the sort that will be examined here.[17]

These questions of the value of risk analysis will be discussed further during the chapters that follow. For the moment, however, it can be noted that one feature of many of the debates over technological risks which has attracted considerable attention is the tendency for technical experts to differ in their expressed judgements of safety. It is clear that there is an especially large scope for disagreement when the sources of evidence may range so widely; moreover, the professional backgrounds of research workers involved in a specific debate may also vary. Robbins and Johnston have studied the effect of these factors in relation to the division of scientific opinion over the harmful consequences of environmental lead pollution.[18] The case study presented by the two authors deals with the dispute between two scientific groups over the establishment of standards for lead in the atmosphere. The first group, the medical scientists, utilised occupational toxicology as its analytical framework. This led it to accept certain levels of lead retention in the body as normal (and therefore acceptable) and to relate these levels to no-effect 'thresholds'. The second group, the environmentalists, based their analyses on totally different theoretical assumptions so that even minute lead levels were seen as distinctly abnormal (and therefore unacceptable). Accordingly, no technical consensus could be arrived at by the two professional groups and the 'risk estimation' process remained in a state of controversy.

Science can, in this way, be presented not as a homogeneous institution which shares a 'pool of knowledge' (i.e. it is not simply a community of scientists acting in organisational and cognitive harmony) but rather as differentiated in its practice and internally diverse. Within the scientific endeavour, separate groups exist, each concerned with the maintenance of its own professional cohesion and the imposition of its own conceptualisations on a problem area. In this manner, the struggle for professional identity and cognitive hegemony tend to reinforce one another.

As Robbins and Johnston have argued, a sociological perspective should admit the possibility that:

... science is differentiated, to the extent that scientists working within widely separated specialties can on strict scientific grounds reach genuinely opposed conclusions, and the heat of dispute between experts may be an indication of attempts by competing groups of scientists to establish their professional authority over a particular issue or area.[19]

This conceptual approach to the production of scientific knowledge owes a considerable debt to the philosophical insights of Kuhn[20] whose fundamental contribution was to highlight the inadequacies of a positivistic conception of science and to stimulate the sociological investigation of not just the institutional apparatus but also the cognitive structures of technical expertise. Kuhn opened up, both directly and indirectly, a new area for sociological enquiry based on the assumption that science is a negotiated social order rather than a corpus of value-free facts. Law and French have labelled this the 'interpretive' approach to sociology of science.[21] A large body of literature has grown up which seeks to study the relationship between scientific and technological knowledge[22] and its social context.[23] This literature has been reviewed elsewhere.[24]

In addition to the stimulus provided by Kuhn's study of scientific revolutions it should also be noted that there has been a long history of Marxist analyses of sciences, prominent among which has been Hessen's seminal work on the social and economic foundations of Newton's *Principia*.[25] Science was presented by Hessen as a straightforward superstructural representation of the substructural economic system. However, since Hessen's 1931 paper, Marxist accounts of science and technology have attained much greater levels of sophistication.[26] In a series of articles, one Marxist writer, Young, has argued for a conception of the science–society relationship based on the notion of science as a 'labour process':

This approach moves away from focusing on what is special about scientific knowledge and considers just how much of the social relations and social processes of the origination, reproduction and dissemination of science, technology and medicine are like those of any other manufactured products on the one hand, and other areas of culture on the other . . . it analyses a social process whereby scientific workers transform raw materials into products by means of instruments and procedures.[27]

This analysis sees social factors as constitutive of scientific knowledge production rather than merely contextual. The influence of society does not, according to this model, impact science after a body of knowledge has been established; social concerns and pressures are rather an integral part of the scientific labour process itself.

If this general perspective (which, for the sake of convenience, will from this point be referred to as the 'sociology of scientific knowledge' approach) is applied to the technical estimation of the nature and severity of risks, a certain departure from the analytical framework provided by Lowrance, i.e. the separation of risk measurement from the social treatment of a hazard, is required. Technical estimations of risk are liable to be affected by the organisational structure within which they are conducted, by the disciplinary and professional commitments of researchers, and by broader social pressures. In this way, it can be seen that risk estimations are open to disagreements between experts which will manifest themselves in the type of technical controversy that abounds in this area. These controversies should be understood, in many cases, not as a competition between inferior and superior expertise, but rather as a conflict over professional or ideological values as embedded in scientific knowledge.

Science can no longer be divorced from the political programme which allows it to develop and which science itself helps to achieve through close association . . . Even though the practice of 'pure' science seems unchanged . . . the choices affecting that project are set in a context of institutions, mechanisms, procedures of which it is no longer the sole master.[28]

This case can be extended to include the whole topic of the control of technological risks. Wynne, for example, has argued that the British Windscale enquiry, although ostensibly concerned with the construction of one reprocessing plant, became, in fact, a debate over the future structure of British society.[29] Thus, the technical analysis of a thermal oxide reprocessing plant (THORP) proved inseparable from a whole range of economic and political arguments. Cotgrove has taken this argument further by producing evidence to suggest that the position taken by different social groups on the general question of nuclear energy policy is less a matter of technical analysis or an appreciation of detailed argument than a question of an individual's overall world view and basic values.[30] Already, however, our discussion of risk analysis has developed into a consideration of risk evaluation. This development lends support to the argument that 'analysis' and 'evaluation' are not strictly separable, but it is still valuable to discuss risk evaluation more explicitly.

Risk evaluation

Following Lowrance, after the nature and severity of a hazard has been subjected to a technical analysis, the evidence must be collected and sifted by a central or local authority. It is at this stage that key judgements have to be made, and a 'balancing act' carried out between the costs and benefits of any regulatory actions. It is here that such notoriously treacherous questions as the value of a human life and the weighting of short-term gains against long-term dangers have to be tackled. There is now a general acceptance that 'zero risk' (or 100 per cent safety) can never be obtained. The issue then centres on the point at which a hazard can be judged as acceptable. This judgement is, in may ways, at the very heart of the present concern over the control of risk-related technologies. How safe is safe enough?

Although it is very difficult to consider the nature of risk evaluation at the general level – and indeed the sterility of over-abstracted discussions of risk is a major argument of this book – it is possible to pinpoint a number of relatively discrete issues within any such judgemental process.[31] First of all, the hazard must have emerged as a distinct problem worthy of attention. It must have found a place on the 'agenda' of the relevant advisory body. This point may appear self-evident, but it is nevertheless important, as it draws attention to at least two further questions. There is a major difference between those authorities that systematically review each and every product or process within their jurisdiction and those that have no such procedure but consider specific hazards only when their attention has been attracted, through either public or technical discussion. Following on from this, there is also the more general political question of the way in which power can be influential within the stage of agenda setting. There is always the possibility that specific decisions can be affected by particular parties, but Crenson has pointed out that power can also be exercised by keeping certain topics in the sphere of 'un-politics'. In this way, 'non-decisions' also become significant – the neglect of particular problems and their exclusion from the regulatory agenda. As Crenson contends:

The most significant fact about these non-decisions is that many – perhaps most – of them have something to do with the distribution of power. They are not all politically random oversights but instances of politically enforced neglect.[32]

The influence of political power over regulatory action is a major concern here, and the notion of 'politically enforced neglect' has proven especially useful, as we shall see.

If one turns now from the stage of *agenda setting* to the actual *decision-making* phase for any regulatory authority, a number of questions become relevant. First, there is the important question of the membership of decision-making bodies. One common British structure is the advisory committee which, in matters of this sort, is predominantly 'expert' in character and may include very little in the way of 'lay' representation. In contrast, the US political system appears far more geared to the inclusion of broader participation via a system of public hearings and also what is often considered a more 'open' decision-making style.[33] Quite obviously, the membership of such bodies can have a major effect on the eventual policy output. Again, this issue will be a matter for discussion and analysis here, as also will the notion of confidentiality/openness and the effect this has on the extent and form of participation.

A second major feature of any decision-making phase which must be stressed is the criteria for choice according to which authorities operate. In certain cases, a statutory framework may exist which establishes the definition of concepts like 'burden of proof' or 'suggestive evidence'. In others, a more flexible series of guidelines may offer considerable discretion to decision makers. Also relevant with regard to criteria for choice is the manner in which questions of need are taken into account: is the social value of a possible hazard considered or simply the risks associated with it? Again, one can ask *how* questions of need are included in decision making. Are techniques such as cost-benefit analysis drawn upon or is the necessary 'balancing act' a more implicit and less openly debated process?

A whole range of other questions can be raised with regard to the decision-making phase. How is the relationship between state sponsorship of an industry and regulation of the same industry organised? An overlap between the two functions can lead to a suspicion that one will tend to dominate the other. How is technical advice (the product of the risk analysis phase) included in the process? How are outside views represented? Are particular bodies, e.g. industrial groups, in an advantageous position in terms of exerting their influence? How has the historical development of particular regulatory authorities influenced the terms of reference and the often taken-for-granted approach adopted regarding certain issues? All of these questions deserve attention, but all of them require the detailed analysis which can come only from the consideration of specific areas of concern. In later chapters we will begin to accumulate the background knowledge which is necessary before these questions can be properly answered in one context.

One final stage of risk evaluation should not be overlooked – the business of *policy execution*. This phase covers the output from authorities and the specific form which this takes (regulations, guidelines, bans, permissions, standards, etc.). It also includes the methods that are used to enforce decisions, often via national inspectorates or systems of 'self-certification' by manufacturers. A particular aspect of policy execution which should be mentioned is monitoring, the steps that are taken to discover whether a regulatory decision actually achieves its intended purpose. This phase can, of course, lead an issue back on to the agenda of the relevant authority and so completes the regulatory circle. At this point, the concept of 'institutional flexibility' becomes apparent: how capable are the appropriate agencies of responding to new information on the effectiveness of a decision or a shift in the 'balancing act' as needs, benefits and costs change over time?

It is in the context of complex questions of this sort and, in particular, the difficulties of balancing costs and benefits while also reconciling the countervailing political pressures generated between the 'risk triangle' of regulators, the regulated industries and the exposed public[34] that (see below) a number of attempts at rationalising the risk assessment process must be seen. Very often, these attempts address themselves directly to the oft-repeated question: How safe is safe enough?

Analytical approaches to risk acceptability

The basic goal of the analytical approaches that will be discussed in this section is to calculate a numerical point at which particular risks may be judged 'acceptable'. Improbable events, such as being struck by a falling meteorite, tend not to cause a high level of anxiety in Western societies. If there is, as perhaps in this case, a relationship between an event's probability of causing a fatality and its social acceptability, then it may be reasonable to correlate these factors for various kinds of hazard and so produce general guidelines for the acceptability of risks. At the very least, it is argued, the probability of fatality provides a basis for the comparison of different risks and so offers a solid foundation for regulatory action. As Lord Rothschild argued in the 1978 Dimbleby Lecture on BBC television:

... there is no point in getting into a panic about the risks of life until you have compared the risks which worry you with those that do not − but perhaps should. Comparisons ... are the best antidote to panic. What we need, therefore, is a list or index of risks and some guidance as to when to flap and when not.[35]

A feature of this approach is the notion that certain 'yardsticks' can assist policy making. One of the earliest attempts at proposing such a yardstick was made by Starr in 1969.[36] Starr argued that the probability of death from disease represented a degree of risk which would not be exceeded willingly by any individual and, therefore, could be taken as a baseline for 'unacceptability'. In contrast, the probability of death from 'natural hazards' is taken to be 'acceptable' for all individuals and, therefore, any risk even more slight than this can automatically be considered acceptable. Individuals are prepared to undertake increasing risks between the level of 10^{-2} and 10^{-6} (of fatality per person-year) provided that the benefits increase proportionately. Starr's grand hypothesis has been extremely influential and a slightly watered-down version of his approach has been advocated by a number of commentators including Rothschild. Chicken,[37] for example, has argued that a hazard will be considered acceptable if its probability of causing a fatality is small when compared with natural hazards. Lord Ashby[38] has proposed the 'rough generalisation' that risks of 10^{-6} (of fatality per person year) are of 'no great concern' to the 'average person'. A risk level of 10^{-4} will render the public willing to 'incur expenditure' to reduce the risk *unless* it is undertaken voluntarily. At the level of 10^{-3}, a risk becomes unacceptable and there will be strong pressure to have it reduced.

As can be seen from Ashby's proposal, the distinction between 'voluntary' and 'involuntary' risk has assumed a certain significance within this approach to risk acceptability. Kletz, for example, has argued that the numerical risk of a hazard provides a logical foundation for regulatory action.[39] He then constructs two indices of risk: one for voluntary risks and including such activities as motor cycling, taking contraceptive pills, smoking twenty cigarettes a day or car driving, and the second for involuntary risks such as being killed by a falling aircraft, a meteorite, a road vehicle or a release from an atomic power station. The basis for this distinction is, of course, the notion that we accept very high risks voluntarily but will not tolerate such levels when we are subjected to them without our expressed wish. Accordingly, the two categories must be kept apart when using risk comparisons as the foundation for regulatory decisions.

What is common to these approaches to risk acceptability are two fundamental ideas: first of all, that it is possible to pinpoint certain levels of risk which are by nature 'socially acceptable'; secondly, that the numerical severity of a risk provides a basis for comparison so that indices can be prepared and priorities established for future action. As Kletz has argued:

Whatever money we make available for safety we should spend in such a way that it produces the maximum benefit. There is nothing humanitarian in spending lavishly to reduce a hazard because it hit the headlines last week and ignoring the others.[40]

Thus, comparisons offer a rational foundation for policy making which avoids the vagaries and emotional reactions of the usual political processes.

A third, but less essential, aspect of this approach to risk is the voluntary/involuntary distinction. In this general form the 'acceptable risk' approach has become increasingly influential among policy makers. For example, the UK Royal Commission on Environmental Pollution's Sixth Report considered the question of *Nuclear Power and the Environment*.[41] In this document, the predicted frequency of a release of iodine-131 from a nuclear reactor is compared with a series of probabilities for other major hazards – air crashes, dam failures, fires and explosions. The resultant chart 'demonstrates' the lower risk level involved in nuclear power production and this is taken as an important argument for the acceptability of that hazard. Similarly, the 1978 Report on Canvey Island included an explicit comparison between the chance of a resident in the Canvey Island area being killed as a consequence of a major accident at the existing industrial installations and the death rate from natural causes for those in the 25–34 age group in Britain as a whole.[42] It was after a consideration of examples such as these that McGinty and Atherley described the 'acceptable risk' philosophy as the 'key element of today's safety catechism'.[43]

What criticisms can be made of this risk philosophy? One might begin by examining the voluntary/involuntary distinction more closely. Whereas it may well be true that an activity like rock climbing can only be described as 'voluntary', and, similarly, the effect of cosmic rays from the explosion of supernovae (to take one of Kletz's examples) is apparently 'involuntary', a large grey area seems to exist which cannot be categorised very satisfactorily. Car driving may not be absolutely voluntary when one must travel to work and public transport systems prove inadequate. Deaths caused by tornadoes are not totally involuntary when buildings could reasonably be modified to reduce mortalities – provided, of course, that the necessary finance was made available. From these examples it can be appreciated that the voluntary/involuntary distinction ignores a whole range of political and philosophical questions about the nature of free will and, furthermore, that these questions become crucial when the distinction is applied to matters of public policy.

The second point of criticism concerns the nature of the comparisons which are being conducted. It would seem essential for any adequate comparison that it must be dealing with equivalent entities. However, as Cohen and Pritchard have noted,[44] there are at least three different kinds of statistical risk: (a) risks for which there is an historical record and for which, accordingly, reliable statistical (perhaps actuarial) information is available (e.g. road deaths, fires, factory accidents, etc.); (b) risks where an effect is believed to exist but where the relationship between cause and effect may not be completely understood (e.g. chemical carcinogens or radiation); (c) risks for which the only information available consists of experts' best estimates of the probability of catastrophe (e.g. a major nuclear reactor accident or an explosion in a petrochemical complex).

It can readily be seen that a comparison between, for example, a risk of the type found in category (a) with one from category (c) is likely to be meaningless. As Griffiths has pointed out:

> It would be highly convenient for all concerned with risk decisions if a common unit could be found by means of which risks could be put on a single quantified scale . . .[45]

However, Griffiths concludes that no such 'common unit' presently exists nor, one might add, is it likely to be developed.

We now turn to the most basic feature of the analytical approach that we are considering – its belief in the existence of an identifiable 'acceptable risk' for any hazard. McGinty and Atherley have challenged the notion of comparison:

> . . . it is impossible to compare risks of different types, undertaken for different reasons in different social circumstances.[46]

and then rejected the 'acceptable risk' concept as not only worthless but also 'profoundly undemocratic':

> The fallacy is that there is only one quantitative level of risk that is 'acceptable'. But acceptable to whom? From whose viewpoint is risk to be judged – its creators, its victims, experts, representative organisations, the community at large, the government? Each viewpoint defines its own, sometimes widely different, level of acceptability.[47]

The Council for Science and Society has echoed this criticism by emphasising the extent to which the 'acceptable risk' notion is fraught with ambiguity:

> . . . there is considerable variety in the situations and values that may be involved in a judgement of whether a risk is 'acceptable'. The risk may appear 'negligible', 'less salient', 'socially permitted', 'unavoidable', 'temporarily tolerated', 'irreducible and intolerable', or finally, 'worthwhile'.[48]

The approach taken by the Council for Science and Society is that a hazard is not an objective phenomenon but rather an 'intellectual construct'. Different people within different social settings will perceive a hazard in individual ways – the numerical severity of a risk is just one dimension of the product or process in question which cannot be separated out from the overall social context. Seen in this light, the potential for risk is simply one aspect of a given technology: we do not judge the risk alone, but rather the whole 'package' of cost and benefit of which it is a part.[49] It follows that any 'rational' attempt to abstract a statistical risk out from its technological and social setting will prove a sterile exercise. Moreover, as McGinty and Atherley point out, it is also likely to be undemocratic: the only people in a position to judge whether a specific risk is acceptable are those who will be directly affected by any consequent death or injury. This represents a powerful argument for public participation in matters of technological risk and its actual practicability will be debated throughout this book.

The immediate consequence of the above discussions for public policies with regard to technological risk is a reorientation of major concern away from the pursuit of 'acceptable risks' and towards a consideration of the regulatory forms within which decisions over risks are taken.

... no single, static conception of the criteria can yield an answer to the question 'What is a fair risk?' ... Rather than continuing to demand an answer to the question whether a risk is fair *in itself*, we should redirect our attention to the ways in which risks come about and are controlled. That is, we should focus on the *procedures* by which decisions are taken on the creation or persistence of risks, and ask whether these procedures are fair.[50]

Accordingly, the prime aim of this book is not to offer a view as to whether the risk of road traffic accidents in Britain and the United States is intrinsically 'fair' or 'acceptable'; rather its focus will be on the institutional mechanisms and regulatory structures that exist for the control of this risk-related technology. The major concern will not be with 'How safe is safe enough?' but with the less nebulous issue of 'In the case of road traffic safety, *who* decides and *how*?' Put in this way, questions of accountability and representation become absolutely fundamental, as do the power relations that exist within regulatory authorities, and between such authorities and outside groups. No less important are the evaluative criteria that are brought to bear on any decision and the relationship between these and technical advice. The question of 'who decides and how?' unites the various themes that have been introduced in this chapter and in Chapter 1. It also encompasses the topics of risk analysis and risk evaluation, which have been presented here as constituting the overall risk assessment process.

A framework for analysis

In the previous chapter the question of who decides and how was expressed in a rather different form: 'How can the adverse consequences of technological risks be controlled in a manner which is both effective and equitable?' It should now be apparent that these two formulations raise identical issues for investigation. It was proposed in Chapter 1 that four major influences over the processes of risk control would be studied here: the state, the outside organisations which may seek to influence specific decisions and general policies, the general public and, finally, technical experts. A number of points have already been made in passing about each of these, but we need to consider each in more detail, paying particular attention to the role of the capitalist state and its relationship to the other groups.

The role of the state

Within the domain of political science, the nature of the capitalist state has been a topic of major concern and attention in recent years. Dunleavy[51] has characterised the 1960s views of liberal democratic politics as falling into two broad camps: 'classical pluralism' and the 'Marxist' view. The former tended to focus on the role of pressure groups in informing governments about preferences and opinions while stressing the separation between economic and political power bases. The underlying assumptions behind this approach were that the state was broadly neutral and that there are multiple (plural) centres of power within the political process. In contrast, the Marxist approach stressed the dominance of capital over decision making, as illustrated by the staffing of the state apparatus by owners of capital or closely allied groups, the favourable position of the owners of capital in terms of the acquisition of political power and, thirdly, the policy outputs of the state, which tend, directly or indirectly, to favour the interests of capital. In addition, the ideology of the 'neutral state' serves as a mask for class conflict and so helps to maintain capitalist societies.

Since that time, research in the Marxist tradition has been given an important boost by Miliband's seminal work *The State in Capitalist*

Society.[52] In this, Miliband systematically detailed the shortcomings of the pluralist approach and provided powerful evidence to suggest that such an approach is a 'profound obfuscation' of reality. Miliband argued that the governments of advanced capitalist countries have never been neutral and that they represent a powerful force in the defence of the capitalist system. The ideological and political persuasions of state personnel have been such as to ensure a strong bias in favour of the owners of capital.

The state bureaucracy, in all its parts, is not an impersonal, un-ideological, apolitical element in society, above the conflicts in which classes, interests and groups engage. By virtue of its ideological dispositions, reinforced by its own interests, that bureaucracy, on the contrary, is a crucially important and committed element in the maintenance and defence of the structure of power and privilege inherent in advanced capitalism.[52]

Such arguments about the nature of the state are especially important in the present context because of the increased involvement of this body in the control of risk-related technologies. As already noted, Ravetz has suggested that a 'risk triangle' exists between the regulated industries, those exposed to risks and the regulatory authorities. This triangle represents a political relationship, and the possibility of a close affinity between 'regulators' (i.e. the state authorities) and 'regulated' (i.e. the owners of capital) cannot reasonably be ignored. As Ravetz has argued:

... the style of the control of risks will mimic, and be influenced by, wider social relations of power. A hazardous environment (at work or at home) is a part of social powerlessness. Hence all debates on risks have an inevitable and inescapable element of politics in them.[53]

Recent developments in the Marxist tradition have undoubtedly provided new insights into the role of the state.[54] Certainly, these attempts at interpretation have achieved a greater level of sophistication than the frequently quoted view of the state in *The Communist Manifesto* as 'but a committee for managing the common affairs of the whole bourgeoisie' suggested. In particular, the growth of a social welfare function within advanced capitalist societies – including education, medical care, housing schemes, pensions, unemployment benefits, as well as hazard control policies – has posed a challenge for Marxist analysis. The response to this has been that it is precisely in providing such services that the state has been able to secure the conditions for reproducing the mode of production. The 'neutral' appearance of the state allows it to reduce class conflict by permitting such progressive developments. In addition, there is a certain 'relative autonomy' in the relationship between the state and the ruling class owing to the existence of working-class pressures. In this way the state does not simply respond to the short-term demands of certain factions of the capitalist class, but must also be responsive to class conflict and the longer term interests of capital as a whole.

If the state is to act as more than a sounding-board for these various pressures, if it is to act in the long-term political interest of the capitalist class as a whole, then it must clearly be distinct and possess a degree of autonomy from this class. Only in this way can it perform such a reconciling and mediating function.[55]

An important area of discussion among Marxist writers has concerned the nature of the link between the state and the capitalist class. A famous debate between Miliband and Poulantzas[56] centred on the issue of whether motivations and ideological inclinations of state personnel are crucial, or whether the relationship between the state and capital is a more 'structural' one. Unfortunately, there is not space to review this debate here. Nevertheless, it may be reasonable to conclude with Gough that, although the constitution of the state certainly deserves attention, the key element of a Marxist approach to the state is that *whoever* occupies particular positions, their actions will be constrained by the imperatives of the process of capital accumulation. However, this is not to suggest that changes in government are unimportant or that the state cannot be used to gain reforms. Within the constraints imposed by capitalism, there is room for manoeuvre so that 'relative autonomy' can be exercised to the benefit of groups outside the ruling class. From this perspective, the state can be seen as involved in a dynamic political process and the adoption of a Marxist approach should not be taken as implying that regulatory authorities have necessarily served only as a passive tool for some single 'capitalist interest'. However, it is an underlying theme of this book that the control of technological risk is very much a matter of political power. Accordingly, one might expect to find that the development of risk-related technologies or, in this case, disputes over the regulation of road traffic safety, are closely linked to the general characteristics of capitalist societies. In the central chapters of this book we will be concerned to locate regulatory developments of the sort discussed here within the context of the capitalist state and the broader society of which it is a part. Of course, we will be contrasting two advanced capitalist countries and a special interest will be in discovering how they have reacted to a similar social problem. Although each may reasonably be described as 'capitalist' in terms of its mode of production, system of exchange and class structure, this does not imply, for the reasons discussed earlier concerning 'relative autonomy' and also because of specific patterns of historical development, that each will necessarily regulate risk-related technologies in an identical fashion.

Pressure-group politics

Much has already been said here concerning the role of extra-state groups and this should not be repeated. Certainly, in matters of regulatory action, industry groups have frequently been to the fore. State controls can have very real economic consequences for specific industrial sectors by increasing production costs or even banning the use of certain processes and products. In addition, the state can actually *create* new markets, e.g. for the ignition interlock or the air bag, as we will discuss in Part III. It is not surprising, therefore, that individual manufacturers will see it as being in their own interest to maintain a dialogue with decision makers and to apply whatever pressures are available to them. Very often, manufacturers band together to fight regulatory action – as, for example, via the Chemical Industries Association in the case of British government intervention over toxic chemicals.[57] Associations of this sort allow considerable resources to be applied to full-time lobbying activities, with the consequent development of informal relationships between industry representatives and government officials. Especially in the United States, the existence of casual links between professional lobbyists and civil servants has given rise to frequent accusations of the 'captured agency' or 'revolving door' variety (whereby individuals move easily from important government posts to senior positions in the regulated industry).[58] In Britain, however, amicable links between 'regulators' and the 'regulated' are certainly tolerated and indeed seem encouraged in the interests of a more flexible and consensual working relationship.

One other element of industrial pressure groups is that the financial strength of some of these organisations may well allow superior access to research facilities and the available scientific expertise. This gives these groups a clear advantage over less pecunious lobbies, in that they are frequently able to marshal impressive technical support for their arguments. There is also the fact that the affected industry is likely to be the only body in a position to make a precise judgement of the economic costs of regulation: here again there is a privileged access to information.

'Non-industrial' or 'public interest' groups are in a relatively weak position when compared with a well co-ordinated and financially solvent organisation such as the Chemical Industries Association. Some of these groups may well be professional bodies or trade unions with adequate resources of their own; others will depend on voluntary and part-time support. The political influences of these groups will depend on a number of factors: their strategic importance in society, their lobbying skill, their size and income, the nature of their case, their expertise and the timing of their demands.[59] The available organisational base may also be of crucial importance in determining whether or not a lobby will form in the first place. Trade unions, for example, can be seen as having a 'natural constituency' for action on occupational health and safety, but there is no readily apparent constituency for mobilisation on consumer safety or hazards of the general environment. For this type of hazard, the affected parties are dispersed throughout society and are not concentrated within any geographical or institutional location. It should be noted, however, that national differences exist on this matter and, for example, the 'consumer movement' appears considerably stronger in the United States than it is in Britain.[60]

Throughout this book an attempt will be made to consider the relationship of industrial and 'public interest' groups to the state so as to assess their relative power and influence.

The general public
In many ways one of the most problematic categories with which to deal in any policy analysis is that of the 'general public'. As has already been noted, the 'public' as a single entity does not exist, but rather a number of overlapping groupings divided according to such factors as social class, locality, occupation, race and gender. The problem for analysis then becomes one of the ways in which such a heterogeneous body can organise so as to exert any political pressure on the state. The lack of a specific 'constituency' can render public opinion weak and undeveloped in terms of the exercise of political power. It is at this point, of course, that questions of public participation and the accountability of institutions and decision-making processes become

especially relevant. Nelkin has argued that the relationship between this and technical expertise has become a central problem in modern societies.

The complexity of public decisions seems to require highly specialised and esoteric knowledge, and those who control this knowledge have considerable power. Yet democratic ideology suggests that people must be able to influence policy decisions that affect their lives.[61]

Given the existence of this problem, how viable is increased public participation in technical decision making? In the specific case of road traffic safety we will discuss this question in some depth. To what extent do the two national systems encourage democratic involvement? How successful have they been in this? Has the technical nature of the debates caused any particular difficulties for lay groups? Has the participation of 'public' representatives served to open up the general political issues for discussion? Alternatively, have debates retreated into a wrangle over technical detail and the presentation of political and economic judgements in scientific guise? This latter development can be termed 'scientisation'.[62] The major argument over public participation in technical decisions seems to revolve around the questions of how capable the general public are of appreciating technical information and whether their inclusion would not lead to emotionality and irrational regulatory actions. These matters will certainly be discussed in later chapters.[63]

Technical expertise

The earlier section on risk analysis devoted some time to a discussion of technical expertise. One can only add here that a considerable literature has developed by way of analysing the relationship between technical knowledge and political power.[64] It should be emphasised that this is very much a 'two-way' relationship for although technical expertise can, as we will see, prove to be an important influence over the exercise of political power, that expertise is itself shaped by the political context in which it is developed. Accordingly, the spheres of 'knowledge' and 'power' are certainly not completely separate although the emphasis may, at times, be on one rather than the other.

In the analysis that follows we will be concerned with at least two different levels at which technical expertise can exert an influence within the decision-making process. First of all, there is the *specific advice* which technical experts make available to policy makers and pressure groups. At this level it can be seen that the membership of key advisory bodies by particular experts can be a crucial factor.[65] The second level is concerned less with the specific advice that is offered than with the *overall framework* within which decisions are reached. It is possible to identify national styles in the control of technological risks; these general regulatory approaches will embody technical as well as political assumptions about the best way of dealing with a specific category of hazard. They may have developed as a consequence of radical changes in policy direction or they may have evolved in an incremental and piecemeal fashion.[66] Gillespie, Eva and Johnston, for example, have identified distinct regulatory philosophies in Britain and the United States with regard to the control of carcinogenic chemicals.[19] In addition to technical assumptions, national frameworks for the control of particular technologies will also contain certain institutional features, such as the state's relationship with particular pressure groups or the degree of confidentiality which may be derived from the broader political system of that nation. The distinction between specific advisory structures and overall policy frameworks is one that will become more apparent as this book continues and, more particularly, in Part II where the major features of British and United States approaches to road traffic safety are considered.

Review

This chapter has provided an introduction to the control of technological risks. It has divided the general topic of risk assessment into the stages of risk analysis and risk evaluation while taking care to note that these phases are not absolutely discrete: no straightforward fact/value distinction can be maintained in this context. Following this, the 'rational' (or, more accurately, 'technocratic') approaches to risk acceptability were considered in some detail before an alternative approach was developed which regards such techniques as fundamentally misguided. According to the latter, there is no justification for comparing risks of different types undertaken in different social circumstances and for different reasons. This led us to a focus on the *procedures* by which decisions regarding risk are taken and to the basic political question, 'Who decides and how?'

The analytic framework outlined in the latter part of this chapter should have made it quite clear that the present focus on procedures does not suggest an exclusive concentration on bureaucratic minutiae (relevant though these may be), but rather an approach which sees the regulatory process as occurring within a historical and political context. Only by adopting this broader framework can the state control of technological hazards be properly understood.

The chapters that follow are somewhat different in character to this introduction. They move away from the general, and somewhat abstract, discussion in which we have been engaged and deal instead with a more specific topic, the control of road traffic safety in Britain and the United States.

Notes and references

1 See: Freeman, C. *The Economics of Industrial Innovation* (Penguin, Harmondsworth; 1974). OECD. *Science, Growth and Society* (OECD, Paris; 1971). Rosenberg, N. *Perspectives on Technology* (Cambridge University Press, Cambridge; 1972). UNESCO. Method for Priority Determination in Science and Technology *Science Policy Studies and Documents No. 40* (UNESCO, Paris; 1978).

2 Steward, F. and Wibberley, G. Drug innovation – what's slowing it down? *Nature,* **284** (1981), 118–20. Teeling-Smith, G. *A question of Balance* (Office of Health Economics, London; May 1980). Available from Office of Health Economics, 162 Regent Street, London W1R 6DD. Weatherall, M. An end to the search for new drugs?. *Nature,* **296** (1982), 387–90.

3 Elliott, D. and Elliott, R. *The Control of Technology* (Wykeham Publications, London; 1976), p.v (their emphasis).

4 *Ibid.* p. 134.

5 See, for example: Braverman, H. *Labor and Monopoly Capital* (Monthly Review Press, New York; 1974). Noble, D. *America by Design* (Oxford University Press, New York; 1977).

6 Collingridge, D. *The Social Control of Technology* (Frances Pinter, London; 1980), p.11.

7 It is worth while at this point to offer a brief note on definitions. Following the categorisation suggested by the British Standards Institution, 'risk' will be taken here to include the combined effects of the probability of occurrence of an undesired event and the magnitude of the consequences. 'Hazard' refers to a set of conditions, a situation or an entity with the potential for causing harm. British Standards Institution, *Glossary of terms used in quality assurance (including reliability and maintainability)*, BS 4778 (1979).

8 Apart from the texts discussed during this chapter, the following provide a useful introduction to this literature: Conrad, J. (ed.) *Society, Technology and Risk Assessment* (Academic Press, London; 1980). Griffiths, R. F. (ed.) *Dealing with Risk* (Manchester University Press,

Manchester; 1981). Schwing, R. C. and Albers, W. A. (eds) *Societal Risk Assessment* (Plenum Press, New York; 1980). Warner, F. E. and Slater, D. H. *The Assessment and Perception of Risk* (Royal Society, London; 1981).

9   Lowrance, W. W. *Of Acceptable Risk* (William Kaufmann, California; 1976).

10 *Ibid.* Chapter 2.

11 Unfortunately, there is not the space here to discuss these two important fields. However, an introduction can be found in the following references: Lees, F. P. *Loss Prevention in the Process Industries* (Butterworth, London; 1980), 2 volumes. McCormick, N. J. *Reliability and Risk Analysis: Methods and Nuclear Power Applications* (Academic Press, London; 1981). See also: Irwin, A., Smith, D. and Griffiths, R. G. Risk analysis and public policy for major hazards. *Physics in Technology*, **13** (6) 1982, 258–65.

12 Health and Safety Executive. *Canvey – an Investigation of Potential Hazards in the Canvey Island/Thurrock Area* (HMSO, London; 1978).

13 Notably: Cremer and Warner. *An Analysis of the Canvey Report*, Oyez Intelligence Reports (Oyez, London; 1980).

14 Health and Safety Executive. *Canvey : A Second Report* (HMSO, London; 1981).

15 United States Nuclear Regulatory Commission. *Reactor Safety Study* (USNRC, Washington, DC; 1975) (the 'Rasmussen Report').

16 Risk Assessment Review Group (the 'Lewis Commission') Report to the US Nuclear Regulatory Commission, Nureg/CR-0400 (1978).

17 Irwin, A. Risk analysis: *whose* choice in science and technology? Paper presented to the STSA/EASST Conference on 'Choice in Science and Technology', Imperial College, London, 16–18 September, 1983.

18 Robbins, D. and Johnston, R. The role of cognitive and occupational differentiation in scientific controversies. *Social Studies of Science*, (6) 1976; 349–68.

19 Ibid. p. p.352. See also: Gillespie, B., Eva, D. and Johnston, R. Carcinogenic risk assessment in the United States and Great Britain. *Social Studies of Science*, **9** (3) 1979, 265–301. Johnston, R. and Robbins, D. The development of specialties in industrialised science. *Sociological Review*, **25** 1977, 87–108.

20 Kuhn, T. *The Structure of Scientific Revolutions* (University of Chicago, Chicago; 1971).

21 Law, J. and French, D. Normative and interpretive sociologies of science. *Sociological Review*, **22** 1974, 581–95.

22 In this book technology will be viewed not as a branch of 'applied science' or a simple craft skill, but rather as possessing its own cognitive dynamic and body of theoretical knowledge. In practice, the distinction between science and technology is very difficult to define and usually reference to just one of these here will not preclude the other. See: Gruber, W. H. and Marquis, D. G. (eds) *Factors in the Transfer of Technology* (MIT, Cambridge, Mass. 1969).

23 For example: Barnes, B. *Scientific Knowledge and Sociological Explanation* (Routledge & Kegan Paul, London; 1976). Barnes, B. and Edge, D. *Science in Context* (Open University Press, Milton Keynes; 1982). Bhaskar, R. *A Realist Theory of Science* (Leeds Books, Leeds; 1975). Latour, B. and Woolgar, S. *Laboratory Life* (Sage, Beverley Hills, 1979). Ravetz, J. *Scientific Knowledge and its Social Problems* (Penguin, Harmondsworth; 1973). Whitley, R. D. (ed.) *The Social Processes of Scientific Development* (Routledge & Kegan Paul, London; 1974).

24 Bohme, G. Models for the development of science, in Spiegel-Rosing, I. and de Solla Price, D. (eds) *Science, Technology and Society* (Sage, London; 1977), Chapter 9, pp. 319–51. Mulkay, M. *Science and the Sociology of Knowledge.* (Allen & Unwin, London; 1979).

25 Hessen, B. M. The social and economic roots of Newton's *Principia*, reprinted in Bukharin, N. I. (ed.) *Science at the Crossroads* (Cass, London; 1971), pp. 149–212.

26 See, for example: Enzensberger, H. M. A critique of political ecology, in Rose, H. and Rose, S. (eds) *The Political Economy of Science* (Macmillan, London; 1976), 161–95. Habermas, J. *Towards a Rational Society* (Heinemann, London; 1971), and *Knowledge and Human Interests* (Heinemann, London; 1978). Levidow, L. and Young, B. (eds) *Science, Technology and the Labour Process: Marxist Studies, Volume I* (CSE, London; 1981). Marcuse, H. *One-dimensional Man* (Routledge & Kegan Paul, London; 1964).

27 Young, R. M. Interpreting the production of science. *New Scientist*, 29 March 1979, p. 1028, and Science *is* social relations. *Radical Science Journal*, 5 1976, 65–129.

28 Salomon, J. J. *Science and Politics* (MIT Press, Cambridge, Mass.; 1973), p. xiii.

29 Wynne, B. Nuclear debate at the crossroads. *New Scientist*, 3 August 1978, p. 349.

30 Cotgrove, S. Risk, value conflict and political legitimacy, in Griffiths, R. F. (ed.) *Dealing with Risk* (Manchester University Press, Manchester; 1981), pp. 122–40.

31 Many of the ideas in this section developed during numerous discussions with Ken Green of the Department of Science and Technology Policy of Manchester University in the course of a joint investigation into the British control of carcinogenic chemicals. This expression of gratitude does not, of course, implicate Ken in any of the weaknesses that there may be in what follows. See: Irwin, G. A. and Green, K. The British control of chemical carcinogens. *Policy and Politics.* **II** (4) 1983, 439–59.

32 Crenson, M. A. *The un-politics of Air Pollution* (Johns Hopkins, Baltimore; 1971), p.184.

33 See: Gillespie, B. F. British safety policy and pesticides, in Johnston, R. and Gummett, P. *Directing Technology* (Croom Helm, London; 1979), pp. 202–24.

34 Ravetz, J. The political economy of risk, *New Scientist*, 8 September 1977, pp. 598–9.

35   Lord Rothschild. Risk. *Atom*, **268**, February 1979, p.30.

36   Starr, C. Social benefit versus technological risk. *Science*, **165** 1969, 1232–8.

37   Chicken, J. C. *Hazard Control Policy in Britain* (Pergamon, Oxford; 1975), p.6.

38   Lord Ashby. The subjective side of assessing risks. *New Scientist*, 3 August 1977, p.399.

39   Kletz, T. A. What risks should we run? *New Scientist*, 12 May 1977, pp. 320–2.

40   *Ibid.* p.322.

41   Royal Commission on Environmental Pollution, Sixth Report. *Nuclear Power and the Environment* (HMSO, London; 1976).

42   Health and Safety Executive. *Canvey – an Investigation of Potential Hazards in the Canvey Island/Thurrock Area* (HMSO, London; 1978).

43   McGinty, L. and Atherley, G. Acceptability versus democracy. *New Scientist*, 12 May 1977, pp. pp.323–5.

44   Cohen, A. V. and Pritchard, D. K. *Comparative Risks of Electricity Production Systems*. HSE Research Paper 11 (HMSO, London; 1980).

45   Griffiths, R. G. A background of risks. Paper given at an Oyez conference on 'Living with Uncertainty: Risks in the Energy Scene', November 1981.

46   McGinty, L. and Atherley, G. Acceptability versus democracy. *New Scientist*, 12 May 1977, p. 323.

47   *Ibid.* p. 324.

48   Council for Science and Society. *The Acceptability of Risks* (Barry Rose, London; 1977), p.36.

49   See also: Otway, H. and Thomas, K. Reflections on risk perception and policy. *Risk Analysis*, **2**(2) 1982, 69–82.

50   Council for Science and Society. *The Acceptability of Risks* (Barry Rose, London; 1977), p.40 (their emphasis).

51   Dunleavy, P. Alternative theories of liberal democratic politics: the pluralist – marxist debate in the 1980s, in Potter, D. *et al.* (ed) *Society and the Social Sciences* (Routledge & Kegan Paul, London; 1981), pp. 200–20.

52   Miliband, R. *The State in Capitalist Society* (Quartet, London; 1973), p.115.

53   Ravetz, J. The political economy of risk. *New Scientist*, 8 September 1977, p.598.

54   For a useful discussion of many of these developments, see: Jessop, B. Recent theories of the capitalist state. *Cambridge Journal of Economics*, **1** 1977, 353–73.

55   Gough, I. *The Political Economy of the Welfare State* (Macmillan, London; 1979), pp. 41–2.

56   The two major papers in this important debate are reprinted in Urry, J. and Wakeford, J. *Power in Britain*. (Heinemann, London; 1973), pp. 291–314.

57   Russell, D. *The role of the chemical industries association in the regulation of the vinyl chloride monomer hazard*. Unpublished MSc

Thesis, Department of Liberal Studies in Science, University of Manchester, 1978.

58 For a discussion of these charges see: Williams, R. Politics and the ecology of regulation. *Public Administration*, **54** 1976, 319–31.

59 Open University. Government and technology. *Control of Technology, Units 3–4* (Open University Press, Milton Keynes; 1978).

60 For further discussion of pressure-group activities see: Dahl, R. A. *Modern Political Analysis* (Prentice-Hall, New Jersey; 1970). Kimber, R. and Richardson, J. (eds) *Pressure Groups in Britain* (Dent, London; 1974). Malecki, E. S. and Mahood, H. R. (eds) *Group Politics – a New Emphasis* (Scribner's, New York; 1972). Rivers, P. *Politics by Pressure* (Harrap, London; 1974).

61 Nelkin, D. The political impact of technical expertise. *Social Studies of Science.* **5** 1975, 37.

62 See Habermas, J. *Towards a Rational Society* (Heinemann, London; 1978), pp. 62–80.

63 For a discussion of some of these points see: Epstein, S. *The Politics of Cancer* (Sierra Club Books, San Francisco; 1978). Green, K. and Hudspith, R. Trade unions and technical expertise: the control of asbestos dust in British workplaces, in Skoie, H. (ed.) *Scientific Expertise and the Public*. Studies in Research and Higher Education (Oslo), **5** 1979, pp.153–70. Mitchell, R. C. Since *Silent Spring* : Science, technology and the environmental movement in the United States, in Skoie, H. (ed.) *Scientific Expertise and the Public*. Studies in Research and Higher Education. (Oslo), **5** 1979, pp. 171–207. Nelkin, D. *Technological Decisions and Democracy* (Sage, London; 1978). Open University. Trade Unions, Technology and the Environment. *Control of Technology, Unit 9* (Open University Press, Milton Keynes; 1978).

64 For a discussion of this topic see: Barnes, B. (ed.) *Sociology of Science* (Penguin, Harmondsworth; 1972). Blume, S. S. *Towards a Political Sociology of Science* (Free Press, New York; 1974). Lakoff, S. A. (ed.) *Knowledge and Power* (Free Press, New York; 1967).

65 Bundy, M. The scientist and national policy. *Science*, **139** 1963, 805–9. Gummett, P. *Scientists in Whitehall* (Manchester University Press, Manchester; 1980). Miser, J. The scientist as adviser, *Minerva* **IX** (1) January 1973, pp. 95–108. Primack, J. and von Hippel, F. *Advice and Dissent – Scientists in the Political Arena* (Basic Books, New York; 1974).

66 Lindblom, C. E. *The Policy-making Process* (Prentice-Hall, New Jersey; 1968), pp. 26–7. See also: *Idem. A strategy of Decision* (Free Press, New York; 1967).

Part II

Chapter 3

Technical approaches to road traffic safety

In this chapter the focus of attention will be on the 'science of road traffic safety',[1] i.e. the various forms of technical expertise that have been developed to analyse the phenomenon of road traffic accidents. The three major explanatory modes, or specialty frameworks, of relevance to road traffic safety will be discussed. However, before examining technical expertise any further, one general point is worth making. In terms of the research work involved and patterns of funding, the technical investigations which are collectively referred to here as the science of road traffic safety have traditionally been neglected when contrasted with comparable areas of safety research. It is certainly the case that there has been a large disparity between the funds allocated from various sources to road traffic accident investigation and, for example, aircraft safety. This is despite the comparatively small number of individuals killed in air crashes in any one year.[2] It should also be noted that, although road traffic safety research as a whole has not been an especially prestigious or well funded area, an additional factor is the uneven distribution of financial support within the field as a whole. This point can only be clarified by a detailed investigation of the science of road traffic safety itself.

As discussed in Chapter 2, an important feature of the analytical framework employed in this study is a conception of science not as a homogeneous structure, but rather as an internally diverse body of expertise in which conflicting assessments of a problem area may evolve. The technical controversies that follow are not necessarily a confrontation of 'good' and 'bad' science but may be the outcome of different disciplinary and specialty traditions finding themselves in competition for professional dominance over a specific question. In this chapter it will be argued that such an intellectual rivalry can be found with regard to the science of road traffic safety.

Within the broad area of technical competence which will be examined below, three distinct cognitive orientations can be discerned and these will be known from here on as 'traffic engineering', 'human factors' and 'occupant protection'. These labels have been chosen for convenience and because they are at least suggestive of the emphasis given by each explanatory model. Before discussing the detail of these three, the basis for the approaches can be presented in straightforward terms.

If the phenomenon of a particular road traffic accident is considered in an attempt to explain its causation, it soon becomes apparent that there are three relatively distinct ways in which to reach such an explanation. One is to inquire into the driver's (or the road user's) *mental state* – including psychological and alcohol or drug-related factors – and attempt to pinpoint the human error involved: failure to adjust vehicle speed to road surface, lack of attention, etc. An alternative approach may emphasise the design of the roads involved, and the general *highway environment*. Did the accident occur on a difficult bend, a badly lit intersection, or an inadequate road surface? The difference between this approach and the former, individual-oriented, perspective should be clear. However, a third type of explanation would again interpret the problem in very different terms. It is quite possible to focus on the structure of the *vehicles* involved, their capacity for accident avoidance and their crashworthiness once a collision has occurred. The above three modes of explanation correspond to our categorisation of the 'human factors', 'traffic engineering' and 'occupant protection' approaches to road traffic safety.

In the analysis that follows, the development of these three as technical specialties will be considered in some detail. It is also important to relate these frameworks to the political context in which they have evolved, e.g. government policies and the interests of vehicle manufacturers. In this and the subsequent two chapters these political elements will be examined.

Traffic engineering

The traffic engineering specialty has evolved from the discipline of civil engineering and has focused on the highway environment of the motor vehicle: the road surface, street lighting, traffic flow, signals and road signs. In 1939 the British Road Research Laboratory (RRL) was transferred to the general authority of the Ministry of Transport, its task being mainly to conduct research of this type.[3] This laboratory continues to be the leading centre of its type in Britain. In 1972, its name was altered to 'Transport and Road Research Laboratory' (TRRL) and this was indicative of a slightly broader ambit.

The earliest publications in this specialty date back to the 1930s and their titles give a reasonable indication of the type of problem which was being tackled: 'Traffic accidents and their relation to town planning and road construction',[4] 'Automatic street traffic signalling',[5] 'Laboratory investigations into the slipperiness of roads'[6]. Of course, not all traffic engineering research is directly concerned with safety, but a reduction in the number of road traffic accidents has always been one of the major themes within this approach. Baker, for example, has suggested that the most substantial advances in transportation safety – at least until the 1950s – emanated from just this area of research through its practical applications such as median barriers, traffic lights, and improved road intersections.[7]

The general case can be made that a training in civil and traffic engineering encourages the use of a type of explanation, and therefore an approach to policy and practice, which at least partially excludes the roles played by the driver and vehicle involved. Accordingly, research into this specialty has produced a number of distinct practical measures, which can be categorised into four types.

The first category is pedestrian protection and includes the zebra (pedestrian) crossing, pedestrian-controlled traffic signals and road-centre 'refuges'. The second set of measures relates to traffic flow. Traffic signals, road intersection design and control, street signs and parking arrangements, fixed speed limits and bypasses can all be said to have had a direct effect on road traffic accidents. A third basic category consists of the design and siting of road furniture: median barriers, safety fences and the layout of features such as side slopes, trees, sign supports and kerbs. A fourth line of research within this specialty deals with road surface characteristics. For accident prevention purposes skidding should be kept to an absolute minimum in all weather conditions[8] and research into alternative road surfaces has been extensive at the RRL.[9]

Perhaps one of the most prominent arguments for the traffic engineering approach in Britain came in the Buchanan Report to the Minister of Transport in 1963, *Traffic in Towns*. The terms of reference were 'to study the long-term developments of roads and traffic in urban areas and their influence on the urban environment'. The overall conclusion of this report as regards safety was that a major reduction in road traffic accidents could only come from 'sweeping physical changes' in the design of roads so that the number of possibilities for collision between vehicles or between vehicles and pedestrians would be reduced.[10]

This view can be seen as the essence of traffic engineering philosophy – that roads and road surroundings should be built so as to minimise the possibility of any serious accident occurring. The philosophy can be attacked by those who argue that the *real* cause of collisions is human failure, or that vehicle design can make collisions less physically damaging than at present, but the traffic engineering approach has been extremely influential in the USA and in Britain. It is also evident that this specialty complies with the interests of what can be termed the 'road lobby', i.e. those industries which are liable to benefit most from the road-building and redesign measures advocated by this technical focus. Hamer has suggested that the British TRRL has a specially close relationship with these groups as a result of technical cooperation and the build-up of strong personal ties.[11] Although such 'amicable cooperation' fits the general pattern set by the Department of Transport in this area,[12] there is no need to adopt 'conspiracy theories' or specify precise communication networks in order to demonstrate a link between this specialty and road-building programmes. That much is quite explicit in a report like *Traffic in Towns* and in the civil engineering background of most of the researchers involved in this area, as Hamer has asserted:

The academic discipline which is common to nearly all road lobby financed research is civil engineering ... Civil engineers in transport are primarily interested in building roads ... They tend to provide the justifications for road projects ...[13]

Although the link between those liable to benefit most from road-building programmes as advocated by the Buchanan Report or TRRL research and the traffic engineering specialty is relatively clear, it is perhaps less easy to understand why vehicle manufacturers (especially in the USA) should invest in this area. For example, Nader has argued that research within this field was the major focus of General Motors' crash investigation work between 1955 and 1965.[14] Nader accounts for this emphasis in two ways: first, that the research itself is relatively cheap to support and therefore serves a public relations function while only involving a handful of engineers and a small expenditure; secondly, the research directs public policy away from vehicle redesign standards and therefore from tooling and manpower costs to the company. In this way, traffic engineering research can serve an important ideological and propaganda function for a motor manufacturer.

One should be aware that Nader is also presenting a case for the occupant protection framework and consequently is highly critical of all other approaches to the road traffic safety problem. Again, one should be careful not to fall into a conspiracy theory account of the research–industrial interests relationship. However, without criticising the quality of individual research projects and the technical expertise involved, it is possible to identify broad research policy and to suggest that there has been a link in this case between the professional interests of the civil engineers involved in this specialty and the financial concerns of the road industry[15] and vehicle manufacturers.

Human factors

The central idea that I have tried to convey is that if we are to arrive at a better understanding of the 'causes' of road accidents we shall need to make a radical appraisal of the *motorist*.[16]

The above statement by a professor of psychology emphasises the contrast between this specialty framework and that of traffic engineering. At the centre of this research tradition can be found not the road environment, but the individual in control of a vehicle. The central precept is that it is the *driver* who is ultimately responsible for the situation: crash performance and road design would become redundant if total and effective human control could be maintained.

This psychologically based approach to road traffic accidents can be traced back to the work of Hugo Munsterberg[17] in 1913, when he was dealing with questions of safety in railways and other transportation systems. Munsterberg was particularly concerned with factors relating to 'job efficiency', i.e. productivity, and developed the notion of 'accident proneness'. The link between these two concepts is, of course, that accidents represent a considerable drain on national and industrial resources. Elimination of so-called accident-prone drivers could possibly produce large financial savings. The connection with occupational safety research should also be noted: both shared the notion of training the operative so as to reduce human error rather than redesigning the machine to compensate for lack of attention and errors of judgement.

In a 1931 study of bus and street railway operators in Boston, USA, Bingham claimed that some drivers had two or three times as many accidents as the overall average. He recommended that accident-prone drivers should be identified via various types of psychological testing and then either replaced or given remedial treatment.[18] A 1938 report[19] for the US Secretary of Agriculture concluded that drivers under the age of 25 had relatively high accident rates, with a decreasing rate thereafter until 60 or 65. This assessment is matched by modern statistical analyses of accident rates, and the concept of 'accident proneness' (normally in regard to age and occupation) has since become extremely important for actuarial techniques of vehicle insurance.

In 1935, Myers, a leading British psychologist, argued in *Nature*[20] that 80 to 90 per cent of road accidents are reducible to 'human causes'. This outlook has been consistently supported by the British Department of Transport, and one recent consultation document on transport policy included the claim that human error 'contributes' to 95 per cent of road traffic accidents.[21] The relationship of this specialty to official British thinking on road traffic safety will be discussed in a later chapter.

One spin-off from the human factors tradition has been the development of driver testing in most countries (since 1935 in Britain). Propaganda, another approach aimed at the 'human cause', has also been used extensively worldwide. Of course, a third method of modifying individual behaviour is via the introduction of compulsory measures and enforced regulations – speed limits, traffic laws, or compulsory seat-belt wear. This mandatory approach rejects persuasion and determines that individual freedom of action should be subordinate to the aims of general public safety[22] in certain areas. The emergence of an ergonomic focus within this specialty must also be noted. This was considered first in aviation around the Second World War period and has gradually filtered into vehicle design. Ergonomics has been widely applied to industrial techniques and processes with the intention of improving worker efficiency (again, the link between this specialty and industrial safety and productivity can be seen). The ergonomic approach seeks to design motor vehicles so that human control can be enhanced to the greatest degree and 'efficiency' maximised. In practice, this involves attention to features such as the careful layout of instrumentation and steering, speed and braking controls, in order that essential information is relayed to the driver without causing undue distraction.[23] Vehicle manufacturers in Britain and the USA do seem to be taking an increased interest in such considerations, possibly because of a concern for safety, but also because features of this type can make cars seem more 'luxurious' to the buyer.

It can be seen from the description so far of the human factors explanatory framework that it includes a whole range of intellectual approaches which share a focus on the individual road user (and especially the driver) as causing road traffic accidents. To these approaches can be added the social psychological investigation of human behaviour. This form of analysis suggests that the motor car has produced a fundamental change in certain social relationships and has created new social roles and types of interaction: between drivers, between driver and pedestrian, etc. Social norms of courtesy and consideration for others are negated by this new social context: a state of anomie prevails among road users, with clear repercussions for road traffic safety.[24]

Klein has developed a rather different form of social psychological explanation, which he terms a 'hydraulic theory'.[25] This sees the major obstacle to progress in accident prevention (at least in the USA) as stemming from the cultural values of society. Klein's view is that American children are inculcated into adopting a set of values which stress aggressive competitiveness, individual initiative, independence of action, risk-seeking behaviour and personal achievement. The expression of these values may have had a place in the 'frontier society', but they are systematically prevented from fulfilment in the routine and risk-minimising systems of capitalist production. Consequently, the individual attempts to compensate in the sphere of consumption rather than production − hence the popular interest in high-energy, high-risk devices such as aircraft, snowmobiles and automobiles, and hence also the frequently 'irresponsible' manner in which these are utilised. The hypothesis is 'hydraulic' because of its implication that whereas efforts to force down the accident rate in one area of activity may be successful, they will merely serve to force the rate *up* in some other, perhaps leisure-related, sector.

The case put forward by Klein is reminiscent of Starr's belief (see Chapter 2) that there are fixed and determinable levels of 'acceptable risk' in society which cannot be reduced without producing counter-tendencies that cause the overall level of risk taking to rise once again. A similar point has also been made by Peltzman[26] with specific regard to the type of automobile regulation that will be discussed in the following chapter. Peltzman argues that such regulation has been ineffective because accident rates are determined not by federal laws but by supply and demand factors. Mandatory safety devices merely produce a compensation effect in the form of greater driver risk-taking. Related arguments have been put forward repeatedly in Britain to oppose compulsory seat-belt wear. Needless to say, the hypotheses put forward by Klein, Starr and Peltzman have been hotly disputed by those concerned to develop stricter vehicle design standards and, in particular, by proponents of the occupant protection approach.

Pease, in a useful paper,[27] has summarised the main theories of individual causation and considered the evidence for each. According to this author the main theories range from the claim that all drivers have equal chances of an accident to suggestions that motorists differ in their physical abilities, psychological traits, or liability to anxiety. Quite clearly, each of the theories also has certain policy implications.

The close relationship between the human factors research tradition and public policies for road traffic safety should be noted. For example, the legal systems of both the USA and Britain tend to pin responsibility for accidents on individuals as 'guilty parties'. In recent years this bias may have altered somewhat so that 'product liability' cases are also being heard in the USA[28] and moves have at least commenced in Britain towards 'no-fault' compensation schemes.[29] Nevertheless, the main emphasis in both countries remains on the assessment of accidents in terms of individual responsibility. This conventional wisdom is also reflected in the normal preparation by the police of accident reports – with a consequent effect on official statistics such as those used by the Department of Transport.

Barry has argued that this individualistic approach (which is typical of the human factors perspective) can be interpreted as a clear example of 'blaming the victim', i.e. pinning responsibility on those actually involved in accidents and, therefore, removing the need for structural changes.[30] The concept of 'victim blaming' was originally developed by Ryan,[31] who saw the underlying notion as serving an important ideological function in regard to a number of social problems, e.g. poverty, family breakdowns, educational failure. For Ryan, 'victim blamers' refuse to relate these problems to the broader social structure of which they form only a part (including income distribution, racial inequality, power structures, etc.), and instead focus their attention on the character and behaviour of the individuals who are actually 'suffering' the problem. This attitude is ideological inasmuch as it presents a 'systematic distortion of reality' – although an unconsciously developed one in many cases – which serves to maintain the status quo.

Barry maintains that human-factors-based policies fulfil an identical ideological purpose: individually-oriented programmes create the illusion that something is being done to improve road traffic safety, but without actually necessitating any more radical – or effective – measures:

... the ideology in particular serves the interest of powerful groups who stand to bear the greatest burden in solving the problem. That is, it protects those groups most able to prevent the problem in the first place.[32]

The 'powerful groups' in this case could be identified most clearly as the 'road lobby', vehicle manufacturers and national governments. However, as with the traffic engineering specialty and its relationship to road-building industries, one must take extreme care in suggesting any type of ideological connection between a specialty and vested social interests. It has been the case that, in the rivalry between these specialties for funding and access to policy making, allegations of 'capitulation to industry' have been prevalent – although only rarely voiced in any public forum. This much is inevitable, given the sudden and explicit 'politicisation' of these frameworks in the USA during the mid-1960s when the policy implications of each specialty became a major public issue. The very fact that, until the 1970s in the USA, so much of research into the science of road traffic safety was funded by industry rather than by 'independent' or academic sources itself leaves much technical data open to such accusations.

Whilst wishing to make the above reservations, it is apparent that vehicle manufacturers and British and US governments have (at least until the 1960s in the USA, and until very recently in Britain) shown a reluctance to back research voluntarily on a significant scale into anything other than the traffic engineering and human factors specialties. There has been a lack of interest in both countries in the sponsorship of research into occupant protection, and it seems more than likely that this fact is related to the policy implications of this specialty. Manufacturers, for whatever reasons, have preferred – at least since the time of Sloan[33] – to concentrate on changes in styling rather than crash protection measures. The lack of enthusiasm from the major research sponsors in this whole area could only have had an inhibiting effect on the third of the traditions of road traffic safety analysis.

Occupant protection

The third specialty differs once again in regard to the element of the 'road traffic safety problem' seen as causative and the cognitive framework brought to bear. The occupant protection approach focuses on the vehicle itself, borrowing from the techniques of automotive and mechanical engineering and also from medical, physiological and traumatological[34] expertise.

One branch of this specialty deals with pre-collision safety (i.e. accident avoidance). Relative to post-collision research (i.e. crash protection) this has been well funded; in Britain a large amount of work has been carried out at the (T)RRL and also at the Motor Industry Research Association (MIRA) on this topic. Research has focused on items such as braking[35] (including tyre adhesion), steering mechanisms[36] and vehicle suspension. Manufacturers have certainly shown more interest in these design developments than in 'collision packaging' (see below). The problem still remains, however, that without any clear economic or regulatory incentive, the industry has demonstrated little zeal for the actual innovation of even collision-avoidance technology. Far more attention has been paid to annual styling changes, in the belief that these have a direct benefit for sales, than on less visible engineering modifications. For example, anti-lock brakes have been considered practicable for over two decades, and yet in Britain they are still only fitted to a minority of 'up-market' motor cars.[37] The introduction of new safety features tends to occur very slowly, with a 'filtering effect' down to the more modest models. This point has been discussed at length by a number of commentators.[38]

The second branch of this specialty, collision phase protection,[39] has risen to political prominence relatively recently, although its roots can be traced back somewhat further. During the early 1960s it became accepted among technical experts and policy makers that it was possible to package the vehicle occupant so that in a collision only physically tolerable forces are transmitted through the body. This view at that time represented a 'new wave' of research which challenged the 'old guards' of the other two specialty frameworks. The following chapter will discuss the political significance of this in some detail.

One of the best sources available for a review of this specialty is an influential book which appeared in the USA in 1964. Entitled *Accident Research — Methods and Approaches*,[40] this work attempted to synthesise the major research papers relating to this topic. In one section (Chapter 9, 'Factors that determine injury') the history of 'injury causation research' is discussed in terms which would later be utilised by Ralph Nader in his *Unsafe at Any Speed*, and also became embodied in US motor vehicle safety legislation in 1966. In fact, the major author of this particular chapter, W. Haddon Jr, later became the first Director of the National Highway Safety Bureau (NHSB).

The first major contribution to the literature on energy transfer during accidents was DeHaven's 1942 paper 'Mechanical analysis of survival in falls from heights of fifty to one hundred and fifty feet' in the journal *War Medicine*.[41] DeHaven's interest in this research followed his own involvement in a mid-air collision in 1917. Of the four pilots operating the two similarly designed aeroplanes, only DeHaven survived. His efforts at resolving this paradox in a scientific manner (i.e. rejecting 'good luck' as a cause) led him to examine a number of cases of the 'miraculous' survival of individuals when falling from great heights. The 1942 paper included eight such case studies which were based on inadvertent falls or suicide attempts. For each incident DeHaven produced an estimation of the velocity of body impact involved and the injuries received. The general conclusions drawn by DeHaven from these eight incidents are highly pertinent to the development of this specialty approach. The overall argument was that the human body is capable of withstanding tremendously large decelerative forces *if* those forces are channelled correctly. DeHaven was extremely aware of the policy implications for automobile safety and this point was also emphasised in his paper.

DeHaven's ideas were taken up by Colonel J. P. Stapp of the US Air Force. Stapp and his colleagues performed a series of experiments on human volunteers and animals with the aim of calculating the limits of human tolerance to rapid deceleration. Beginning in 1946 and using a rocket-propelled sled and 2000 ft of railway track, a number of tests were carried out. Stapp subjected himself at one point to a force of 40 **G**. In this way, data were accumulated on the effects of different levels of deceleration. This information has since provided the basis for many studies of crash protection measures. In a 1957 paper, Stapp stressed – just as DeHaven had done before him – the importance of applying this knowledge of the structural strength of the human body to automobile design so as to produce 'a great saving of lives and prevention of disabilities'.[42]

By the late 1950s, a number of projects in the USA were developing the 'energy management' framework which is central to this specialty. What these studies shared in terms of overall framework can be better explained by an idea developed in the late 1940s;[43] the notion of the 'second collision'. The first collision – the impact of the vehicle with an external object – may well be unavoidable, but it is the *second* collision, when occupants are thrown into the vehicle interior, which causes passenger injury and death. The work of individuals like Stapp and DeHaven concentrated on this second collision from the occupant's perspective.[44] Furthermore, it is basic to this approach that the circumstances surrounding a particular road traffic accident (driver carelessness, bad road conditions) become entirely irrelevant. The only pertinent factor in determining the extent and nature of injuries is the magnitude of decelerative forces involved and their concentrations throughout the human body.

... it is the manner in which energy is dissipated that determines the results of mishaps, not the antecedent causes, whatever they might be. This has been overlooked in most accident prevention and research.[45]

In 1959, D. P. Moynihan, who was subsequently to become US Ambassador to the United Nations and a leading political figure, wrote an article[46] which was based on occupant protection and aimed at a general audience. In the same year, Ralph Nader's first publication on automobile safety appeared[47] and again this drew heavily on the same research tradition. As will be discussed in the next chapter, the energy management concept had begun to be translated from a little-explored theoretical insight into a major political focus as a whole popular movement rose to prominence. As McCarry has observed,[48] both Moynihan and Nader blamed the vehicle manufacturers for the rising numbers of road traffic accidents, attacked the inertia of the government on this issue, and argued that the regulatory policies of the time were totally inadequate.

It is significant that at least three of the major exponents of the occupant protection framework in the USA became directly linked to the preparation and enactment of the 1966 Vehicle Safety Act (to be discussed in the next chapter): Moynihan as head of the policy planning staff that drafted the legislation, Nader as a major public figure, and Haddon as first head of the regulatory agency. By the late 1960s, the 'new wave' of occupant protection formed the basis for the US government control of road traffic safety; although this should certainly not be interpreted as suggesting that total consensus had been reached between the specialties. Havelock[49] has described US inter-specialty rivalry during the late 1960s as a 'tug of war' in which occupant protection had made steady gains, but certainly had not established complete dominance. The relationship of this rivalry to British and US public policies is explored throughout this book.

In Britain, occupant protection research has developed rather more slowly. The original Road Research Laboratory had, as its name suggests, been involved mainly with the traffic engineering framework. However, by 1963, the RRL could report that a number of such studies had been undertaken, e.g. an examination of accident-damaged vehicles, an analysis of occupant injuries, on-the-spot accident investigations, laboratory tests of seats, steering wheels and windscreens, and the design of safety devices.[50] Nevertheless, all these studies were being undertaken on a smaller scale than parallel work in the United States at that time. In its defence the RRL argued that the British 'accident profile' is rather different from that of the USA: whereas in the United States most of the injuries are sustained by vehicle occupants, in Britain a larger proportion of pedestrians, cyclists and motorcyclists are affected. (This point will be discussed in Chapter 10.)

One accusation which has been made by those involved in the political dimensions of the occupant protection framework is that manufacturers wilfully ignored design-related safety features because of the cost this would incur in re-tooling, increased prices and consequent loss of sales. Furthermore, Nader has argued that the motor industry's resistance to such measures has hampered the development of this research tradition.[51] Automotive engineering has been inextricably linked to the manufacturers who provide its only practical outlet and this fact has moulded the whole direction of research into an *industry*-based focus. Technical investigations have not been conducted solely for the sake of improving scientific understanding: they have largely been channelled so as to fit the requirements of the motor companies.

The lack of a 'critical science'[52] type of occupant protection approach in the USA until the late 1950s may indeed have been linked to the automobile industry's dominance over this branch of the science of road traffic safety, but this is not to suggest any 'buying off' of research workers. It seems inevitable that the manufacturers will show greater enthusiasm for developing technical expertise which will further existing design strategies (better styling, greater comfort for the occupants, smoother engines, etc.). Until the mid-1960s in the USA no political force had emerged to counter this dominance; the emergence of such a force in that country will be the subject of the next chapter.

Conclusion

In this discussion a sociological approach to technical expertise has been advocated which is based first, on an examination of the internal cognitive structures of scientific research, and secondly, on the study of the relationship between the available branches of knowledge and broader social interests. By an analysis of the different bodies of expertise which have focused on the single problem area of road traffic accident causation, it has been shown that no single, definitive 'scientific explanation' may exist but rather an array of explanations, each based on separate intellectual traditions and advocating rather different public policies.

The analytical approach presented here also suggests a valid basis for understanding the relationship between technical expertise and social interests in this context. Given the existence of relatively distinct specialties in this problem area, it is not surprising for an organisation to provide facilities for the development of research work which it sees as ultimately to its own advantage. There may be a *direct* relationship between research and self-interest (as in the case of the road industry and traffic engineering), or a more *indirect* link (as with vehicle manufacturers and human factors). In the former case, public policy is directed towards certain strategies; in the latter, it is diverted away from undesirable courses of action. The emergence of other forms of social interest to challenge the relevant industries may alter this knowledge – social interest relationship and lead to the strengthening of specialty approaches which have previously been ignored.

An important aspect of the interaction between the development of technical expertise and wider social forces as presented here is the *relative autonomy* of each entity. Although it is being argued that there is a definite relationship between the two, this is not to imply that either necessarily dominates the other, or that the relationship is static. Industry strategies may change, so that a company sees it as being to its commercial advantage to exploit the occupant protection framework (as certain European manufacturers have done since the 1970s).[53] Specialty approaches may also adopt new lines of thought and research directions which no longer reinforce the self-interest of dominant social groupings. The type of interaction being described here is not a simplistic notion of some direct link between the sponsorship of research and the emergence of 'expedient knowledge', but rather a more complex association between technical expertise and interests, the precise nature of which in any particular context can only be determined by careful examination. The analysis of this association as it relates to road traffic safety will continue throughout the rest of this book. Clearly, however, it is also desirable for a similar theoretical approach to be applied to other areas of technical and social concern, in order to test its general validity.

As a final note at this juncture, it should be emphasised that it is not the argument of this chapter that the three specialty approaches are completely divided from each other as entirely 'watertight' intellectual traditions. In fact, there are overlaps between the three so that, for example, the accident avoidance strand of occupant protection (brakes, lights, tyres, etc.) may well borrow insights from the ergonomic principles found with the human factors framework. Communication *is* possible between practitioners of the three specialties, but this exchange of information is substantially hindered by the fundamental assumptions about accident causation which lie behind each approach.

Notes and references

1   This is an appropriate point at which to explain the use of 'road traffic safety' and 'road traffic accident' in this book. There is a definite semantic problem in that the selection of a term like 'road safety' implies a specific (i.e. road-oriented) approach to the problem and this is true also of 'traffic safety' or 'vehicle safety'. Accordingly, 'road traffic safety' has been adopted as the most appropriate term.

2   For example: Baker, R. F. *The Highway Risk Problem – Policy Issues in Highway Safety* (Wiley, New York; 1971), p.28. Hartman, C. H. The evaluation and improvement of motor vehicle safety through regulation, in *Proc. Fourth International Congress on Automotive Safety* (USGPO,

Washington, DC; 1975), p.270.

3 Before 1939 the laboratory had existed as a branch of the Department of Scientific and Industrial Research. Two RRL publications serve as excellent reviews of Traffic Engineering research until the early 1960s: RRL Library Bibliography. *Guide to Reference Literature in the Field of Traffic Engineering Published since 1932.* No. 293/PON, April 1958. RRL. *Research on Road Safety* (HMSO, London; 1963), Chapter 14.

4 Muller, F. *Verkehrsunfalle in ihrer Beziehung zum Stadte und Strassenbau* (Verlag Konrad Triltsch, Wurzburg; 1933).

5 Harrison, H. H. and Priest, T. D. *Automatic Street Traffic Signalling* (Pitman, London; 1934).

6 Saal, R. N. J. Laboratory investigations into the slipperiness of roads. *J. Soc. Chem. Ind.* **55** (1) 1936 3–7.

7 Baker, R. F. *The Highway Risk Problem – Policy Issues in Highway Safety* (Wiley, New York; 1971)

8 On dry road surfaces approximately 8 per cent of accidents involve skidding; for wet roads this figure varies from 15 to 40 per cent. Mackay, G. M. *A Review of Road Accident Research.* University of Birmingham, Department of Transportation and Environmental Planning, Departmental Publication No. 10, 1965, p.26.

9 See: RRL *Research on Road Safety* (HMSO, London; 1963).

10 *Traffic in Towns* (HMSO, London; 1963), p.16.

11 Hamer, M. *Wheels within Wheels* (Friends of the Earth, London; 1974), p. 23.

12 See later chapters.

13 Hamer, M. *Wheels within Wheels* (Friends of the Earth, London; 1974), p.32.

14 Nader, R. *Unsafe at Any Speed* (Pocket Books, New York; 1966), p.136.

15 'Road industry' in this sense would include the cement and concrete, quarrying, asphalt and coated macadam, tar, sand and gravel industries represented in the UK by the following trade associations: Cement and Concrete Association (CCA), British Quarrying and Slag Federation (BQSF), Asphalt and Coated Macadam Association (ACMA), British Tar Industries Association (BTIA), and Sand and Gravel Association (SAGA).

16 Cohen, J. and Preston, B. *Causes and Prevention of Road Accidents* (Faber & Faber, London; 1968), p.115.

17 Munsterberg, M. *Hugo Munsterberg – his Life and Work* (Appleton, New York 1922).

18 Bingham, W. V. The prone to accident driver. *Proc. Seventeenth Annual Conference on Highway Engineering.* Ann Arbor, Michigan; 1931, pp.1–12.

19 Secretary of Agriculture. Motor Vehicle Traffic Conditions in the United States, Part Six. *The Accident Prone Driver.* House Document No. 462 (USGPO, Washington, DC; 1938).

20 Myers, C. S. The psychological approach to the problem of road accidents. *Nature* **86** 1935, 740–2.

21 Department of the Environment. *Transport Policy* Vol. 1 (HMSO,

London; 1976), p.75.

22   This issue will be discussed in greater detail during the analysis of compulsory-seat-belt debates in Chapter 7.

23   See, for example: Black, S. *Man and Motor Cars* (Secker & Warburg, London; 1966), p.43.

24   Godart, A. Approche sociologique de la securité routière. *Revue de l'Institut de Sociologie* (4) 1970, 638.

25   Klein, D. The influence of societal values on rates of death and injury. *J. Safety Research*, **3** 1971, 2–8. See also: Dowie, J. and Pym, C. Risk to life and limb. *Risk: a Second Level University Course*, Unit 11. (Open University, Milton Keynes; 1980), pp.21–3.

26   Peltzman, S. The effects of automobile safety regulation. *J. Political Economy*, **83**(4) 1975, 677–725.

27   Pease, K. A study of accident proneness. *Care on the Road*, August 1972, pp.8–9.

28   See Chapter 8.

29   Royal Commission on Civil Liability and Compensation for Personal Injury. (Chairman: Lord Pearson). Cmnd 7054/978.

30   Barry, P. Z. Individual versus collective responsibility for safety: an unexamined policy issue, in *Proc. Fourth International Congress on Automotive Safety* (USGPO, Washington, DC; 1975), pp.37–47.

31   Ryan, W. *Blaming the Victim* (Orbach and Chambers, London; 1971).

32   Barry, P. Z. Individual versus collective responsibility for safety: on unexamined policy issue, in *Proc. Fourth International Congress on Automotive Safety* (USGPO, Washington, DC; 1975), p.40.

33   Alfred Sloan at GM in the USA was largely responsible for taking production away from 'Fordism' (utility models at ever lower price) and towards a greater diversity of models with annual design changes and 'improvements' (usually of a stylistic nature). This policy is usually known as 'Sloanism' and has dominated the market since the 1950s. See: Rothschild, E. *Paradise Lost* (Allen Lane, London; 1973), Chapter 2.

34   Traumatology is the branch of surgery dealing with injury from accidents (trauma).

35   See: Curtis, A. Taking the skid out of braking. *New Scientist*, 12 August 1971, pp. 358–61. Institute of Mechanical Engineers (I.Mech.E.) *Braking of Road Vehicles* (I.Mech.E., London; 1976). RRL. *Research on Road Safety* (HMSO, London; 1963), Chapter 11.

36   Curtis, A. Revolution in car steering. *New Scientist*, 15 September 1977, pp.670–1.

37   Dunlop Rubber Company. Anti-skid device. Preliminary report on a Dunlop development that is a significant contribution to road safety. *Auto Engineer*, **48**(7) 1958, 248–54.

38   Rothschild has described the automobile industry as being in a state of 'technological inertia': Rothschild, E. *Paradise Lost* (Allen Lane, London; 1973). See also: Abernathy, J. *The Productivity Dilemma – Roadblock to Innovation in the Automobile Industry* (Johns Hopkins University Press, Boston; (1978). Ensor, J. *The Motor Industry*

(Longman, London; 1971). White, L. J. *The Automobile Industry since 1945* (Harvard University Press, Cambridge, Mass.; 1971).

39   The third branch, which we will not discuss here, is the 'post-collision' phase, i.e. the provision of ambulance and medical services to ensure the best possible accident recovery rate.

40   Haddon, W. Jr, Suchman, E. A. and Klein, D. *Accident Research – Methods and Approaches* (Harper & Row, New York; 1964).

41   *Ibid.* pp.539–46, and De Haven, H. Mechanical analysis of survival in falls from heights of fifty to one hundred and fifty feet. *War Medicine*, **2**, July 1942, 586–96.

42   Haddon, W. Jr, Suchman, E. A. and Klein, D. *Accident Research – Methods and Approaches* (Harper & Row, New York; 1964), p.561, and Stapp, J. P. Human tolerance to deceleration. *Am. J. Surg.* **93**(4), 1957, 740.

43   In fact by an Indiana State policeman, Elmer Paul, who later worked with DeHaven on the Cornell project.

44   The protection of pedestrians, etc. did not feature as a focus in the USA until much later. However, British emphasis on this problem emerged somewhat sooner – see reference 50.

45   Haddon, W. Jr., Suchman, E. A. and Klein, D. *Accident Research – Methods and Approaches* (Harper & Row, New York; 1964), p.596.

46   Moynihan, D. P. Epidemic on the highways. *Reporter*, 30 April 1959.

47   Nader, R. The safe car you can't buy. *The Nation*, 11 April 1959.

48   McCarry, C. *Citizen Nader* (Saturday Review Press, New York; 1972), p.71.

49   Havelock, R. G. with Markowitz, E. A. *A National Problem-solving System: Highway Safety Researchers and Decision Makers.* Report from Centre for Research on Utilization of Scientific Knowledge, Institute for Social Research, The University of Michigan, Ann Arbor, Michigan, May 1971, p.158.

50   RRL *Research on Road Safety* (HMSO, London; 1963), pp.462–3.

51   Nader, R. *Unsafe at Any Speed* (Pocket Books, New York; 1966).

52   See Ravetz, J. R. *Scientific Knowledge and its Social Problems* (Penguin, Harmondsworth; 1971), p.424.

53   Volvo and Rover represent examples where safety has been used as a major selling point.

Chapter 4

Road traffic safety policy in the USA

In the following two chapters, the general national approaches to road traffic safety which have been adopted in the United States and Britain will be described and discussed. This broad treatment will thus serve as background to the particular case studies that will be considered in later chapters. A full understanding of contemporary debates over specific issues like the air bag or mandatory seat-belt wear depends upon an awareness of the assumptions about road traffic safety which are embedded in the British and United States 'styles' of policy making.

For the USA, the single most radical change in national strategy took place in September 1966 when President Johnson signed the National Traffic and Motor Vehicle Safety Act[1] following its unanimous passage through both the Senate and the House of Representatives. The special significance of this legislation makes it appropriate to divide the discussion of US policy into two parts. First of all, there is the background to the Act (from here simply known as the '1966 Safety Act') and its antecedents. Following this, the actual content of the law will be reviewed and federal controls up till the present date will be considered.

The background to the 1966 Safety Act

Perhaps the most popular explanation for this Act and its political impact focuses on one man, Ralph Nader. Just as Rachel Carson and her book *Silent Spring*[2] are often portrayed as the initiators of a new concern with the environment in the 1960s, Nader is judged to have played a similar role in making road traffic safety an important national issue for the USA in 1965–66 and the subsequent years.

There is little doubt that the publication in November 1965 of Nader's *Unsafe at Any Speed*[3] had a considerable effect on public attitudes towards road traffic safety. The book represented a damning indictment of the motor manufacturers' approach to vehicle design and of the 'designed-in dangers' of the American automobile. Nader drew upon the occupant protection approach outlined in the previous chapter and made an explicitly political case regarding the need to concentrate on crashworthiness rather than changes in styling. However, Nader's contribution to the US debate on road traffic safety must be seen in context and, in particular, with regard to the political developments that had taken place since the mid-1950s in the USA and the various attempts that had been made to 'translate' the technical arguments about occupant protection into the domain of public policy. Accordingly, we will return to a discussion of Nader's role after an examination of other major events and key figures.

Although this account of events leading up to the 1966 legislation will concentrate on the preceding decade, it is worth reviewing the years prior to the mid-1950s very briefly. During this earlier period, there had been a strong consensus between the state and federal legislatures, the vehicle manufacturers and those organisations like the National Safety Council (NSC) who formed the 'safety establishment' of the time that road traffic safety was not a contentious or, in any way, a political issue. It was accepted by these groups that action along the lines suggested by the traffic engineering and human factors frameworks was the best way of dealing with the problem of road traffic accidents, i.e. the encouragement of road-building programmes and attempts to alter driver behaviour by education or propaganda.[4] The NSC was the main independent body operating in the area and this organisation has consistently emphasised the central importance of the 'human factor' in matters of safety.[5] The parallel between this period in the United States and present British policies will be explored in the next chapter.

In 1937, the Automotive Safety Foundation was founded. This was largely supported by the American Manufacturers Association (AMA) and it acted as an intermediary between the AMA and the White House. In 1954, a 'President's Committee for Traffic Safety' was established – largely on the initiative of Harlow Curtice, head of General Motors. However, there is no record of any recommendations for major policy reform emanating from either of these groups.

A fresh initiative on road traffic safety took place in 1956 when Congressman Kenneth Roberts was Chairperson of a House subcommittee on traffic safety (Appendix 1 contains a chronology of events for the years 1956–66). Hearings began on 16 July of that year and they represented a new forum for representatives of industry, government and research centres to express their views. The hearings continued until 1963 when Roberts lost his seat in Congress. At least one commentator has suggested that the approach taken by the motor manufacturers at that time was to encourage greater 'consumer education' and 'further research' without actually undertaking any of these tasks themselves.[6] The industry favoured stricter vehicle inspection as a means of maintaining safety (of course, such inspection would encourage the removal of old vehicles from the population and so increase demand for newer models), but any serious discussion of design standards was discouraged. Congressman Roberts frequently expressed frustration at the attitude of federal officials towards motor vehicle safety standards. Indeed, until 1969 these fell under the jurisdiction of the Department of Commerce, and Roberts certainly felt that the responsibility of this department for the commercial viability of the motor industry made it totally unresponsive to any attempts at controlling vehicle safety.[7]

The Roberts hearings are particularly interesting because they illustrate the lack of public or media interest in road traffic safety during the 1956–63 period and also the apathy and opposition shown by Congress towards any regulatory changes. However, there were some groups – mainly related directly or indirectly to the medical profession[8] – that did lobby for a more radical approach to safety. A small number of independent engineers also testified[9] and many of these opposed the traffic engineering/human factors consensus by presenting a case for national vehicle design standards.

The most active opposition to the development of safety controls on the motor vehicle came from the manufacturers, either individually or via the AMA. The industry were of the opinion that 'Safety doesn't sell', this viewpoint being expressed as long ago as 1929 by Alfred P. Sloan, former President of General Motors and a very important figure in the development of the motor industry, in correspondence with the president of a US safety glass manufacturing company.

I may be all wrong, but I feel that General Motors should not adopt safety glass for its cars and raise its prices even a part of what the extra cost would be. I can only see competition being forced into the same position. Our gain would be that both competition and ourselves would have reduced the return on our capital, and the public would have obtained still more value per dollar expended . . .[10]

Sloan's argument against safety glass (a particular topic to which we shall return in a later chapter) can be accommodated within Galbraith's analysis of 'oligopolies'[11] where a small number of companies dominate a particular market and share a monopoly between them – in this case General Motors, Ford and Chrysler. In such a situation, companies see stability and regular, constant profits as the key to maintaining their success rather than fluctuations in turnover and 'business wars'. Externally imposed standards serve to create uncertainty in the market and are judged as undesirable for two major reasons: first, because the cost impact, if passed through as price increases along with the effects of inflation and increased production costs, may well affect sales adversely by growing faster than consumer income; secondly, because the industry is resistant to such standards simply on the grounds that they are *externally*-imposed and threaten the sovereignty of the industry to plan for the future as it sees fit.

These points concerning the economic and political unacceptability of national standards are clearly interrelated. Even after the 1966 legislation was enacted, they emerged once again during the mid-1970s and early 1980s. Also related to both these points is the view that 'Safety doesn't sell', i.e. price increases for the purpose of improving vehicle crashworthiness are viewed by potential customers in purely negative terms.[12]

Nader and others have countered this argument by claiming that safety never has been 'sold'. Safety features tended to be available only on the customer's special request. In this extract, Nader uses seat belts as an example of the manufacturers' down-playing of safety:

Although they had a long record of success in creating a public demand for even the most superficial automotive features, the manufacturers lamented the absence of demand for seat belts while they made it difficult for such a demand ever to materialize.[13]

This treatment of safety was not a reflection of the consumers' lack of interest but rather of the manufacturers' fear that vehicle safety might become a major issue – to the detriment of their trade. Such attention, according to Nader, would highlight the more undesirable and deleterious aspects of the motor car. This argument provides yet another reason for the industry's antipathy towards vehicle safety standards.

One controversy over the effects on sales of safety innovation relates to an important instance before the late-1960s in the USA of a manufacturer opting to incorporate safety as a major feature of its

model range. Robert McNamara, then a vice-president of Ford Motor
Company, made the decision to sell the 1956 model range of Ford cars
largely on the basis of 'Lifeguard Design'. McNamara had in fact been
impressed by the work on occupant protection conducted at Cornell
University. Ford models for that year were fitted with a number of
features that had developed from the occupant protection specialty
approach. These included safety door latches and impact-absorbing
steering wheels as standard, with padded instrument panels, seat belts
and sun visors as optional extras. Not only did Ford offer this
equipment, it also marketed safety in a most aggressive manner.

One of the new vehicles sold with the 'Lifeguard Design' strategy
was the Ford Edsel, which came into direct competition with a new
General Motors product, a V-8 powered Chevrolet. However, the
'Lifeguard Design' concept was soon withdrawn, giving rise to two
quite different accounts of the episode. What *is* undoubtedly true is
that Ford returned to their previous strategy of emphasising the
stylistic virtues of their motor cars rather than their crashworthiness –
after a period of only one year. What is less clear is why Ford should
make this sudden change in strategy. Many accounts have seen the
'Lifeguard' concept as a simple commercial mistake, thus reinforcing
the notion that 'Safety doesn't sell'. An alternative interpretation was
offered by a 1966 article in *Fortune*, the US business magazine.

General Motors officials were dumbfounded, and then furious. Ford's tactics,
they believed, would not sell its own cars and would frighten buyers away
from everyone else's. Some of them, moreover, made their views known
forcefully to their counterparts at Ford. The auto industry, for all its
competitiveness, is a clubby business, and many an outraged telephone call
went out from the G.M. building in Detroit to Ford headquarters in nearby
Dearborn – and not without effect . . .[14]

Or, to continue the story in Nader's less compromising prose:

G.M. said stop and Ford literally screeched to a halt, with . . . ex-G.M. Ford
executives getting McNamara to switch gears to an advertising campaign that
emphasised styling and performance rather than safety.[15]

This version of the events has not been accepted by either company
and it is perhaps debatable whether even General Motors' market
dominance could make Ford 'screech to a halt' when the latter had a
massive investment in 'Lifeguard Design'. However, it is interesting to
note John DeLorean's conviction, based on his own broad experience
of working for General Motors, that the company's competitors only

survive on 'GM's sufferance'. According to DeLorean, the other large firms could be forced out of existence, within as little time as one year, by General Motors simply lowering their prices across the range.[16] Ford's action was certainly not designed to perpetuate the oligopolistic harmony of the industry, and the reaction of other manufacturers, including General Motors, to this was perhaps very predictable. Whatever the case, the 'Lifeguard Experiment' is still used to demonstrate both the 'Safety doesn't sell' *and* the 'Industry refuses to sell safety' arguments. Certainly, at least under the leadership of Henry Ford II, the Ford Motor Company made no further attempts to market vehicle crashworthiness as a major sales feature.

We could build a tank that would creep over the highways and you could bang 'em into each other and nobody would ever get a scratch. But nobody would buy it either. The American people want good cars, good looking cars, fast cars, cars with power and styling and that's the kind of car we build.[17]

It was in a similar mood of hostility to even voluntary safety innovation that the motor industry appeared before the Roberts hearings between 1956 and 1963. What Roberts did achieve despite this opposition was a small, but symbolic, change in the operation of a law which allowed the federal government to establish safety standards for motor vehicles purchased for its own use. From 30 August 1964,[18] jurisdiction for the establishment of such standards was transferred from the Department of Commerce (whose attitude was discussed earlier) to General Services Administration (GSA). The latter was now in the position of specifying standards for 36 000 vehicles a year and the new law laid down that the first of these standards should be published by 30 June 1965 for application to 1967 model-year vehicles. Although this was federal control on a relatively small scale, it did set an important precedent for future political action, and created a practical basis for the first Federal Motor Vehicle Safety Standards (FMVSSs), which were mandated by the 1966 Safety Act.

In January 1965, GSA published seventeen preliminary safety standards and invited comment.[19] Considerable industry criticism followed, and, although each of the seventeen survived, many were relaxed from their original specifications. The final standards were published on 20 June 1965. Although there was some criticism of the relaxing of these standards compared with their original specifications,[20] the establishment of any controls whatsoever on vehicle design was undoubtedly a significant extension of governmental powers. Certainly, in the absence of any strong 'public interest' group pressure for safety standards (even as late as 1965), considerable credit must go to Roberts himself for this achievement.

The apparent apathy of this time – especially when contrasted with the events of 1966 – should not be allowed to conceal the fact that changes were taking place during the early 1960s. It was during this period that certain arguments began to be voiced at the local state level. One of Roberts' other successes was in gaining Congressional approval in 1958 for the establishment of local state cooperation on vehicle safety. The underlying aim was to establish uniformity of action between states rather than the isolation of each one. In 1962 Senator Edward Speno made New York State the first to adhere to this agreement and also to the national Vehicle Equipment Safety Commission (VESC), which was its adjudicating body. However, by 1965 the VESC had produced only one standard (on tyres) and many of its critics asserted that its chief function was in public relations for the industry rather than design control.

Other developments were taking place at the national level in the early 1960s which were to prove more successful than the voluntary VESC system. The first, enacted on 5 September 1962, authorised the Secretary of Commerce to establish specifications for hydraulic brake fluid sold or shipped in interstate commerce.[21] The second law, passed on 13 December 1963 allowed the Secretary of Commerce to establish safety standards for the manufacture of seat-belt assemblies involved in interstate commerce.[22] Although these laws were very specific and also uncontroversial, in that the industry made no very evident attempt to block the legislation, they did establish the general principle of federal vehicle design controls which was to be extended in 1966.

At the same time as these political activities were taking place, a number of articles and popular publications were appearing which argued the case for design changes. As discussed in the previous chapter, both Moynihan and Nader published articles at this time and the contribution by Haddon, Suchman and Klein was also influential in certain circles. In 1963, Moynihan became Assistant Secretary of Labor with particular responsibility for policy planning. The following year, Nader, who was known for his occasional articles and also for his experience as a lawyer in a number of cases relating to vehicle safety, was invited to join Moynihan's staff as a consultant on highway safety. Nader accepted this offer and began work on a policy document for Moynihan which was subsequently entitled 'A report on the context, condition and recommended direction of federal activity in highway safety'. Only a few copies were produced and it was never made available to the general public, but it was out of this document that Nader was to develop his famous book *Unsafe at Any Speed*.

On 22 March 1965, Senator Abraham Ribicoff commenced the hearings of the Subcommittee on Executive Reorganisation, which intended to investigate the federal role in road traffic safety. The general stance of the US motor manufacturers during the early 'Ribicoff hearings' was that the federal government should concentrate its involvement by assisting state legislatures, providing research funds and improving highways.[23] They argued for 'consumer sovereignty' – that the industry should in no way force the pace of safety innovation but simply react to customer preferences. This complacent mood was dispelled as the Ribicoff hearings progressed.

One line of inquiry followed by subcommittee members in general and Senator Robert Kennedy in particular focused upon the precise amount which General Motors were spending on occupant protection research. At first, the company's representatives argued that it was impossible to give a precise figure for this because such research work could not be separated from other types of engineering Research and Development. Under harsher questioning, however, the vice-president in charge of engineering staff (H. Barr) could cite only the $1 million grant to MIT as an example of crashworthiness research – and this study was couched in the broadest terms[24] with the grant expected to cover a four-year period.

Senator Ribicoff had already made clear his own determination not to treat the motor industry as a 'sacred cow':

... I think a lot of us would be happier if they would spend some of their profits on safety features on automobiles. Unless there is a hue and cry from people who have the responsibility, I don't think the manufacturer is going to do it voluntarily.[25]

From all accounts at that time, the industry representatives who appeared at the hearings were visibly shaken by the unexpectedly critical onslaught which they faced.[26] However, Ribicoff's own view, as publicly expressed, was that a 'war of attrition' would be required before any firm regulatory controls could be established.[27]

Part Two of the Ribicoff Hearings began in July 1965, and by that time there were already some signs of increasing public interest in road traffic safety. The Illinois State government had approved a bill extending GSA standards to all state-owned vehicles. A Harris poll taken in that month suggested that traffic safety was perceived as one of the six or seven major American problems. A bill was being proposed to establish the 'National Highway Traffic Safety Act of 1965', which was more commonly referred to as the 'Ribicoff–Kennedy Bill' after its originators. The aim was to improve R & D activities, partly by the creation of a National Highway Traffic Safety Center, and also to provide financial assistance for states to accelerate their own highway safety programmes. However, the crucial social and political change occurred between July 1965 and February 1966, when Part Three of the Ribicoff hearings took place. This change must to some extent be attributed to Ralph Nader and the circumstances that surrounded his book.

The appearance of *Unsafe at Any Speed* in the latter part of 1965 was to have great consequences for the American control of road traffic safety. As noted already, Nader focused on the occupant protection approach in such a way as to denounce the motor industry for its culpable neglect of the best interests of its consumers. In addition to this general accusation, Nader wrote a powerful condemnation of one particular automobile – the Chevrolet Corvair. Nader had already been involved in a number of damages cases relating to this vehicle and he managed to produce a good deal of evidence to suggest that it was particularly susceptible to rollover. One 'insider' account has suggested that General Motors officials were aware of this design fault, but that it had been ignored owing to the perceived need for increased sales.[28]

Nader argued forcefully that the neglect of the safety aspects of vehicle design was the result of a conspiracy between greedy and irresponsible manufacturers, apathetic government officials and research workers who could be 'bought off' by the occasional grant or conference sponsorship. For Nader, the Corvair was symptomatic of an American society which was prepared to tolerate such corporate behaviour without establishing any democratic controls over the activities of giant firms like General Motors. Nader's basic argument certainly found a sympathetic audience in a United States which, despite the relative affluence of the period, was racked by social unease and racial tensions.[29] Nader's criticism of the neglect of road traffic safety was also linked by the public to the general concern with the environment which was growing during the 1960s. The political philosophy behind Nader's attack on 'corporate America' was summarised in a statement of his made in 1966. In this, he described his own outrage at the 'injustice and brutality' that exists in industrialised societies largely as a consequence of the lack of public accountability or institutional social responsibility. Nader went on to argue:

This is not an ideological problem. This is a problem of individuals confronting complex organisations, whether they are complex organisations in the United States – corporations, labor unions or what not – or whether they are complex organisations in other countries of the world.[30]

The 'non-ideological' nature of the analysis is interesting because of its implication that Nader and his supporters were not trying to revolutionise the economic and social structures of US society in any socialist sense. Their goal was the more limited one of reforming existing institutions. The contrast between this reformist attitude and the explicitly radical approach taken by certain British pressure groups such as the Socialist Environment and Resources Association (SERA) will be considered in the next chapter. The nature of Nader's political philosophy should also be borne in mind when discussing the receptivity of various politicians and public representatives to his ideas during the 1960s. Although a deeply challenging perspective, the arguments in favour of occupant protection and stronger regulatory powers were not intended to bring US capitalism to its knees. The 'public interest' group leaders were not confronting the right of companies like General Motors to continue profit accumulation nor, and this is equally important, were they challenging the place of the automobile as a key mode of personal transport.

Early sales of Nader's book were fairly good, if not overwhelming. By the end of February 1966, approximately 22 000 copies had been sold. It really took the publicity of the events that followed to make the book into a major success. Before discussing these, it is worth pointing out the fact that *Unsafe at Any Speed* was certainly not as original as some commentators have suggested. Moynihan had argued a similar case in 1959 and a book by O'Connell and Myers, published in 1966 but written in 1965, bears a striking likeness in its basic argument and also its detail.[31] Nader also borrowed freely from the literature relating to the occupant protection framework (and was quite open about doing so).

When the new session of the Ribicoff hearings was called in February 1966, Nader was invited to appear. Ribicoff opened the hearings with a reassessment of what he interpreted as a new public mood with regard to road traffic safety. He contrasted the 'here we go again' attitude surrounding the 1965 hearings with the 'vastly different' mood of 1966.[32] Although there were pleas (notably from the President of the National Safety Council) for the federal government to leave responsibility in the hands of local state authorities, the subcommittee seemed to be moving in favour of national legislation to cope with road traffic accidents. This point was emphasised in strong statements by Nader and Senator Kennedy.

It was in the month after Nader gave testimony at this hearing that the young lawyer suddenly became world famous. General Motors had been particularly interested in Nader because his book's critique of the Corvair appeared at a time when the company was vigorously defending itself in a number of damages cases relating to the vehicle. These amounted to a potential sum of $40 million on the date of publication. A private investigator was commissioned to delve into Nader, his professional qualifications, and his personal background. Nader alleged that this 'investigation' was in fact 'harassment' – that he was being kept under surveillance, that blackmail attempts were made, and that his friends had been cross-examined on details of his sexual preferences and possible character flaws.

News of these accusations became public on 12 March in a hard-hitting magazine article.[33] Press coverage was immediate and the whole issue became a major scandal.[34] General Motors published a press release which admitted that Nader was under 'routine investigation prompted by Mr Nader's extreme criticism of the Corvair ...'.[35] Suddenly, public interest in Nader and the topic of road traffic safety was immense. Ribicoff, in an attempt to 'clear the air', but also to ensure that this general concern was channelled appropriately, announced a new hearing for 22 March 1966.

I have called this special meeting today to look into the circumstances surrounding what appeared to be an attempt by General Motors Corporation to discredit Mr Ralph Nader, a recent witness before the subcommittee.[36]

The hearing has been described as having 'all the fascination of a public whipping'.[37] The room in which the session took place was packed with reporters, photographers and television crews. Never before had a discussion on road traffic safety taken place before such an enthusiastic and excited audience. At the witness table, and to all intents and purposes 'on trial', sat James Roche, president of the world's largest manufacturing company. The drama heightened even further when Nader was called as the opening witness but was found not to be present. Roche took the stand and offered his sincere apologies to Nader and the subcommittee, but only 'to the extent that General Motors bears responsibility'. Roche denied any suggestion of infringing Nader's civil rights and insisted that there had been no attempt 'to annoy, harass, embarrass, threaten, injure or intimidate Mr Nader'.[38]

Under some very aggressive cross-examining, especially from Senator Kennedy, Roche admitted that the margin between detective 'investigation' and 'harrassment' in this case may have been very faint. He also admitted that the earlier press release from GM might well have been rather misleading in that it failed to suggest the full extent of the investigation.

For General Motors – and by extension the other motor manufacturers – this was certainly a humiliating occasion. The revelation of the investigations into Nader's private life caused considerable public outrage. Perhaps even more damaging for the manufacturers was the suspicion that General Motors had shown itself to be a less than trustworthy organisation in the attempted 'cover-up' of its activities. The company was seen to be out of tune with popular demands for more responsible and accountable corporate institutions. The effect of this whole escapade was to turn public opinion towards stronger government intervention rather than a continuation of *laissez-faire* policies. Nader's eventual testimony certainly expressed this view:

. . . a civilized society will not tell the victims of the automobile that it is up to them to prove that the automobile is defective when the difficulty of that proof staggers the imagination. Although in court the plaintiff must prove his case, I think beyond that, that we should have standards and legislative frameworks by government that will in effect make sure that the automobile manufacturer has to prove that his vehicle is safe before he puts it on the market. That is where the burden of proof has to lie, it seems to me.[39]

The demand for 'standards and legislative frameworks' was met by the 'Safety Acts' signed by President Johnson on 9 September of that year – less than four months after the crucial Ribicoff hearing just

.described. The major effect of these laws was to establish the institutional mechanisms whereby FMVSSs could be promulgated. In fact, the bills in question passed through both the Senate and House with unanimous votes.[40] The climate was such that even those politicians who felt that the automobile industry was quite blameless still made no attempt to block the bill. For Ribicoff, the 1966 acts represented above all a symbolic breakthrough. The issue, as he expressed it, was not 'how many lives will be saved?' but '*who decides* whether these lives should be saved?'[41]

Discussion

This review of the years prior to the 1966 legislation began by acknowledging the place of Ralph Nader in creating the necessary political climate. We have now examined the part played by Nader in 1965–66 and noted that his expressed political philosophy and specific demands for change made him an appropriate figurehead for a social movement, especially after the 'General Motors scandal'. However, our examination has also revealed the inadequacy of viewing the road traffic safety issue as simply being fuelled by one 'great man'.

If we consider the 1966 legislation in the context of political developments from 1955 onwards, then a more gradual process can be discerned based on the accumulation of minor breakthroughs such as the standards for hydraulic brake fluid and seat belts. Lindblom has proposed the notion of 'disjointed incrementalism' to describe changes of this sort where politicians 'muddle through' over a period of time and only occasionally engage in more radical or rational decision making.[42] For at least a decade, individuals such as Roberts and Ribicoff strove in the face of general opposition to formulate acceptable proposals for road traffic safety policy. The elements which were to constitute a more receptive political climate (and Nader was certainly one of these) only came together in 1966.

One other factor that played its part in 1966 was the growth of popular concern with the environment and with the physical effects of technological developments such as the automobile. The social movement that surrounded *Silent Spring* had begun to spawn a number of 'public interest' groups and lobbying organisations, and many of these came to see road traffic safety as another cause for concern.[43] The philosophy of increased government intervention in regulating US corporations was politically acceptable at that time and the establishment of a federal agency to control road traffic safety was only one demonstration of a wider trend which led to the creation of a number of similar institutions in the USA for other areas of control.[44] Seen in this perspective, the regulation of road traffic safety in 1966 was not a completely isolated event but rather one part of a broader pattern of social and political activity in the United States during the 1960s.

While noting these features of the debate over road traffic safety, other, more enduring, facets of the US political system must also be considered. To present the argument simply: it is possible to suggest that certain characteristics of the system of government — such as public hearings, 'watchdog' committees, the formation of 'public interest' pressure groups — allowed this issue to emerge in the way it did. This point will become particularly clear in the next chapter when we examine the equivalent British decision-making processes and their more confidential and consensual nature. However, one simple illustration of this contrast can be offered now. It is extremely difficult to imagine the head of a major British private corporation being put 'in the witness box' by an official committee in full public view. This, of course, was the position in which James Roche found himself on 22 March 1966. It can accordingly be argued that the structural characteristics of the US political system provided substantial assistance to the emergence of road traffic safety as a political issue. This comparative political analysis will be continued in later chapters of this book.

One final factor which helped shape legislative action in 1966 and the years prior to this was discussed at length in the previous chapter: technical expertise. From the late 1950s onwards, the occupant protection specialty approach — with its focus on energy management and crash survival — became increasingly important within the science of road traffic safety. As noted earlier, many of the political actors involved in discussion of road traffic safety had written public articles in support of the occupant protection approach and its policy implications. The 'overlap' of the research and political communities was particularly evident when Moynihan reviewed Haddon *et al.*'s book for a popular magazine in 1964.[45] The point was made even more clear when Haddon was appointed as the first head of the new National Traffic Safety Agency in October 1966. Of course, Nader's *Unsafe at Any Speed* was also based on the occupant protection framework. This research tradition provided a coherent case for reform and suggested the philosophy that should form the basis of this. In this instance, the relationship between technical expertise and political power was a particularly close and symbiotic one.

It can be concluded on the basis of the analysis so far in this chapter that a number of factors together, rather than any single element or political actor, constituted the social and political circumstances in which the 1966 legislation could be formulated and unanimously carried. Any attempt at unravelling as complex a series of historical events as occurred in this case is of necessity subject to challenge and qualification.[46] However, this analysis has not relied on any single conceptual model, nor has it clutched at a narrow, monocausal form of explanation. Rather, the underlying case has been that it is necessary for a satisfactory policy analysis to study the conjunction of social, political and technical factors in such a way as to appreciate their interrelationships. It can be concluded, for example, that the arguments that emanated from the occupant protection framework provided the intellectual basis for policy reform. It must also be seen, however, that such arguments would have had little effect (as, one can assert, has been the case in Britain) if the political structures had not been present in which they could be heard nor pressure groups existed to relate the technical analysis to their emerging political philosophies. The very combination of these factors, and not any single overriding determinant, made 1966 ripe for policy reform in a way no other year had been.

The structure of federal controls

Three items of legislation came into existence in 1966 which directly related to the automobile. The first, the DOT Act,[47] created a unified Department of Transportation (DOT). The second, the Highway Safety Act,[48] allowed for the establishment of highway safety standards by individual states. Finally, the National Traffic and Motor Vehicle Safety Act (the '1966 Safety Act') created the institutional apparatus and administrative procedures for developing automotive safety standards.

There is little doubt that this third act represented a significant intervention by the US federal government into the design of motor vehicles. Whereas, previously, manufacturers had enjoyed an almost free hand in constructing whatever automobiles they themselves judged to be fit for sale, the 1966 legislation gave an important power over product design to federal officials.

One of the major functions of the act was to create a federal agency to set national standards for motor vehicle safety. In its original form, this agency was known as the National Traffic Safety Agency (NTSA) and it was under the jurisdiction of the Secretary of Commerce. By 1971, jurisdiction had been transferred to the Secretary of Transportation and the body had been renamed the 'National Highway Traffic Safety Administration' (NHTSA). The 1966 Act required publication of the first set of Federal Motor Vehicle Safety Standards (FMVSSs) by 31 January 1967; these took effect on 1 January 1968.

Before continuing our discussion of the NHTSA and the standards which it had produced, it is important to note some general features of FMVSSs as laid down by the 1966 Safety Act. The legislation defined an FMVSS as a

... minimum standard for motor vehicle performance, or motor vehicle equipment performance, which is practicable, which meets the need for motor vehicle safety, and which provides objective criteria.[49]

The 'need for motor vehicle safety' was in turn defined largely in terms of the occupant protection framework. The emphasis was on the protection of the public against

... unreasonable risk of accidents occurring as a result of the design, construction, or performance of motor vehicles and ... also ... against unreasonable risk of death or injury to persons in the event accidents do occur.[50]

FMVSSs were defined as being 'minimum standards', i.e. they should specify the *lowest* acceptable performance.[51] They should be 'reasonable' and 'practicable' – the agency must consider economic costs, technical feasibility and lead times for compliance with standards. A statutory requirement was established that standards should be expressed in the form of 'objective criteria' with appropriate testing procedures specified.

One vital point relating to US federal safety standards is the focus on 'performance-' rather than 'design-based' requirements. Performance standards specify only the structural tolerances that must be built into a vehicle. They say nothing about how such tolerances are to be achieved. The intention behind this is to give maximum freedom to manufacturers in deciding how to comply with a standard and also to encourage engineering innovation. This approach contrasts with the general European reliance on design rather than performance in standard setting (see the following chapter for a review of British practice in this regard).

Although government regulators in the United States generally see performance standards as granting a very free hand to manufacturers and suppliers in complying with FMVSSs, a number of problems with performance-based requirements have been raised. The first and most obvious point is that the regulatory authority must at least consider existing design capabilities before establishing a standard; the requirement may therefore be more design related than is immediately apparent. Secondly, performance standards shift the burden of financial risk on to the manufacturer in a manner which the motor companies have generally considered unreasonable. As at least one commentator has suggested,[52] performance regulations allow the federal government 'to stand in splendid isolation' while the industry has to cope with the painful process of achieving compliance – and then shifting the costs to the consumer. From the NHTSA's perspective, however, performance standards allow the highest degree of initiative to the manufacturers in applying their own special knowledge of designing and manufacturing motor vehicles.

A third aspect of performance standards which should be stressed at this early stage in the discussion is their dependence on relatively sophisticated testing procedures. A standard may, for example, specify the maximum decelerative forces that should be transmitted to parts of the human body in collisions at a certain speed. In order to establish whether such a standard has been met, various laboratory crashes must be conducted and a heavy reliance is placed on the comparability of humans and anthropomorphic dummies in terms of physical trauma. The whole area of testing procedures has provided fertile ground for controversy between the motor industry and federal regulators, as will be seen when we discuss various specific case studies of vehicle safety regulation.

One other controversial topic has been the granting of exemptions. This power was bestowed by a 1968 amendment to the 1966 Act[53] and it allows the Secretary of Transportation authority to offer limited exemptions to individual manufacturers.[54] As Heffron has noted,[55] the agency has three main choices when confronted with a manufacturer who, for financial reasons, cannot meet a standard before its effective date. These are, first, to delay the effective date of the standard, thus granting all manufacturers the same delay; secondly, to retain the date and so cause financial losses for the company in question, or, thirdly, to retain the date but grant a limited exemption. The NHTSA has very often taken advantage of this third option. However, exemptions have been awarded to even very large manufacturers, and strong political pressure has nevertheless been maintained by the industry for the extension of deadlines. Despite this, the power of exemption could be a useful tool for the agency in avoiding the 'lowest common denominator effect' whereby overall standards are set at the level acceptable to the smallest or least commercially viable firm in the sector. Of course, we have yet to examine how this has worked in regulatory practice.

Many of the objections put forward by British and US motor manufacturers to the establishment of federal safety standards concentrate on the problems arising from the technical complexities of motor vehicle production. One obvious complication for the introduction of any national standard is the nature of vehicle production itself. The design and construction of machinery for the production of a great number of vehicles involves capital investment on an enormous scale, and also a large amount of time. A typical vehicle pre-production schedule commences 43 months before the first vehicles roll off the production line. Product planning must take place, followed by advanced engineering, design and styling, quality assurance and then assembly tooling (which itself takes approximately two years).

If only for the reason of receiving a good return on their investment, the manufacturers are eager to maintain basic production runs whenever possible. An additional problem for any new standard is that manufacturers produce more than just one vehicle; for example, Ford in 1966 had nine basic lines of passenger cars in production. If one then considers that there are approximately fifteen major car manufacturers (foreign and domestic) selling in the United States, it is clear that the establishment of a federal standard is by no means a straightforward matter. The industry will impose great pressure on the NHTSA to allow the latest deadline possible – and then only after it has agreed the feasibility of a specification. Consequently, the agency is confronted time and again with the difficult question of how to evaluate industry's arguments about the retooling and design costs of a proposed standard and also the required lead time. The NHTSA simply cannot compete with the industry in terms of detailed knowledge of the practicality of a standard – nor does it have technical personnel or research facilities on a scale comparable to those of the manufacturers.[56] The result of this is that the agency must use whatever informal channels are available to acquire 'inside' information and then set proposed standards in somewhat stringent terms so as to draw out the opposition and negotiate a more lenient specification from this point. This is a crucial part of rulemaking, and the bargaining involved and the strategies adopted by the agency will be a major focus of the case studies in this book.

Compliance to finalised FMVSSs is based on a 'self-certification' principle – manufacturers must themselves ensure that their products match all existing regulations. The 1966 Act fixed a civil penalty for violation of regulations at $1000 per vehicle up to a maximum of $400 000 for one company. Within the NHTSA, an Office of Vehicle Safety Compliance is responsible for the random testing of vehicles for conformity.

An additional feature of the NHTSA is its Office of Defects Investigation, whose task is to act as a central information centre for safety-related design or production faults in the vehicle population. In 1977, NHTSA was receiving 36 000 consumer reports a year dealing with defects. A telephone 'hotline' service is also maintained for reports on individual vehicles and these are fed into a computer, together with information concerning manufacturers' service bulletins, recall campaigns, previous investigations and known problems. If the agency determines that there is a safety defect or noncompliance, a letter is written to the manufacturer and a notice is published in the *Federal Register*. A public hearing will be held to discuss the alleged defect and evidence will then be presented by the various parties. If judged necessary by the Administrator of the NHTSA, a recall campaign will be initiated. However, the major onus is always on the manufacturer to notify the agency of any defect that could affect the safety of a motor vehicle.[57] The contrast between the US and British approaches to defect notification and recall campaigns has been studied by the British Safety Council and this issue will be considered in the following chapter.

An understanding of the rulemaking procedures that have been established for the NHTSA is extremely important for our later discussion of specific standards. The complexity that rulemaking can involve will become clear in later discussion, but it is worth while to note here the basic administrative steps. Each stage must be publicised in the *Federal Register* with a 'docket' number for comments. The 'docket' is a file kept in the agency headquarters which contains all remarks and information submitted relating to specific issues or standards. These files are then open to the inspection of any interested member of the public.

Although not a legal requirement, in many cases the NHTSA's first official step is to publish an Advance Notice of Proposed Rulemaking (ANPRM). This announces the agency's intention to establish a regulation – but it does not specify details and merely invites general comments on a particular topic. After a possible ANPRM, the agency may decide to take the first formal steps and publish a Notice of Proposed Rulemaking (NPRM). This will announce specific details and application dates for the proposed standard and, in many cases, the final FMVSS will be established with precisely the same wording. Once again, public comment is invited – usually with a deadline for submissions. If these comments force any major reconsideration of the standard by the agency, then a new NPRM will appear in the *Federal Register* with amended specifications. Of course, the agency could also terminate rulemaking at this stage if sufficient opposition had been mounted.

If the agency is still satisfied with the proposed regulation after time has been given for discussion, then a full FMVSS will appear in the *Federal Register*. Within 30 days of the publication of an FMVSS, any individual or organisation may file a 'petition for reconsideration' and the agency will give its judgment on this petition usually within 120 days. There is also scope for external groups or individuals to sue the agency as a challenge to a standard; this action must be taken within 60 days of publication. A federal court will then rule on the claim. It should also be noted that any individual or organisation can petition at any time to initiate rulemaking. The agency must consider all such petitions and either accept or reject them within 120 days.

The above brief account describes what can be termed for present purposes the formal policy-making operation within the federal government. A grasp of this is important if one is to understand the framework within which political activity relating to vehicle safety must operate. However, it is also necessary to examine the more implicit and less formalised aspects of the negotiation between interested parties and this will be carried out in the later case studies.

Road traffic safety in the USA since 1966

As stated above, the 1966 Safety Act created an agency to produce rulemaking on road traffic safety matters. This body is now known as the National Highway Traffic Safety Administration (NHTSA). The 'Administrator' of the NHTSA is directly responsible to the Secretary of Transportation. The Administrator, and also the DOT Secretary, are appointed by the US President and, therefore, the holders of each post tend to change at least with every new administration.

The first set of safety standards under the new statute took effect on 1 January 1968. The NPRM for these appeared in the *Federal Register* on 30 November 1966,[58] only two months after Haddon took office: the time constraints on the nascent agency were clearly enormous. Perhaps unsurprisingly, the twenty original FMVSSs tended to be based on GSA standards and 'existing practices'. Some concessions were also made to the manufacturers following the consideration of their comments to the agency.[59] It was at this point (i.e. almost immediately) that 'public interest' groups began to criticise the agency for having surrendered to industry pressure. Ralph Nader, for example, has persisted throughout the 1970s with a critical attack on the US government and the motor industry in terms similar to those of *Unsafe at Any Speed* in the mid-1960s. Writing in 1972, Nader asserted that;

The government's permissiveness toward the indifference and greed of the automobile manufacturers is less excusable than ever. However, political leadership toward human engineering will grow only as fast as a strong auto safety constituency makes its demands and strategies undeniably known at the scene of the action in Washington and Detroit.[60]

Again, in 1976, Nader attacked the 'corrupt and callous' manner in which the White House had attempted to block regulatory programmes and also criticised the 'lethargic and unimaginative leadership' of the NHTSA.[61] The 'Naderite' group which has attempted to provide a 'strong auto safety constituency' is the Center for Auto Safety and this has played an important critical and 'consciousness-raising' role during the 1970s and early 1980s. Even the NHTSA head under the Carter administration, Joan Claybrook, who had once been a member of Nader's Congress Watch, was subject to a strong attack on her inactivity – only a few weeks after she took office in 1977.[62] Through the Center for Auto Safety and his public appearances at hearings and meetings, Nader has, despite his broad interest in regulatory matters outside vehicle safety and also the tensions caused within 'Naderite' groups by his unyielding and populist style, remained a significant voice for stricter federal standards.

One other 'public interest' group which rose to prominence during the 1970s is the Insurance Institute for Highway Safety (IIHS). This was founded in 1959 and, as its name suggests, is supported by various insurance companies. William Haddon Jr, on leaving the agency, became President of the IIHS and, under his leadership, it has become a major party to the policy-making process, as will be seen in relation to the later case studies of passive restraint and fuel system integrity. Unlike the Center for Auto Safety, the IIHS is not a lobbying organisation, but its research reports and analyses have figured prominently in public hearings, and the Insurance Institute publication *Status Report*[63] is certainly influential and widely circulated.

Whereas Nader and his supporters have accused the NHTSA of being a 'captured agency', the manufacturers have adopted a starkly different perspective on the evolving situation. Vehicle safety standards are just one part of a body of legislation that relates to the American automobile. Other federal controls deal with emissions,[64] fuel economy[65] and maintenance costs.[66] For the industrialists these standards, when taken together, represent an unwanted constraint on the industry's freedom to design vehicles as they see fit. Moreover, the requirements of one area of federal regulation, e.g. fuel economy, may cut across the requirements of another enforced goal – so that lighter vehicles which use less fuel are, other things being equal, less damage resistant. The US motor manufacturers argue that the collective regulatory power of the federal government threatens to stifle their very existence. Henry Ford II has expressed the feelings of the industry's leaders in typically blunt fashion:

We now have a silent partner who has no equity in our business but has a strong voice in management. They control everything we do practically speaking. They control the design of our product – both from an operating standpoint and a looks standpoint. They control our prices, control our salaries, control our wages, control our profits.[67]

Ford's remarks also raise questions regarding the government regulation of industry at a broader level. In this book, we will concentrate on the *control* rather than the *promotion* of the motor

vehicle sector. However, it is relevant to note one assessment of the
role of international governments in relation to the motor industry.
The Economist Intelligence Unit[68] has characterised the state –
motor industry relationship as taking different forms throughout the
world. The role of governments in developing countries has been that
of *initiator*; in Japan the government has been the *promoter* of the
motor industry; in Western Europe the *owner* and in the USA the
legislator. Although this is a very broad generalisation and seems to
relate above all to the 1970s, it does highlight a difference of
emphasis between national approaches.

Arguments about the restrictive effect of different federal controls
have taken on particular force since the early 1970s, largely because
of the changing economic climate. Lee Iacocca, when President of
Ford Motor Company, stated that federal regulations had added
$500 to the price of a new car.[69] General Motors estimated that it
would cost the company $1.3 thousand million to meet total
regulatory demands for 1974.[70] In addition, a 1977 study for the
Department of Transportation counted 237 regulatory changes
relating to cars and light trucks which had come into effect between
1960 and 1975.[71]

The response of the more committed NHTSA Administrators,
such as Joan Claybrook, has been to express extreme scepticism at
the industry's financial assessment of regulatory cost. The agency has
also criticised the failure of the motor manufacturers to innovate in
the area of safety or to make any voluntary effort towards meeting
the social need for a cheap, safe and non-polluting form of transport.
The philosophy behind federal regulation has been that the industry
needs a spur to product development where consumer demands are
not sufficiently influential. In order to remove excess monetary risk
for individual manufacturers who may innovate in such areas,
uniform standards are brought into effect and each company is
challenged to find the least costly way of achieving the required
performance level. However, the motor industry has tended to
concentrate on the cost impact of regulatory standards and the
likelihood that, if these are passed along to the consumer together
with other cost increases, then annual price rises will exceed rates of
inflation or growth in consumer income. Such increases could be
expected to affect particularly the smaller domestic manufacturers,
such as Chrysler or American Motors. They may also have more
general adverse consequences for the industry in reducing the funds

available for investment and, therefore, lengthening the average product cycle with possible effects on competitiveness.[72]

The arguments between regulators and the regulated have in no way been dampened during the 1970s and early 1980s but they have, as one might anticipate, been extremely susceptible to changes in the political and economic climate of the USA. For example, the political mood of the mid-1970s was in favour of the reduction of constraints on private enterprise and for 'deregulation', or at least a moratorium on new standards. In October 1974, President Ford issued an executive order that all new regulations should be accompanied by an 'inflation impact statement'.[73] During the mid-1970s, regulatory reform became a major issue and moves in this direction undoubtedly had the sympathy of the Republican administration. This political belief was also, of course, reflected in the choice of NHTSA Administrators and DOT Secretaries during that period.

President Ford and the Council on Wage and Price Stability had advocated cost-benefit analysis (CBA) as a way of determining the worth of any proposed standard. Three major reports – by the agency,[74] by the White House Office of Science and Technology,[75] and by the Government Accounting Office[76] – had sought to place a 'dollar value' on human life so that potential savings could be weighed against the cost of meeting a standard. In 1972–74 this figure was taken to be approximately $200 000. However, the conceptual and methodological difficulties of this technique cannot be ignored. Not least of these is the problem of pinning an objective, monetary value to such factors as the loss of a human life.

The NHTSA was also criticised from the 1970s onwards for its lack of an independent data base. The Research and Development section of the agency had come under attack in Congressional hearings[77] and elsewhere from both the Comptroller General[78] and the Center for Auto Safety[79] for its failure to publicise findings and, more fundamentally, to produce a counterbalance to industry data. Even in 1980, as Joan Claybrook has stated,[80] the budget for governmental research and development into the motor vehicle was only $21 million and funds showed every sign of decreasing – even before inflation had been taken into account.

In an area of negotiation and confrontation between manufacturers, regulators and public interest groups, which has mostly been conducted via technical analyses rather than via explicitly political argumentation, the lack of an 'alternative' knowledge base to that of the industry poses distinct problems. However, as Nelkin has pointed out, oppositional groups may not need to match the manufacturers' research capabilities, but merely have sufficient background knowledge to identify weaknesses in the 'opposition' case and exploit these to the utmost.[81] The phenomenon of 'scientisation', whereby an essentially political argument is carried out in the language of technical expertise, will be explored in later chapters. For the moment, it can be seen that Nelkin's argument was well illustrated by the 1966 legislation where a receptive public climate allowed a small group to overpower an immense industry and the body of specialist knowledge which it had at its disposal. Whether oppositional groups can enjoy similar success in a more hostile social climate without the necessary technical support is more open to doubt.

The susceptibility of federal vehicle safety regulation to the changing political climate was demonstrated once again in 1977 with the incoming Carter administration. The new President sought to renew the flagging vitality of agencies by appointing 'consumerist' or 'public-interest' advocates at sub-Cabinet level.[82] This general policy brought Joan Claybrook, an enthusiastic supporter of firm regulatory policies, into the post of NHTSA Administrator. Claybrook quickly earned herself a reputation as a tough negotiator who was prepared to meet the manufacturers in open confrontation. However, as the case of FMVSS 208 shows very clearly, this determination and strength of purpose did not lead to the NHTSA finding it any easier to gain acceptance for new safety standards. The motor industry argued throughout this period that the particular economic difficulties which it was facing precluded any significant new regulatory controls. The manufacturers have also found many allies within Congress who are prepared to lead the opposition to measures like the proposed passive restraint standard.

The election of President Reagan came at a time when the US motor manufacturers were experiencing the most severe financial difficulties in their history. In 1981, Ford, General Motors and American Motors all announced substantial losses and the particular problems being faced by Chrysler were given massive worldwide publicity.[83] The new Republican administration had always made clear its intention of reducing federal regulation and this spirit was reflected in the choice as NHTSA Administrator, Ray Peck, who was known to be in favour of measures such as compulsory seat-belt wear rather than passive safety measures. Almost immediately on taking office, the Transportation

Secretary under the Reagan administration announced his intention of seeking a 48 per cent reduction in the NHTSA's budget for 1982.[84]

As a final comment on the changing pattern of federal regulation from the late 1960s until the early 1980s, the attitude of the manufacturers themselves should be noted. It could be suggested that this attitude towards regulation has evolved from one of questioning whether any federal controls whatsoever should exist towards an acceptance of this principle but with a more realistic concern for costs and practicability. According to this view, the stonewalling or 'head in the sand' posture of the mid-1960s has given way to more complex and differentiated strategies for meeting the public interest. Although some support for this evaluation can be found in the activities of the manufacturers and their public statements, in general terms an underlying industry opposition to stricter performance standards has barely waivered since the mid-1960s. However, it may be true that the *terms* in which this opposition has been voiced have altered somewhat over the last two decades.

Conclusion

A number of points relating to the control of road traffic safety since 1966 should be stressed at this stage. The first, and perhaps most obvious, feature is the *emphasis on occupant protection*. The particular circumstances that led to this were discussed at some length in the early part of the chapter.

The second point to be made is the *mode of control* adopted to deal with this problem area. The federal government has relied upon regulation in the form of performance standards rather than any alternative approach such as economic and fiscal controls, financial inducements, advice and services or encouragement and exhortation. Authority for detailed regulation has been granted to a single agency, thus localising responsibility for this specific topic. We have noted that this mode of control was also adopted by the federal government for a variety of other regulatory contexts.

One important feature of the US negotiation over road traffic safety is the *adversarial manner* in which proceedings are typically conducted. This can be seen partly as a reflection of the 'style of government'[85] in the USA and partly also as a consequence of the 'mode of control' specific to this issue (these two characteristics themselves being interconnected). The NHTSA typically finds itself in the middle of a constant battle between industry lobbyists and public interest group activists (as represented by Nader, the Center for Auto Safety, the Insurance Institute for Highway Safety, and other similar groups). The pressure group network is particularly well-developed and the agency is subject to a continual barrage of exhortations, petitions and accusations from each party.

The adversarial style is often linked to a perceived 'openness' in the US system of government. The existence of various public interest groups and the availability of information relating to present and future agency actions has encouraged a greater citizen involvement in road traffic safety issues although, as will be noted, public concern has certainly not maintained its 1966 pitch. Very often, the 'openness' of debate is effectively limited to highly committed participants who tend to be based in Washington, DC. However, this is due more to public indifference than to the restriction of information. At the same time, an open/adversarial system also has various disadvantages, which may include a distinct lack of flexibility. Once an FMVSS has been established, it becomes exceedingly difficult to alter − even if one or more of the parties begins to change its attitude or new evidence emerges. New rulemaking becomes, almost inevitably, a very slow process and the most minor points can assume immense symbolic significance as no party (not the 'regulators', not the 'regulated' nor the 'exposed') wishes to concede defeat.

All these points will become clearer in the later chapters of this book which deal with specific examples of NHTSA rulemaking. Before this, we need to gain a comparative perspective on US policies by examining the background to British regulatory strategies.

Appendix 1: Chronology of major events

1956, July:	Roberts hearings commence.
	Ford 'Lifeguard' project.
1958:	Vehicle Equipment Safety Compact established (for state cooperation).
1959:	Moynihan and Nader articles appear.
1962, September:	Hydraulic brake fluid national standard authorised.
1963, December:	Federal seat-belt standard.
1964, August:	General Services Administration given authority to set standards for federal vehicles.

	Haddon *et al.* publish *Accident Research.*
1965, March, July:	Ribicoff hearings.
November:	*Unsafe at Any Speed* published.
1966, February:	Ribicoff hearings.
22 March:	Roche and Nader appear before special Ribicoff hearing.
9 September:	President Johnson signs 'Safety Acts'.
September:	W. Haddon Jr. appointed first head of federal agency.

Notes and references

1 Public Law 89–563, 80 Stat. 718, 15 USC 1381, September 9, 1966.
2 Carson, R. *Silent Spring* (Fawcett Crest, Greenwich; 1962). See also: Dunlap T. R. *DDT: Scientists, Citizens and Public Policy* (Princeton University Press, Princeton; 1981). Graham, F. *Since Silent Spring* (Pan/Ballantine, London; 1970). Mitchell, R. C. Since *Silent Spring*: Science, technology and the environmental movement in the United States, in Skoie, H. (ed.) *Scientific Expertise and the Public.* Studies in Research and Higher Education (Oslo), **5**, 1979, pp. 171–207.
3 Nader, R. *Unsafe at Any Speed* (Pocket Books, New York; 1966).
4 This emphasis on altering driver behaviour by scare campaigns of various sorts has been termed the 'exhortatory approach to safety'. See O'Connell, J. and Myers, A. *Safety Last – an Indictment of the Auto Industry* (Random House, New York; 1966).
5 Tofany, V. L. Factors contributing to the reduction of motor vehicle fatalities in 1974, in *Proc. Fourth International Congress on Automotive Safety* USGPO, Washington; 1975), pp. 783–90.
6 White, L. J. *The Automobile Industry since 1945* (Harvard University Press, Cambridge, Mass.; 1971), pp. 241–2.
7 See Nader, R. *Unsafe at Any Speed* (Pocket Books, New York; 1966), p. 225.
8 Representatives of the American Public Health Association, the American College of Surgeons and the American Medical Association all testified at the hearings.
9 Including James Ryan, W. Stieglitz, F. Crandell, H. Wakeland and A. White.
10 Sloan, A. P. quoted in Nader, R. (ed.) *The Consumer and Corporate Accountability* (Harcourt-Brace-Jovanovich, New York; 1973), p. 78.
11 Galbraith, J. K. *The New Industrial Estate* (Houghton Mifflin, Boston; 1967).
12 In addition to the statements of industry representatives such as Sloan, this view has been expressed by Ensor in his study of the industry and, more recently, by Schnapp. See: Ensor, J. *The Motor Industry* (Longman, London; 1971). Schnapp, J. B. *Corporate Strategies of the Automotive Manufacturers* (Lexington Books, Lexington; 1979).

13   Nader, R. *Unsafe at Any Speed* (Pocket Books, New York; 1966), pp. 91–2.
14   Cordtz, D. The face in the mirror at General Motors. *Fortune*, August 1966, p. 207.
15   Nader, R. *Unsafe at Any Speed*, 2nd edn (Grossman, New York; 1972), p. xiii.
16   Wright, J. P. *On a Clear Day you can see General Motors* (Sidgwick & Jackson, London; 1980), p. 224.
17   Henry Ford II quoted in Ensor, J. *The Motor Industry* (Longman, London; 1971), p. 203.
18   Public Law 88–515, 78 Stat. 696, 40 USC 701.
19   These preliminary standards related to seat-belt anchorage points; padded dashboards and visors; recessed instrument controls; impact-absorbing steering columns; safety door latches and hinges; seat anchorage; indicator units; safety glass; dual braking systems; automatic transmission design; windscreen wipers and washers; glare-reducing surfaces; exhaust emission; tyres; lighting; outside mirrors.
20   See, for example, O'Connell, J. and Myers, A. *Safety Last – an Indictment of the Auto Industry* (Random House, New York; 1966), p. 221.
21   Public Law 87–637, 76 Stat. 437, 15 USC 1301–3.
22   Public Law 88–201, 77 Stat. 361, 15 USC 1321–3.
23   US Congress Senate. *Federal Role in Traffic Safety*. Hearings before the Subcommittee on Executive Reorganisation of the Committee on Government Operations, 89th Congress. 1st Sess., July 13, 1965 ('Ribicoff Hearings'), p. 666.
24   The study's goal was a 'long-range, in-depth, quantitative analysis of all facets of the safety problem – the car, the road, the driver and their various interactions'.
25   *Ribicoff Hearings* 25 March 1965, p. 241.
26   A good account of this can be found in Cordtz, D. The face in the mirror at General Motors. *Fortune*, August 1966, p. 208.
27   *Ribicoff Hearings* 26 March 1965, p. 441.
28   Wright, J. P. *On a Clear Day you can see General Motors* (Sidgwick & Jackson, London; 1980), pp. 53–7.
29   Piven, F. P. and Cloward, R. A. *Regulating the Poor* (Tavistock, London; 1972).
30   Nader, R. *Ribicoff Hearings* 22 March 1966, pp. 1511–12.
31   O'Connell, J. and Myers, A. *Safety Last – an Indictment of the Auto Industry* (Random House, New York; 1966).
32   *Ribicoff Hearings* 2 February 1966, p. 1977.
33   Ridgeway, J. The dick. *New Republic*, 12 March 1966, pp. 11–13.
34   For a detailed account of the 'Nader Scandal' see: Sethi, S. P. *Up against the Corporate Wall: Modern Corporations and Social Issues of the Seventies* (Prentice-Hall, New Jersey; 1977), pp. 353–68. See also: McCarry, C. *Citizen Nader* (Saturday Review Press, New York; 1972).
35   General Motors Press Release, 9 March 1966.

36   *Ribicoff Hearings* 22 March 1966, p. 1380.
37   *Newsweek*, 4 April 1966, pp. 77–8.
38   *Ribicoff Hearings* 22 March 1966, p. 1382.
39   *Ibid*. p. 1500.
40   Senate: 76–0. House of Representatives: 331–0.
41   McCarry, C. *Citizen Nader* (Saturday Review Press, New York; 1972), p. 80.
42   'Usually . . . what is feasible politically is policy only incrementally, or marginally different from existing policies. Drastically different policies fall beyond the pale . . .' Lindblom, C. E. *The Policy-making Process* (Prentice-Hall, New Jersey; 1968), pp. 26–7.
43   See Mitchell, R. C. Since *Silent Spring*: Science, technology and the environmental movement in the United States, in Skoie, H. (ed.) *Scientific Expertise and the Public*. Studies in Research and Higher Education (Oslo), 5, 1974, pp. 171–207.
44   For a useful discussion of this, see Reppy, J. The control of technology through regulation, in Johnston, R. and Gummett, P. (eds) *Directing Technology* (Croom Helm, London; 1979), pp. 135–55.
45   Moynihan, D. P. A plague of our own. *The Reporter*, 31 December 1964, pp. 32–4.
46   One analysis of these problems which can be recommended is: Allison, G. T. *Essence of Decision* (Little, Brown and Co., Boston; 1971).
47   Public Law 89–670, 80 Stat. 031, October 15, 1966.
48   Public Law 89–564, 80 Stat. 731, September 9, 1966.
49   Public Law 89–563, 80 Stat. 718, September 9, 1966, Section 102(2).
50   *Ibid*. Section 102(1).
51   For an excellent discussion of FMVSSs, see: Heffron, H. A. *Federal Consumer Safety Legislation* (USGPO, Washington, DC; June 1970), pp. 15–105.
52   Mills, D. Q. The techniques of automotive regulation: performance versus design standards, in Ginsburg, D. H. and Abernathy, W. J. (eds) *Government, Technology and the Future of the Automobile* (McGraw-Hill, New York; 1980), pp. 64–76.
53   Public Law 90–283, 90th Congress, 2nd Session (1968).
54   That is, those who produce less than 500 motor vehicles per year.
55   Heffron, H. A. *Federal Consumer Safety Legislation*, pp. 27–8 (see reference 51).
56   See: Dodge, L. A critique of vehicle safety programs from the viewpoint of a consumer advocate, in *Vehicle Safety Research Symposium*. US Dept Transportation (USGPO, Washington, DC; 1973), pp. 191–3.
57   Public Law 89–563, 80 Stat. 718, September 9, 1966, Section 113(a).
58   National Traffic Safety Agency, US Dep. Commerce. *Report on the Development of the initial Federal Motor Vehicle Safety Standards issued January 31, 1976* (USGPO, Washington, DC; 1967).
59   Three major changes were made. The effective date for application was extended; non-destructive tests were allowed; and the definition of 'multipurpose passenger cars' as opposed to regular passenger vehicles was accepted.

60   Nader, R. *Unsafe at Any Speed*, 2nd edn (Grossman, New York; 1972),
     p. lxxxvii.

61   Nader, R. *Washington under the Influence: a Ten-year Review of Auto
     Safety amidst Industrial Opposition*. (Mimeo.), 23 February 1976.

62   Cameron, J. Nader's invaders are inside the gates. *Fortune*, October
     1977, p. 262.

63   Available from the Insurance Institute for Highway Safety, Watergate
     Six Hundred, Washington, DC 20037.

64   The Clean Air Act Amendments of 1970.

65   The Energy Policy and Conservation Act of 1975.

66   The Motor Vehicle Information and Cost Savings Act of 1972.

67   Cordtz, D. Henry Ford, Superstar. *Fortune*, May 1973, p. 284.

68   See Pearce, M. C. International competition in the world automotive
     industry, in Ginsburg, D. H. and Abernathy, W. J. (eds) *Government,
     Technology and the Future of the Automobile* (McGraw-Hill, New
     York; 1980), pp. 259–69.

69   Singer, J. W. Regulatory Report 9. *National Journal Reports*, 7, p.
     658.

70   Thayer, H. E. Business in an era of legislation and regulation.
     Chemistry and Industry, 19 March 1977, p. 226.

71   Goodson, R. E. *Federal Regulation of Motor Vehicles: A Summary
     and Analysis*, Report to the DOT (Purdue University, March 1977).

72   A study prepared for the NHTSA has discussed these issues in some
     depth with particular emphasis on the way they will affect individual
     companies. Schnapp, J. B. *Corporate Strategies of the Automotive
     Manufacturers* (Lexington Books, Lexington; 1979).

73   The part played by the Council on Wage and Price Stability in
     opposing NHTSA plans for a new passive restraint standard will be
     examined in the appropriate case study.

74   US DOT, NHTSA. *Societal Costs of Motor Vehicle Accidents*.
     Preliminary Report, May 1972.

75   Office of Science and Technology. *Cumulative Regulatory Effects on
     the Cost of Automotive Transportation* Final Report of the *Ad Hoc*
     Committee (USGPO, Washington DC; 1972).

76   US Congress, Government Accounting Office. *Need to Improve
     Benefit–Cost Analyses in Setting Motor Vehicle Safety Standards*, July
     1974.

77   House of Representatives. Hearings before the Subcommittee on
     Oversight and Investigations of the Committee on Interstate and
     Foreign Commerce. *Regulatory Reform Vol. IV*. 94th Congress, 2nd
     Sess., 27 February 1976, Serial No. 94–83 (USGPO, Washington, DC;
     1976).

78   US Comptroller General. Report to the Committee on Commerce, US
     Senate. *Improvements Needed in Planning and Using Motor Vehicle
     Safety Research*, 16 September 1974.

79   Dodge, L. A critique of vehicle safety programs from the viewpoint of a
     consumer advocate, in *Vehicle Safety Research Symposium*, US Dept
     Transportation (USGPO, Washington, DC; 1973), pp. 185–95.

80 Claybrook, J. Regulation and innovation in the automobile industry, in Ginsburg, D. H. and Abernathy, W. J. *Government, Technology and the Future of the Automobile* (McGraw-Hill, New York; 1980), pp. 319–33.

81 Nelkin, D. The political impact of technical expertise. *Social Studies of Science*, **5**, 1975, 53–4.

82 Cameron, J. Nader's invaders are inside the gates. *Fortune*, October 1977, p. 262.

83 In fact, the announced losses for 1980 were as follows: Chrysler – $1.71 thousand million, Ford – $1.54 thousand million, American Motors Corporation – $198 million, General Motors – $763 million (the company's first loss since 1921). Source: *Fortune*, 23 March 1981, p. 21.

84 This would have taken the budget down from $325 million (the figure for 1981) to $170 million. The Carter administration had been seeking $357 million for 1982. This cut would imply a 25 per cent reduction in the agency's workforce.

85 Gillespie, B. F., Eva, D. and Johnston, R. D. Carcinogenic risk assessment in the US and Great Britain. *Social Studies of Science*, **9** (3), 1979, 265–301.

Chapter 5

Road traffic safety policy in Britain

Three immediate points must be realised about the British system for road traffic safety. First, unlike the USA, there has been very little 'radical' policy making: the present processes are the outcome of a long, incremental development which has not openly been directed towards any specific goals or objectives. This suggests that the current situation can only be comprehended by adopting a somewhat longer historical period for discussion that was the case for the USA. Secondly, the British system is characteristically informal; no one framework exists for rulemaking and the topic has only rarely emerged as a visible public debate. Consequently, there is a sharp contrast with the United States in terms of the availability of information concerning the relevant political processes. In addition, there is, of course, the characteristic confidentiality of the British style of government which serves to render the everyday operation of the administrative system relatively opaque. A third notable aspect of the British regulatory process in recent years has been the effect of decision making in two European organisations, the United Nations Economic Commission for Europe (ECE) and the European Economic Community (EEC). However, this chapter will focus on specifically *British* political developments; the European sphere of influence will then be introduced in Part III. In the first section of this chapter, a brief analysis of the evolution of the present administrative processes will be carried out. Following this, the structure of the contemporary policy-making system will be analysed.

The historical development of legislation

The first (and most drastic) policy for controlling road traffic safety in Britain came with the Highways and Locomotive Acts of 1861 to 1878.

These now famous laws limited 'road locomotives' to a maximum speed of 4 mph and required a person with a red flag to walk in front warning of their approach. By 1903 the speed limit had been raised to 20 mph as the motor car began to be accepted as a mode of transport.

The 1930 Road Traffic Act laid the foundations for a large part of modern British practice in regard to road traffic safety. A number of specific clauses came into operation: third-party insurance became obligatory; the penalties of licence endorsement and disqualification were introduced; 'careless driving' became an offence and police were given the power to arrest without warrant motorists for driving while under the influence of alcohol or drugs. The Minister of Transport was also granted wide powers – as in other government departments – to introduce new legislation and put it before Parliament.[1]

The 1930 Act also established the statutory basis for 'Construction and Use Regulations'. These are the nearest equivalent to Federal Motor Vehicle Safety Standards in that they set specifications for certain aspects of vehicle and vehicle equipment design. According to the new act, public service vehicles (buses and coaches) were subject to special construction regulations and had to be 'certified' by government inspectors before going into operation. For all other road vehicles (including motor cars), the *user* was held responsible for compliance, although this did of course put the onus on manufacturers to produce legally roadworthy vehicles. Construction and Use (C. & U.) Regulations now set out the minimum construction, equipment and safety standards for most vehicles in Britain. Since 1930, the law has changed so that it is now an offence to sell a vehicle for use on British roads unless it meets these requirements. In order to increase the responsibility of manufacturers in this area, a type approval scheme now covers many of the major vehicle safety requirements. Type approval has been developed in many European countries and its procedures were made compulsory for Britain in 1978. The main consequence of type approval has been that all cars must be approved by the Department of Transport, following tests on such features as windscreen glass, steering systems and braking, before they can be licensed for British use.

In 1931, a set of Motor Vehicles (Construction and Use) Regulations were passed by Parliament. These covered 87 items and were typically couched in rather vague and even subjective terms, e.g. 'vehicles must be able to stop in a reasonable distance under the most adverse conditions'. As one Director of the Department of Transport

Vehicle Safety Division has commented on vehicle standards as they existed until 1951:

To the Legislators it seemed quite unnecessary to specify by regulation such items as the steering mechanism – after all it was obvious that the vehicle must be capable of being steered.[2]

It can be argued that a similar approach still dominates British thinking on vehicle design standards. As an example of this one can take the C. & U. Regulation defined in 1973 to deal with the integrity of petrol tanks in motor cars. This specified that such a tank be

... made only of metal, and in a position as to be reasonably secure against damage and any leakage of liquid or vapour is adequately prevented ...[3]

Terms like 'reasonably secure' and 'adequately prevented' assure a high degree of flexibility for manufacturers which would not be permitted by more precise specifications (whether of the 'performance-' or 'design- based' varieties). The nature of British design standards will be discussed in later sections. However, it is important to note that, as a general characteristic of British policy in this area, the safety of the vehicle itself has not been a major focus of attention. Instead, of the three specialty approaches presented in Chapter 3, two have been given particular emphasis, traffic engineering, and human factors. At least in this respect British practice resembles the years in the USA before the 'conceptual shift' of 1966.

At the same time it should be appreciated that *all* government policy has tended to shy away from strong regulatory control, as the Parliamentary Secretary for Transport expressed it in 1955:

In a democratic country, the government cannot go further in enforcing safety regulations than public opinion is prepared to support. We believe that inspection of vehicles would make for a reduction in the number of road accidents, but if public opinion is not prepared to put up with the added interference and inconvenience it is clearly unwise to try to legislate ahead of public opinion.[4]

This argument for what Plowden has termed the somewhat 'anachronistic view of government as night-watchman' has been used on more than one occasion by representatives of the Department of Transport. (See below in relation to the British Safety Council.) It suggests that the department is not prepared to engage in any new policy until public pressure has *forced* a rethink of present strategies. It can be further suggested that there has been a 'non-interventionist' philosophy behind Department of Transport practice. Again, Plowden has noted that, although there has been economic intervention in, for example, the British motor industry, this intervention has not altered the *laissez-faire* consistency of the state approach to transport planning and general transport policy.[5]

The only possible exceptions to this *laissez-faire* approach have been when a particular Transport Minister has pushed through new legislation and been prepared to move away from a purely incremental strategy. Two notable examples of this in the last twenty years are Ernest Marples (Conservative, 1959–64 as Minister) and Barbara Castle (Labour, in office 1965–68). Both personalised government activity in this area and took the Department of Transport away from its more usual 'low profile'. Both were also the specific target for a large amount of opposition.

In 1960 the Ministry of Transport initiated a study of the problems of traffic in urban areas which, it was hoped, would provide the basis for a British transport policy. Colin Buchanan, who had been the author in 1958 of an analysis of the motor vehicle entitled *Mixed Blessing*,[6] was put in charge of the study group, and a steering group was chaired by Geoffrey Crowther. The report eventually appeared in the summer of 1963.[7]

The basic argument that emerged was essentially similar to that found in Buchanan's book. According to *Traffic in Towns*, there should be a fundamental distinction between routes for traffic and for pedestrians. These two should then be physically separated from each other. The implications of this approach for road traffic safety would be that 'the sheer number of opportunities for conflict'[8] would be reduced and therefore fewer accidents should occur.

Both the Conservative government and the motoring organisations publicly welcomed this report; it was certainly not anti-motorist in any sense and it also encouraged new building programmes. In the Commons debate that followed its publication,[9] there was little dissent voiced: transport policy and road traffic safety in Britain have never emerged as major political issues. Nevertheless, there were some critical voices in the discussion. Tony Benn, then a Labour back-bencher, spoke of the 'most hideous lobby of all – the motorists' lobby'. Richard Marsh (who became Transport Minister himself in 1968) struck a similar note by arguing that the road lobby was too strong to suffer any radical changes in policy. Indeed, argument over the strength or otherwise of the 'road lobby' has been conducted since the appearance of the motor car.

If the Buchanan Report's recommendations for road traffic safety are considered, it can be seen that these fall within a traffic engineering framework. In fact, the report explicitly rejected a human factors type of approach and it failed even to consider the occupant protection specialty. Overall, there is little doubt that the focus on vehicle crashworthiness which was fast developing in the United States during the 1960s remained peripheral to discussion in Britain.

The Conservatives left office in 1964 but there were few immediate changes in the outlook and policy of the Ministry of Transport. However, in December 1965 Barbara Castle became Transport Minister. Although this meant little change in official policy, Mrs Castle became very strongly identified with the 70 mph speed limit and the controversial 'breathalyser' and drinking and driving laws, as embodied in the 1966 Road Safety Bill. In its original form, this bill had included random check powers for the police; the clause was eventually dropped when the proposal re-emerged after the March 1966 General Election so that blood-alcohol tests could only be carried out by police officers on drivers suspected of having already committed an offence, or who had been involved in a road accident.[10]

The issue of random check authorisation for the police assumed great importance in regard to the possible infringement of personal liberty. The question has certainly not been forgotten, and in 1976, a Department of Environment committee published its conclusions (usually known as the Blennerhassett Report) on the mandate it had been given in July 1974, 'to review the operation of the law relating to drinking and driving, and to make recommendations'.

The Blennerhassett Report made a number of specific points, but its general argument in favour of increased police discretionary powers was as follows:

While the basic rights of the suspect must be safeguarded, we consider that other road users' right to be protected from dangerously unfit drivers is paramount. Those who have done so much to combat the drinking driver should now be given better tools to continue the job, and be relieved of the handicaps under which they work.[11]

In 1979 the Conservative Minister of Transport, Norman Fowler, stated his intention of introducing legislation to change the present drinking and driving laws. A consultation paper on this matter was published at the end of 1979 which advocated new techniques for breath analysis and removed certain loopholes in the existing law. These proposals then became part of the 1980 Transport Bill. However, despite pressure from organisations such as the Royal Society for the Prevention of Accidents (RoSPA), no major change was made on the matter of increased discretionary powers for the police. The British Medical Association (BMA) had argued for 'random' breath tests and even motorists' organisations such as the Automobile Association (AA) had come to a similar conclusion following the diminishing effectiveness of the existing law. There are certain obstacles to any future implementation of Blennerhassett's recommendations: – the granting of powers to police to stop 'on suspicion' could only take place after a discussion of notoriously treacherous questions such as 'What is human liberty and how is it to be maintained?' Certainly, parallels exist between this issue and compulsory seat belt wear legislation.

In the 1960s the mandatory inspection of vehicles for roadworthiness became applicable to a greater proportion of motor cars than ever before. Ministry of Transport tests became compulsory from July 1966 for all cars of more than four years in age. From April 1967 this requirement extended to cars that had been on the road for only three years. These tests were to be carried out yearly. An additional piece of legislation meant that seat belts had to be fitted in all cars built after 1967.

Although these changes may have been taken as an expression of a growing concern for road traffic safety, a policy document published by the Ministry of Transport in 1966 certainly did not suggest anything but the broadest of strategies. This topic was touched on for only one page of the document, and the section in question appeared as an urgent call for action – with no indication of what that action might be. An argument was made for a 'positive and ambitious approach' to road safety, but only one clue was given to the direction this activity might take. This came in a reference to the Road Research Laboratory:

... the Laboratory is intensifying its research into road safety generally and into particular aspects of it such as human behaviour, which is at the root of the road safety problem.[12]

Here we see a very direct reference to the human factors approach to road traffic safety.

In July 1967, an important government White Paper appeared, *Road Safety — a Fresh Approach*.[13] This document proposed a 'scientific' approach to road traffic accidents, with particular emphasis on the cost effectiveness of the various possible measures. It backed the creation of a centralised and coordinated link between the parties involved (focused on a Central Road Safety Unit at the Ministry), an extended propaganda campaign (to cost £3 million spent over three years and based on the 'You know it makes sense' slogan) and also a review of vehicle design legislation. Fundamental to this proposed strategy was a holistic approach to road traffic safety, an assessment of the problem as essentially *diverse*. No individual aspect of road traffic safety was singled out for particular emphasis and the range of government departments, local authorities, industries and problem areas involved was noted. In addition, the report looked forward to the continuation of a consensual relationship between government and industry so that a 'forward programme of action' could be agreed between the two parties. This emphasis on consensus between regulators and the regulated is quite typical of British state involvement within this area; the contrast with US political developments during the same period is absolutely clear.

Also in 1967 a Ministry of Transport 'study of trends in the design of vehicles with particular reference to their use in towns' was published.[14] One particular focus of the report was on the contribution vehicle design could make to urban road traffic safety. On this theme, the study was a good deal less single-minded than US policies of that time. Instead, a variety of factors such as safety harnesses, stability and handling qualities were stressed. As with the 1967 *Road Safety* document, the overall impression to be gleaned was that the British government was not committing itself to any one policy framework. The Ministry of Transport was prepared, at least in principle, to back various types of measure and encompass each technical specialty (traffic engineering, human factors, and occupant protection). A more recent consultation paper suggests a narrower approach:

... research suggests that while vehicle failures can be held largely responsible for about 8% of accidents, and deficiencies of the road environment for 28%, human error contributes to 95%. There is still scope for improving the engineering of roads and vehicles, but the law of diminishing returns is beginning to operate. It is human behaviour that lies at the root of the road safety problem. If the struggle is not to be abandoned in the longer term, growing emphasis must now be placed on policies for helping road users to behave more safely.[15]

This view is interesting for a number of reasons. First, there is its confident assertion that human behaviour 'lies at the root of the road safety problem', which represents a clear indication of support for the human factors framework. Secondly, there is the imputation of 'diminishing returns' to the traffic engineering and occupant protection approaches. The focus on road user behaviour is indeed very similar to that argued by the 1966 document.

In its actual practice, the Ministry of Transport has consistently emphasised driver and pedestrian education, via driving (and cycling) proficiency tests and also propaganda. As far back as 1939 a House of Lords Select Committee has given its backing to propaganda as a means of ensuring care and attention on Britain's roads.[16] The Ministry of Transport's evidence to this committee had included the argument that 90 per cent of accidents were directly attributable to road-user error. Again, in the years immediately following the Second World War, propaganda became a major activity of the Ministry of Transport.[17] These attempts at behaviour-modification still continue although their effectiveness has often been criticised, the argument being that any success is essentially short lived. Propaganda is, of course, relatively cheap to operate and has the political advantage of attaining large visibility (and is therefore evidence that road traffic safety is not being ignored) without – in this case – impinging on the interests of any particular group.[18]

One of the most recent examples of the official British approach to road traffic safety can be found in the evidence submitted by the Department of Transport (D.Tp.) to the House of Commons Transport Committee in March 1983.[19] This evidence dealt with 'road safety' in the broadest terms but began from the premiss that human factors contribute to 95 per cent of all accidents, road factors to 28 per cent and vehicle factors to $8\frac{1}{2}$ per cent (allowing for multiple causation). However, the D.Tp. evidence was careful to add the following:

It should not be assumed from these figures that all effort at improvement should be applied to influencing human behaviour directly. While an attack on this aspect of the problem offers the greatest scope for casualty saving, influencing behaviour is clearly far more difficult and long term than improving roads or vehicles. In some cases the answer to accidents caused by human error may lie in engineering rather than behavioural solutions. Furthermore, while vehicle factors are a small proportion of contributory factors in accidents, the vehicle is a major contributory factor in the injuries suffered as a result of accidents.[20]

This statement puts the case for an occupant protection approach in terms which are essentially similar to those used by US policy makers and 'public interest' lobbyists, i.e. the *causation* of an accident is less significant than the means adopted for diminishing its *consequences*. Nevertheless, this point is not followed through in the form of appropriate policy recommendations. Instead, the D.Tp.'s evidence focuses on traffic engineering, drinking and driving, highway lighting, driver training and pedestrian behaviour. The main reference to occupant protection comes in a discussion of monitoring procedures for the 1981 Transport Act and, in particular, of its compulsory seat-belt wear provisions (see Chapter 7). Although seat-belt wear certainly falls within the area of occupant protection it does not – as we will see – infringe on the manufacturers' power to design vehicles as they see fit. Furthermore, the D.Tp. evidence says nothing about the need to develop stricter design standards, but assumes instead that 'car safety' has improved since the 1970s without producing any evidence to support this claim.[21] The regulatory climate within which these statements can be made will be explored throughout this book. For the moment, the reluctance of the Department of Transport to take on a 'NHTSA-style' standard-setting role can merely be noted.

The political structure of road traffic safety

Department of Transport (D.Tp.)
The D.Tp. has gone through numerous organisational changes in its history. In October 1976, the Labour Secretary of State for Transport, William Rodgers, announced the formation of the present administrative structure. The Vehicle Standards and Engineering Division (VSE) within the Directorate is now in charge of Construction and Use Regulations and specific topics have been allocated to its eight subsections (VSE 1–8).

The D.Tp. has its own research facilities, the Transport and Road Research Laboratory (TRRL) in Berkshire. Before 1939 the Laboratory, then simply the Road Research Laboratory (RRL), was under the control of the Department of Scientific and Industrial Research and its focus was very much on road building. The TRRL has since developed into an extremely large civil service research centre and its activities cover a broad range of safety-related topics (and also other fields of study), including road user behaviour, traffic management, vehicle design, road surfaces and accident prevention.[22] The TRRL functions as the research wing of the D.Tp. and, although the department is not obliged to support its findings, it is at least expected to take careful note of its research results.[23] This relationship is of particular interest in regard to the debate over windscreen glass. The D.Tp. also sponsors research into many topics, including road traffic safety, in 'outside' laboratories such as universities and the British Standards Institution (BSI).[24] It must be added that the TRRL has been suffering in recent years from government expenditure cuts. There was a loss of 28 per cent in the average number of staff employed at the Laboratory between 1975–76 and 1981–82 (from 1084 to 776). Further staffing reductions were also planned for 1982–83 (to a total of 690, with this figure including support staff of every kind). The main safety department had only 60 staff in 1983 compared with 103 in 1976. Throughout these cut-backs, priority has been given to civil engineering research, which has suffered a smaller reduction than the average across the TRRL.[25] As an attempt to reduce the consequences of these reductions in government funding, 'TRRL Ltd' was created to compete for external contracts and tailor previous research to industrial users. Overall, however, these cuts in government research can only diminish the ability of TRRL to function as an alternative 'knowledge base' to that available to industrial companies.

The development of vehicle safety regulations

Within the broad area of British practice in the area of road traffic safety it is possible to single out for particular attention the development of legislation relating to vehicle design. In this way, sufficient information will be provided for a comparison of this with its US equivalent. For the moment, only the rulemaking which has been carried out within Britain will be considered. The involvement of European organisations and their influence over British policy will be examined later.

(a) *Type approval* As discussed earlier, until August 1978 it was a feature of British law that Construction and Use Regulations did not distinguish between responsibility for the original design of the car and its subsequent condition when in use. Manufacturers were involved in a rather loose 'self-certification' system whereby it was their responsibility to translate standard specifications into engineering practice. One consequence of the new type approval scheme has been to force manufacturers to destruction-test their products as proof of compliance – although the standards applied are different in many ways from their US equivalents (see Part III). The financial consequences of this change can be especially great for the makers of only a small number of vehicles. The Italian firm, Lamborghini, announced the curtailment of British sales when it calculated that gaining type approval for its cars would cost £30 000 for a total sale of only 12–20 vehicles per year.[26] The type approval scheme was introduced into Britain as a result of standardisation steps in the European Economic Community.

(b) *Rulemaking*   The procedure by which a British vehicle standard emerges is based on the principle of *flexibility*. There is not a specific number of administrative stages to be followed, nor a requirement for the speed with which a regulation should be finalised. Consultation occurs before, during and after each step, and not just on certain prescribed occasions. One other major characteristic which must be noted is the *confidentiality* of all documents in this process: the D.Tp. is usually unprepared to make public its justification for new legislation or its assessment of the evidence. The whole process is *closed* to any individual or group outside the consultation network, and the first indication of a new standard will frequently be when the Transport Minister presents it to Parliament for approval. It is possible, however, to reconstruct the typical pattern of administration which leads up to this stage.

The first step, the initiation of a proposal for a new standard, can follow a number of causes – a new international regulation, a technological advance, a development in accident statistics – or it can emanate from a change in the public assessment of a particular risk or a new pressure-group demand.[27] At this point a (confidential) report is prepared by the D.Tp. to calculate the costs and benefits of the proposal and assess its effectiveness. The content of this report can only be guessed at later by examining the arguments put forward by the Minister. The proposal will not proceed to formal consultation unless the Secretary of State has given her/his approval.

The next major stage is the preparation of a draft regulation which is then circulated to up to 200 organisations on the D.Tp.'s consultation list (a limited number of these groups will be discussed in this chapter). What should be emphasised is that the formal consultation process will, in fact, have been continuous since the proposal's inception – especially as regards the manufacturers. A draft regulation is only prepared after discussion with the motor industry over cost and lead times. This dialogue then proceeds throughout the whole policy-making process. The comments received from outside groups are absolutely confidential as far as the D.Tp. is concerned.

The Department will next consider the suggestions and recommendations it has collected, and possibly prepare another internal policy document or amend its original draft. Following this review stage the regulation is submitted to the Secretary of State who, provided s/he deems it worth while, signs it and has it tabled in the House of Commons for acceptance.

One point relating to the D.Tp.'s operation in this and other areas is the *consensual* nature of policy making and implementation. In most cases, the process will be carried from initiation through to final regulation without any public controversy or major confrontation between civil servants and industry officials. As with the administration of health and safety law,[28] it is assumed that there is an 'identity of interest' between the regulators and the regulated. Accordingly, manufacturers will be canvassed for their opinions from an early stage, and informal communications between the two groups will be maintained. The D.Tp.'s philosophy is based on a 'reasonable' approach to standard setting so that a dialogue with the manufacturers is conducted with a view to avoiding 'unnecessary' constraints on industrial performance. This dialogue is aided by the fact that British public interest groups have historically had very little influence on decision making – a theme which will be explored later.

(c) *The British Standards Institution (BSI)* One excellent illustration of the British consensual approach to the area of vehicle design standards is the operation of the BSI. The D.Tp. will frequently adopt a British Standard (i.e. one developed by the BSI) as the basis for a construction and use regulation. Very many other standards relating to vehicle design are formulated by the BSI and then function as voluntary agreements. The 'Kitemark' scheme is an example of this. The BSI will certify certain products as being in compliance with its specifications. The Institution then undertakes annual testing of the product to ensure conformity; approval is terminated if standards are being consistently violated.[29] A fee is paid by firms for the right to use the 'Kitemark'.

On most topics the D.Tp. allows voluntary compliance to continue. Out of the 161 British Standards in existence in 1974, only 1 per cent had been made compulsory by law.[30] A third option for the Department is to set a totally new standard – but the relevant British Standard would certainly be considered beforehand.

The British government and the BSI have had a 'special relationship' since 1942 when the organisation was officially recognised as the sole authority (apart from the government) 'for issuing standards having a national application'.[31] Of course, only a small proportion of the total BSI activity is concerned with motor vehicles. What is interesting, however, for our present purposes is the way in which British Standards are actually formulated. This quotation comes from a BSI booklet of advice for its committee members:

The consensus procedure employed in producing British Standards is designed to ensure that all interested parties have the opportunity to put forward their views and that substantial support for the standards is secured. In other words, the aim in a technical committee is to produce a standard that commands general agreement.[32]

It is this 'safety philosophy' which lies at the roots of the British road traffic safety policy.

The most important pressure groups in this area will now be considered.

(d) *The Society of Motor Manufacturers and Traders (SMMT)*   The SMMT was organised in 1902 and has since assumed the position of main negotiator and coordinator for motor manufacturers. Until the early 1940s, the industry and the Automobile Association (AA) had combined their lobbying activities in a 'Motor Legislation Committee', but this was dissolved and the manufacturers established the SMMT as their collective voice to the government. At the same time, the major manufacturers each have their own divisions devoted to road traffic safety, e.g. Ford UK have an Automotive Safety Planning Department. However, the industry tends to feel that a 'united front' via the SMMT is their best strategy for negotiation at present. Both the D.Tp. and the SMMT characterise their relationship as being one of 'continuous dialogue'. As one might expect, the SMMT stance in this relationship is generally to favour caution and to accept change only when absolutely necessary from their own perspective.

The Society has organised seven or eight technical committees to study such topics as occupant restraint, safety glass, emissions, fuel tanks and wheel/tyre construction. The committees consist basically of industry 'experts' plus representation from involved vehicle and vehicle component manufacturers. A recurrent theme of these committees is an argument over whether the technical evidence for a proposed amendment is sufficient to merit its adoption. The D.Tp. also looks to the manufacturers for its assessments of cost and for its opinion of the practicality and viability of a proposal. The amicable relations between civil servants and industry officials extend into most areas of policy formation relating to road traffic safety.

At present, the SMMT has more than 1500 member companies and a central staff of 120. Its funding comes solely from member subscriptions – around £1.5 million for 1982. The SMMT also operates jointly with the Motor Agents Association (MAA), a Motor Industry Code of Practice aimed at improving customer services in Britain.

(e) *The motoring and consumer organisations*   In Britain there are two principal organisations for motorists, the Royal Automobile Club (RAC), founded in 1897, and the Automobile Association (AA), founded in 1905. Their stance has always been a 'consumerist' one: protecting what they see as the interests of the private motor vehicle owner. The AA and RAC have in general fought against increased costs to the motorist and in so doing they have frequently argued the case for the manufacturers (against increases in vehicle insurance or taxation). A consequence of this is that the motoring organisations have often been seen as part of the 'motor lobby'. However, the organisations have, in fact, been critical of the lack of clarity in the present network of standards and voluntary agreements relating to vehicle design safety.[33]

The AA has been active in this area during the 1970s and early 1980s through its *Drive* magazine, which includes tests of new and old cars, and also equipment and components. One particular campaign has been conducted relating to child restraint systems and the apparent inadequacy of some of these for child protection.

The Consumers' Association has also been active in product testing, mainly through the magazine *Which?* and its supplement *Motoring*

Which?. As with the AA and RAC, its research capability is restricted
and this creates many difficulties for technical analyses and active
lobbying. *Motoring Which?* features occasional articles specifically on
vehicle safety and the regulations in existence.[34]

The four main 'independent' groups and their assessment of road
traffic safety as an issue will now be discussed.

(f) The Royal Society for the Prevention of Accidents (RoSPA)

Few accidents just happen. More often than not they are caused by the human
factor – carelessness, ignorance, tiredness, stress, or simply a break in a
routine. RoSPA believes that more so-called 'accidents' could be prevented.[35]

The Royal Society for the Prevention of Accidents is a registered
charity with an annual budget of around £2 million, received from its
20 000 members, from government grants, and from the sale of
publications and general services. Of course, only a fraction of
RoSPA's total effort is in the area of road traffic safety.

The Society's involvement in road traffic safety dates back to 1916,
but its intervention was extended considerably in 1945 when it began
to plan and run the government's National Road Safety Campaign.
RoSPA today has a National Road Safety Committee to coordinate its
activities. This body draws its members from the civil service, local
authorities, road safety offices (run by local government),
manufacturers and the motoring organisations. As suggested by the
quotation, many of RoSPA's major activities have concentrated on the
human factors framework. This specialty and its 'education and
training' implications for practical implementation have led RoSPA to
become involved in 'defensive driving' courses (usually as a service to
particular private companies), the National Safe Driving Award
Scheme, the National Cycling Proficiency Scheme and publicity,
training and propaganda work. Local authorities now have a statutory
requirement placed upon them to promote road traffic safety.
Accordingly, RoSPA's former function as organiser of these activities
has altered to the present role of providing materials and advice.

However, it must be noted that RoSPA has also been involved in a
range of lobbying activities and campaigns. The organisation has
keenly supported mandatory seat-belt wear and it has petitioned MPs
before a vote on any such bill. Indeed the President of RoSPA, Lord
Nugent, introduced an unsuccessful Private Member's Bill in 1980–81
on this issue. RoSPA's magazine *Care on the Road* has spoken

repeatedly in favour of stricter drink–driving laws and advocated implementation of the Blennerhassett Report (discussed earlier). The magazine has also been one of the few British publications to highlight research on occupant protection and to pay attention to such specific issues as the design of public services vehicles, the safety of Reliant Robins, US regulatory developments or 'space-saver' temporary spare tyres. Although RoSPA enjoys good relations with government officials and also manufacturers, it has at times been hostile towards existing practices, e.g. the manufacturers' promotion of their products as 'dream machines' rather than as potentially lethal modes of transportation.[36] It would be fair to argue, therefore, that although RoSPA has traditionally focused on human factors, its publications have at least been prepared to adopt a critical stance towards the vehicle companies and (to a lesser extent) the D.Tp.

(g) *The Pedestrians' Association (PA)*   In contrast to the 'insider' status of RoSPA, the PA has, from its inception, taken upon itself the role of 'outsider' critic. The association was formed as the 'Pedestrians' Association for Road Safety' (this remains its official title) in 1929, largely through the efforts of Viscount Cecil of Chelwood. Lord Cecil had sat on a Select Committee which was considering a bill to introduce mechanical speed controls on vehicles and also compulsory insurance. In the course of this work, he was struck by the power of the 'motor lobby' and the lack of any opposing pressure group. The PA's hostility to the motor lobby continues today:

The interests of the *consumers* of transport must not be compromised by the interests of those who produce the *means* of transport.[37]

They are also critical of the lack of political action on road traffic safety. The PA remains a small organisation with an annual income of £5000 and a membership of around 1000. Its resources are therefore clearly limited when compared with RoSPA's. The association has nevertheless continued to argue the case for the pedestrian's interests, and especially those of the young, old and infirm. The PA considers that motor vehicles need to be controlled far more strictly and that, for example, road traffic accidents involving child pedestrians should be reduced not by keeping children indoors but by eliminating the possibility of such accidents at source.

Streets without overpowered cars driven by speed-obsessed idiots are perfectly safe for children. Castigate the cause of the danger, not the victims.[38]

This emphasis on the pedestrian rather than the motorist has led the PA away from applying political pressure over vehicle design modifications. There are signs, however, that the PA is becoming interested in the question of design for the minimisation of pedestrian injury in a collision.[39] It should be noted that the association, despite its critical tone and attacks on the motor lobby, has never taken on an openly *political* role. Road traffic safety is not seen as an ideological issue; rather it offers the opportunity for the major political parties to unite so as to end British society's dependence on the motor car. This non-ideological posture is reinforced by the selection of establishment figures for its higher offices: the Bishop of Birmingham (Rt Revd H. W. Montefiore) is its President, and the Archbishop of Canterbury and the Lord Bishop of London as well as several members of the British aristocracy are among its Vice-Presidents. The Pedestrians' Association has presented a 'respectable' image despite its frequently critical tone.

(h) *The Socialist Environment and Resources Association (SERA)*   It is interesting to compare the critical but non-ideological tone of the PA with one group which has a manifestly political[40] approach to transport questions, SERA. This organisation was founded in 1973 and enjoys 'consultative status' with the Labour Party. Its membership includes Labour MPs and affiliates from trade unions, trades councils, cooperative societies and the Labour Party. SERA describes its objectives as follows:

– to alert the labour movement and the public generally to the resource/environment crisis.
– to highlight its political, social and economic causes and effects.
– to put forward positive proposals to counter them.[41]

The organisation has been involved in a number of campaigns relating to the 'right for socially useful and responsible work', the anti-nuclear–power movement, greater self-sufficiency in food production and resistance to public service cuts. On the topic of road traffic safety its political viewpoint has led it to a similar focus to that of the Pedestrians' Association.

Members of SERA tend to emphasise the need to reduce the danger to those outside a car (cyclists, pedestrians, etc.) by traffic reduction and control rather than measures that assist only those inside a car *after* an accident has taken place.[42] This argument can be translated into more explicitly political terms by arguing that safety measures such as seat belts and passive restraint help the middle-class motorist but do little for the less-privileged members of society (the old, the young, the poor) who may find themselves the victims of road traffic accidents.[43] Accordingly, road traffic safety becomes a matter of broader transport policies and, more profoundly, of the distribution of power in society.

This view of transport policy and road traffic safety as intensely political matters is certainly not the conventional approach to the problems in Britain. SERA has consistently attempted to demonstrate in all the areas with which it has been concerned that such policy decisions involve crucial choices about the basis on which our society will be run. Friends of the Earth have played a similar role for many topics, as also have Transport 2000. Like SERA, this group is arguing that a fundamental change in transport policy is required that would remove the present emphasis on the private motor car and replace it with better provision for mass transport. Many of the problems of road traffic safety would then disappear. These groups are not primarily interested in 'tinkering' with vehicle design, road-user behaviour or highway layout: they are concerned with the development of a radically different transport technology. The *Changing Directions* study prepared by the Independent Commission on Transport[44] is in essential agreement with SERA and Friends of the Earth on this point.

One's attitude towards road accidents may be influenced by one's opinion on whether our transport arrangements are in other ways desirable, necessary or even inevitable ... we conclude that the transport system does not serve the nation's transport needs very well, quite apart from accidents and other side effects. We therefore find ourselves unimpressed by the prospect of a reduction only in casualty *rates* if this does not also produce a reduction in the absolute number of casualties.[45]

This distinction between *rates* and *absolute numbers* of casualties is an important one because it divides the British groups which have been examined so far. The industry, government, motoring organisations and RoSPA all argue for a reduction in rates and consider any decrease in these to be a measure of success. The groups which have just been discussed are seeking the kind of major and absolute fall which can only follow a drastic reduction in the vehicle population and a radical new transport policy for Britain. The first group accepts the place of the private car in our transport system; the second does not, for a variety of reasons (e.g. energy resources, the environment, inefficiency, social inequality) of which road traffic safety is but one. In the USA, on the contrary, a large number of lobby organisations fall into the first group, despite their hostility to the vehicle manufacturers. This is an important contrast between the two countries, although it is itself a reflection of the differences in political climate. We will return to these points somewhat later in the book.

The next organisation that will now be examined is of special interest because its approach to road traffic safety bears a certain similarity to that taken by US pressure groups. In fact, it represents an attempt to import an American safety philosophy to a rather different social and political context.

(i) *The British Safety Council (BSC) and vehicle defects*   The British Safety Council is a large and well established organisation, registered under the Charities Act of 1960. Its monthly newspaper *Safety* has a circulation of 70 000 and an estimated readership of 200 000. It is funded by membership subscriptions and revenue from training courses, which mostly relate to occupational safety and hygiene. In recent years the BSC has involved itself not just in health and safety at work, but also in a new area, vehicle safety with a particular emphasis on defects. The handling of vehicle defect recall and notification schemes in Britain has not been discussed in this chapter, and will therefore be examined here.

In September 1978 and April 1979 the BSC produced and circulated a report to MPs on the general topic of vehicle defects. These documents asserted that Britain had a 'totally inadequate system for dealing with car safety' and that this was a consequence of 'commercial camouflage, public ignorance and government complacency'.[46] The Council's argument is that, even if the official D.Tp. figures are accepted (the BSC does not believe that they should be) and vehicle defects contribute to no more than $8\frac{1}{2}$ per cent of accidents, and are the sole cause of only $2\frac{1}{2}$ per cent, then, using the Central Statistical Office's own cost-benefit analysis,[47] this involves a minimum 'cost to the country' of £32 325 000 for the annual figure in question of 164 deaths, 2000 serious injuries and 6340 slight injuries. The Council claims that a basic vehicle defects monitoring system incorporating a telephone hotline and computer facilities (as in the

USA) could be established for £50 000 per annum and that this would lead to clear financial and humanitarian savings. In fact, the BSC is presenting a case for a US-type recall and notification system. Indeed, the NHTSA and Nader gave advice to the Council on the organisation of such a system. At the time of both the BSC reports there was operating in Britain a very informal and voluntary system for defect recall.

One case which highlighted the problem of vehicle defects related to the Austin Allegro. A change in roller bearings fitted to the rear wheels of these cars posed certain problems for servicing.[48] A consequence of this was a tendency for the vehicles to lose a rear wheel – often at high speeds. Following a compensation case in which 'substantial damages' were awarded to a woman who had been left totally paralysed after a motorway crash in such circumstances, a High Court judge, Mr Justice Willis, made a number of comments about British Leyland, the manufacturer of these vehicles. The judge accused the company of 'commercial camouflage' in that they were aware of the mounting evidence regarding the dangers of this component. It was also claimed that at least a hundred such accidents had already occurred.[49] British Leyland argued that they had advised garages and the motoring organisations about the design changes and that this action removed them from liability. The AA have estimated that the typical owner response to such a campaign is around 17 per cent. However, there is some dispute over this: BL claimed a successful recall rate of 80 per cent. Nevertheless, many cases similar to that of the Allegro were known where companies had made recalls – but only at their own discretion.[50]

The BSC argued that an independent monitoring system would demonstrate very effectively the fundamental inadequacy of the present arrangements. The D.Tp. was invited to cooperate in a short trial but it declined, for reasons explained by John Horam, then the Under-Secretary of State:

I appreciate that you are only asking us at this stage to join in a week's trial of the suggested arrangement, but even this would be misleading as it would imply that we saw ourselves in a more direct and detailed consumer protection role than, in fact, is the case.[51]

This statement is very instructive as an indication of the D.Tp's general approach to road traffic safety. Sir Peter Baldwin, the Permanent Secretary to the D.Tp., also wrote to the Safety Council expressing his concern at the effect the 1979 document could have on the motor industry:

... this could harm the prospects of British motor manufacturers at a time of acute competition with foreign manufacturers.[51]

If economic factors are indeed put before questions of public safety in the D.Tp., then there seems little possibility of any radical policy making in this area in Britain. In the 1979 BSC report, Ralph Nader is quoted as suggesting that the British Minister of Transport should be relieved of his job so that he can work for the motor manufacturers 'whose interests he seems to be reflecting' in his present position. The D.Tp. has been able to maintain close and amicable links with the motor industry without generally coming under direct attack of this sort. Whereas statements such as those above from the D.Tp. would elicit howls of protest in the United States if uttered by the NHTSA, in Britain this industry–D.Tp. relationship is generally accepted. The contrast between the two nations in this respect is extremely clear.

The British Safety Council made two specific criticisms of the vehicle defect recall system as it operated in Britain at the time of the report. The first was of the voluntary nature of any recall and the lack of fixed responsibilities and official procedures. In July 1979 a new code of practice was announced by the D.Tp. and SMMT. This, according to Norman Fowler, the Transport Minister, would operate as an 'open book' policy with 'rigorous monitoring' by the Department.[52] The basis of this new system is a better notification system for owners, with access to the Driver and Vehicle Licensing Centre at Swansea for those who cannot be traced. The D.Tp. also has power to demand information from a manufacturer if a defect is suspected and then to publish relevant data if it is in the public interest to do so. However, the prime responsibility for deciding when a recall is necessary will still lie with the manufacturer, and in this way the code is based on a continuation of the old voluntary procedure.

The second basic point being made by the Safety Council is that the issue of vehicle defects should itself be located within a larger discussion of the need for the greater availability of information to the public and the benefits of a more open style of government. In order to discuss the demands being made by the BSC and other groups for the greater availability of information in Britain, the BBC 'Panorama' television team prepared in 1979 a documentary programme entitled 'Do you want to know a secret?' The Safety Council collaborated in the making of this and took the opportunity to gain wider attention for their campaign for a more open defect-recall system. Industry and government officials were also allowed to express their views on this and other related issues. However, British Leyland later protested to the BBC about the showing of this programme on the grounds that it was unfair to the company, and that it might damage the sales of British vehicles. The BBC acceded to this demand and screening was delayed for an indefinite period. It is perhaps unsurprising that these events were interpreted by many of those involved in road traffic safety as yet another indication of the power of the British 'road lobby' and a suggestion of the difficulties to be faced in producing any radical shift in policy making.[53]

The vehicle defect Code of Practice has remained in operation since 1979 so that, for example, between January 1981 and June 1981, 41 recall campaigns were initiated. Some quarter of a million vehicles were involved in this and the successful-recall rate was 73 per cent for cars, 75 per cent for commercial vehicles and 84 per cent for public service vehicles.[54] Defects with steering systems have been the single most important safety problem (accounting for approximately one-third of all recalls); brake defects and electrical problems have also been especially common.

In 1981, the D.Tp. requested various views on the operation of the Code of Practice. At that time the Consumers' Association pointed out a number of weaknesses in the scheme:[55]

> the need to extend it to include motorcycles, caravans, trailers and vehicle components;
> the largely unexplored possibility of using the Driver and Vehicle Licensing Centre (DVLC) to contact owners;
> the absence of a defects 'hotline' as advocated by the British Safety Council;
> the need for more information about how manufacturers monitor their vehicles after sale.

(j) *The Parliamentary Advisory Committee for Transport Safety (PACTS)* The Parliamentary Advisory Committee for Transport Safety[56] is one of the newest organisations to become involved in matters of road traffic safety, although some of its leading members, such as Dr M. Mackay (of the Accident Research Unit, University of Birmingham) or Barry Sheerman MP, have a longer-running interest in this area. The Council sees itself not so much as a lobby group but more as a source of information which can be fed into the policy-making process. It argues that there is a large gap at present between 'what is known to be correct' and 'what is actually practised and accepted'. At the same time, however, PACTS also emphasises the generally low level of funding made available to transport safety. It asserts that the money spent on research is approximately *0.1 per cent* of the annual cost of transport accidents in Britain. Accordingly, PACTS has argued that there is a need for professional expertise on this topic, which is just not being met by either the private or public sector. This matches well the view expressed here at the beginning of Chapter 3 that the 'science of road traffic safety' is generally under-resourced. The group is particularly critical of the rundown in TRRL research and considers that the Laboratory can no longer function as an 'independent national focus' for research.

In 1983, PACTS submitted evidence to the House of Commons Select Committee on Transport (the D.Tp. evidence to this committee was discussed earlier). The PACTS document covered a whole range of safety-related issues but gave particular emphasis to certain points:

mandatory fitting of three-point rear safety belts in all post-1981 cars;

the provision of additional resources for the implementation of low-cost engineering measures by highway authorities;

the provision of additional resources for initiating and improving traffic education programmes at primary, secondary and tertiary schools.

In addition PACTS has made recommendations about many other important topics: the need for mandatory fitting of laminated windscreen glass (see Chapter 9), the fitting of front-seat head restraints, the design of vehicles for maximum pedestrian protection (see Chapter 10). Although PACTS is still a small organisation, it has grown since its inception in 1979 so that it has 70 members from a variety of backgrounds. Organisations represented on PACTS include the Automobile Association (AA), the Royal Automobile Club (RAC), the Institute of Road Safety Officers, the Institute of Mechanical Engineers, the British Medical Association and the Association of Chief Police Officers. Such support can only be to the benefit of PACTS as a source of influence over regulation. However, it is worth stressing that this body does *not* see itself as 'political' in its aims, nor has it tried to appeal to a wider, more public, audience. It is thus attempting to play the role of an 'insider' to the policy process but without the resources of industrial lobbies such as the motor manufacturers. Many of PACTS' recommendations do deserve very serious attention and these will be considered at various stages in this book. The other point to be made about PACTS is that it has provided a source of new ideas in the British context which can only serve to stimulate debate in an area of long-held – and largely unchallenged – consensus.

Discussion

In Chapter 4 some general points were made about road traffic safety policies in the United States. In particular, attention was paid to a number of features: the radical burst of policy making in the mid-1960s, the emphasis on occupant protection, the mode of control chosen (mandatory performance standards), the adversarial political process and the relatively open manner in which decisions are made. We have seen that the equivalent British system of technological risk control is rather different in character.

The British approach to road traffic safety has developed in a most incremental fashion (to use Lindblom's influential terminology once again).[57] Sudden change has been avoided and the D.Tp. has, in general, kept road traffic safety away from public controversy, hence the perceived lack of interest in this topic in Britain and its general status as a 'non-issue'. Whereas the emergence of occupant protection in the United States served to provide a fresh political perspective on the all-too-familiar phenomenon of road traffic casualties, that perspective has not been forthcoming in Britain. Instead, British policies have stressed a view of human error as the major causative factor although with a certain additional importance – through such publications as the Buchanan Report – being attached to traffic engineering. In terms of the motor car itself, the emphasis has been on inspection and, more recently, recall campaigns for defective vehicles. The issue of crashworthiness has been left largely to the manufacturers themselves, with the D.Tp. setting various minimal standards rather than adopting the NHTSA style of 'forcing the technological pace'.

This latter point about vehicle design standards introduces also the British 'mode of control'. Whereas 'legal regulation' has been the form in the United States, Britain has adopted a whole range of devices – advice and services, encouragement and voluntary agreements, as well as legal regulations (in the form of Construction and Use Regulations). However, all of this has taken place within a framework of close cooperation between state officials and the motor industry – a consensual rather than an adversarial relationship. Of course, as with all the other points being made here, a better understanding of this relationship will be gleaned from our examination in Part III of the 'micro' as opposed to the 'macro' level of policy making. To complete the initial comparison with the United States, it can be argued that the political processes in Britain have typically been closed to 'outsiders'. Confidentiality plus an unwillingness to allow 'cause' as well as 'industrial' groups to participate directly in decision making serve to exclude outside involvement and to build barriers to open and informed discussion. In these circumstances, it is inevitable that 'public interest' groups (only some of which have been discussed here) who do wish to participate will compare their status with that of motor industry representatives and come to the conclusion that there is a powerful road lobby at work in Britain.

Hamer, for example,[58] has voiced the suspicions of groups such as Friends of the Earth by arguing that the road lobby is the most powerful pressure group at work in Britain: its understanding of the fine detail of the policy-making process and the resources that it can bring to bear make it extremely difficult for opposing groups to compete in terms of political influence. Other organisations such as the Pedestrians' Association and SERA would echo this view by claiming that it is because of this lobby's power that questions of road traffic policy (including safety) have been viewed by the mass of the public as non-contentious issues. As discussed in Chapter 2, we enter the realm of 'un-politics' where issues may be kept off the political agenda in order to protect certain economic interests.

Quite clearly, the notion of un-politics is very applicable to the question of why occupant protection has not been influential in Britain. The opposition of motor manufacturers to this approach was demonstrated in Chapter 4. Their greater influence over the British state has certainly served to deaden contradictory demands. Furthermore, just as the US political system has facilitated the presentation of 'public interest' views, the closed nature of the British political process has ensured that the views of oppositional groups have been barely visible on this issue. It is in the nature of 'un-politics' that power can be wielded by keeping matters away from discussion just as much as by 'outvoting' propositions once they are under scrutiny.

It should be said, however, that there is some disagreement among political commentators about exactly how powerful the road lobby really is. Plowden, for example, has provided the classical pluralist justification for existing policies and his defence merits quotation in full:

It is hard to show that either motorists or the motor industry now 'make policy' towards the car more directly than they did. In the 1900s both were often consulted . . . and sometimes ignored; exactly the same is true today. Despite their greater scale the organisations have found it if anything harder to succeed in their demands; the development of other interests and above all, in a managed economy, of the notion of the government's responsibility to the electorate as a whole, has kept their influence in check.[59]

The evidence against this view which we have uncovered so far includes the stated concern of the D.Tp. for the economic viability of the motor industry, the closed nature of the system so far as 'public interest' groups are concerned and the immense imbalance of resources between 'cause' and 'industrial' groups. However, our very general survey of the British political system in this area does not permit anything like a final conclusion on the power of the road lobby at this stage. Nevertheless, it is worth noting that many of the more radical pressure groups who might have been looked to for energetic lobbying over road traffic safety have, in fact, analysed general transport needs rather differently from 'Naderite' groups in the United States. For that reason the motor industry has come under little pressure about occupant protection standards largely because no 'public interest' group has mounted a serious and sustained campaign on this issue. This point was touched upon during our discussion of the Socialist Environment and Resources Association, but it needs emphasising here as it provides an additional reason for the strength of the road lobby (almost by default) in this area.

The distinction between groups such as SERA (or Friends of the Earth) and US 'public interest' organisations such as the Center for Auto Safety or the Insurance Institute for Highway Safety revolves around two related points. First of all, there is the view taken about the role of the motor car in society. The American groups tend to accept the importance of the car in future transport policies and, therefore, set themselves the task of 'living with the automobile' in the most socially harmonious manner. The British groups, however, argue vehemently in favour of alternative transport technologies and consider that the car has only a limited place within future networks for mass transportation. If successful, their case would solve problems of automobile safety in the most fundamental fashion – by drastically reducing the number of automobiles. Given this broad assessment, it is hardly surprising that groups such as FoE, SERA or the Pedestrians' Association show little enthusiasm for 'tinkering' with the design of an unacceptable technology. The motor industry must inevitably gain in terms of their freedom of action from this reluctance to engage in the battle over vehicle crashworthiness.

The second point of comparison between the national 'public interest' groups concerns more general political philosophies. Although the 'Naderite' groups can be portrayed as 'radical' elements within US society, their own statements reveal an acceptance of that nation's capitalist system. Their argument is a 'consumerist' or, more accurately, a reformist one. They wish to redress the balance between the ordinary citizen and large institutions such as the motor companies. In this way, the existing system could be improved and democracy would flourish. Accordingly, the demands made by US groups have little to do with socialism or the desire to cause more profound social changes. In contrast, British 'cause' groups are often ambivalent on this point. Groups such as SERA would certainly claim a broader political purpose. Here we can certainly see how debates over road traffic safety in Britain and the United States are affected by far more than simply the specific arguments over this form of technological risk.

As a final point in this chapter it should be emphasised that only a brief review of the relevant industrial and public interest pressure groups has been offered here. A more detailed analysis of the membership, resources and philosophies behind these and other groups is still awaited.[60] The main purpose of this chapter has been instead to characterise British discussions on road traffic safety as background to the more specific cases discussed in Part III.

Notes and references

1   Road Traffic Act, 1930. Sections 59 and 94.
2   Furness, J. W. Administrative requirements – UK legislative scene. in Institution of Mechanical Engineers *International Vehicle Legislation – Order or Chaos?* (I.Mech.E., London; 1976), p.72.
3   Duckworth, J. (ed.) *Kitchin's Road Transport Law 1977* (Butterworth, London; 1977).
4   *The Guardian*, 5 July 1955.
5   Plowden, W. *The Motor Car and Politics, 1896–1970* (Bodley Head,

London; 1971), p.342.

6   Buchanan, C. D. *Mixed Blessing – the Motor in Britain* (L. Hill, London; 1958).

7   *Traffic in Towns* (HMSO, London; 1963).

8   *Ibid.* p.16.

9   House of Commons. *Debates*, Vol. 689, 10 February 1964, Cols 32–160.

10   The important Second Reading of this bill is in: House of Commons. *Debates*, Vol. 735, 7 November 1966, Cols 981–1048.

11   Department of the Environment. *Drinking and Driving. Report of the Departmental Committee* (HMSO, London; 1976), p.14.

12   Ministry of Transport. *Transport Policy* (HMSO, London; 1966), p.11.

13   Ministry of Transport. *Road Safety – a Fresh Approach* (HMSO, London; 1967).

14   Ministry of Transport. *Cars for Cities* (HMSO, London; 1967).

15   Department of the Environment. *Transport Policy – A Consultation Document* (HMSO, London; 1976), Vol. 1, p.75.

16   House of Lords Select Committee on Prevention of Road Accidents (Alness Committee). *Report and Evidence*, March 1939.

17   A Ministry of War Transport report had advocated this approach in 1945. Ministry of War Transport, Road Safety Committee. *Interim Report* 1945.

18   One notable instance of safety propaganda which did upset certain interests was an anti-drinking and driving poster with the slogan 'One for the road may be one for the grave' prepared by the Royal Society for the Prevention of Accidents in 1953 under commission from the Ministry of Transport. In Birmingham a local brewery objected to this and the British Transport Commission decided that the posters were 'knocking copy' and thus in breach of the poster display code. The Ministry of Transport eventually concurred with the ban, deciding that 'these posters chose to criticise even the moderate use of alcohol'. See Plowden, W. *The Motor Car and Politics 1896–1970* (Bodley Head, London; 1971), p.332.

19   Transport Committee, House of Commons. *Road Safety*. Minutes of evidence from Department of Transport, 22 March 1983 (HMSO, London; 1983).

20   *Ibid.* p.2.

21   *Ibid.* p.47.

22   See RRL *Research on Road Safety* (HMSO, London; 1963). TRRL *Towards Safer Road Vehicles* TRRL Report LR481, 1972.

23   As a D.Tp. official expressed it: 'We would soon be taken to task for ignoring the evidence that is being developed on our own doorstep.'

24   See Departments of the Environment and Transport. *Register of Research 1977*. Part III: Roads and Transport.

25   *New Scientist*, 28 January 1982, p.212. *Care on the Road*, March 1983, p.2.

26   *Autocar*, 18 July 1978, p.19.

27   One possible example of this latter factor is the growing interest in legislation to protect child passengers, either by the standardised fitting

of rear seat belts or a law to prevent children from travelling in front seats.

28   Green, K. Health and safety at work and the radical science movement, in *Trade Unions, Technology and the Environment*. Control of Technology Unit 9. (Open University Press, Milton Keynes; 1978).

29   For a description of this process see: Feilden, G.B. The standards challenge, in *International Vehicle Legislation − Order or Chaos?* (I. Mech. E., London; 1976), pp. 47−55.

30   Bradwell, P. The car, the law and the consumer, in *International Vehicle Legislation − Order or Chaos?* (I.Mech.E., London; 1976), p.101.

31   *BSI News*, (12) 1976, p.8.

32   BSI. *BSI − its Activities and Organization*. PD4845:1977, p.2. Available from BSI, 2 Park Street, London W1A 2BS.

33   See Bradwell, P. The car, the law and the consumer, in *International Vehicle Legislation − Order or Chaos?* (I.Mech. E, London; 1976), pp.101−5. (Bradwell was Editor of *Drive* magazine.)

34   See *Motoring Which?* for April 1966, October 1972, April 1975, and September 1983. Available from Consumers' Association, 14 Buckingham Street, London WC2N 6DS.

35   *RoSPA − What it is, What it Does*. Available from RoSPA, Cannon House, The Priory, Queensway, Birmingham B4 6BS.

36   Bishop, J. The dream machine. *Care on the Road*, December 1981, pp.6−7.

37   *Arrive*. September 1978, p.3 (their emphasis). Available from Pedestrians' Association, 1/4 Crawford Mews, York Street, London W1H 1PT.

38   Bendixson, T. Letter to *Care on the Road*, June 1982, p.4.

39   *Pedestrians and the General Election*, PA leaflet, August 1978. See also the PA's evidence to the House of Commons Transport Committee in March 1983 (HMSO, London; 1983).

40   By 'political' in this context, we are referring to a group which explicitly either involves itself in party politics or introduces broader questions about the future of British society into its arguments.

41   *Introducing SERA*. Pamphlet available from SERA, 9 Poland Street, London W1.

42   Robson, P. Personal communication, 25 September 1978.

43   Robson, P. Letter to *The Guardian*, 17 July 1978.

44   This study was initiated by Bishop Hugh Montefiore (also of the PA), to investigate the UK transport system. The 'Commission' included trade union leaders, academics, planners and industrialists.

45   The Report of the Independent Commission on Transport. *Changing Directions* (Coronet, London; 1974), p.66 (their emphasis).

46   Chick, L. and Harrison, M. *Second Report to Members of Parliament on Vehicle Defects*. April 1979, p.1. BSC publication available from National Safety Centre, 62−64 Chancellor's Road, Hammersmith, London W6 9RS.

47 Central Statistical Office. *Facts in Focus* (HMSO, London; 1978).
48 All Allegros had tapered roller bearings rather than the more conventional straight units. There are reasonable engineering reasons for this modification, but there is the problem that tapered bearings need to be tightened to lower pressure than straight ones. Over-tightening can cause wheel seizure and the loss of that wheel.
49 *The Guardian*, 14 July 1978, p.6. *Sunday Times Business News*, 16 July 1978, p.1.
50 A list of UK car recalls for 1978 was obtained from the D.Tp. (although such information was not usually available to the public) and is contained in Chick, L. and Harrison, M. *Second Report to Members of Parliament on Vehicle Defects*. April 1979, pp.24–7. (See reference 46.)
51 *Ibid.* p.21.
52 *The Guardian*, 11 July 1979, p.5.
53 *The Guardian*, 18 August 1979, p.2.
54 *Care on the Road*, January 1982, p.1.
55 *Motoring Which?*, April 1982, pp.231–2.
56 Further information about PACTS is available from: The Co-ordinator, PACTS, c/o Barry Sheerman MP, House of Commons, London SW1A 0AA. See also: *The Guardian*, 18 July 1983, p.16; *The Times*, 15 July 1983, p.25.
57 Lindblom, C. E. *The Policy-making Process*. (Prentice-Hall, New Jersey; 1968).
58 Hamer, M. *Wheels within Wheels* (FoE, London; 1974).
59 Plowden, W. *The Motor Car and Politics*, 1896–1970 (Bodley Head, London; 1971), p.416.
60 See also: Lowe, P. and Goyder, J. *Environmental Groups in Politics* (George Allen & Unwin, London; 1983).

Part III

Chapter 6

Debates over Occupant restraint – I : USA

In the third section of this book the control of road traffic safety will be further examined through the consideration of a number of specific issues: occupant restraint, fuel system integrity, and laminated and toughened windscreen glass. These more detailed chapters will permit an analysis of how the general policies of Britain and the USA (as discussed in Part II) have actually been translated into regulatory practice. Of course, a study of the 'micro' level of decision making should also allow the nature of each nation's approach to emerge more clearly. The first of these case studies concerns the protection of vehicle occupants in the 'second collision' phase, i.e. after their vehicle has struck an external object and at that point when they are themselves about to collide with the vehicle interior.

There are a number of reasons why occupant restraint deserves particular attention in this book. In both countries this issue has been a major topic of public debate and has thus been one of the more 'visible' areas of decision making. Because of this prominence the whole matter has assumed an inevitable 'symbolic' significance inasmuch as it has epitomised the style of regulatory strategy adopted in each country and also the 'risk philosophy' which lies behind it. An important aspect of this – especially in the USA – has been the obvious tendency for occupant restraint to assume significance as a major test case over 'Who should determine design decisions – industry or the state?' However, although the 'regulatory battlefield' has been much more evident in the USA than in Britain, this is not to say that similar power struggles have not also taken place in the latter country.

One other reason for devoting a relatively large amount of space to this issue here is that it illustrates especially vividly the difference between the two countries in their assessment of the road traffic safety problem. In this case, the US debate over 'passive' technology, which is

not under the immediate control of the individual automobile
occupant, is in sharp contrast to the British emphasis on compulsory
seat-belt laws which demand the 'active' cooperation of driver and
passengers. The arguments that lie behind this difference of emphasis
deserve attention, as also does the actual outcome of each approach in
terms of implemented legislation. Accordingly, in the discussion and
analysis that follow in the next two chapters, every attempt is made to
see the national debates over occupant restraint not as single issues
which stand apart in themselves, but rather as debates which are
symptomatic of different styles of regulatory philosophy and political
process. It is in studying the actual conduct of decision making in this
way that it is possible to evaluate ways of coping with technological
risk as opposed to simply drawing broad conclusions from general
statements of policy intent.

FMVSS 208

Federal Motor Vehicle Safety Standard (FMVSS) 208 can be viewed
as a key example of the National Highway Traffic Safety
Administration's intention − at least in the early 1970s and again
under the Carter Administration − to 'force the technological pace'
with regard to safety innovation. The ensuing controversy has been
central to the political debate in the United States over road traffic
safety and has developed into a crucial trial of strength between the
regulatory agency, the motor industry and various 'public interest'
pressure groups. From a very early moment in its existence, the
NHTSA has been prepared to stake its credibility on a successful
resolution to the occupant restraint issue. Likewise, the US motor
industry has developed a common opposition to the new standard and
has blocked and delayed its implementation whenever possible. What
the debate over 208 demonstrates especially well is the way in which
such conflicts are (or are not) resolved within the apparently pluralistic
system of US government. As a study in the realities of decision
making over technological hazards, 208 contains, therefore, many of
the elements that may also be found in controversies over nuclear
power or carcinogenic chemicals. The events surrounding this
standard should also serve as an antidote to many of the more abstract
(and unreal) accounts of risk management and the determination of
'risk acceptability'. It should also be noted that at the time of writing
(1984) the issue is still unresolved and doubt remains about whether

the standard, which was first proposed in 1969, will ever be implemented in the form originally intended.

One important aspect of the US debate over occupant restraint which has received particular attention is the 'air bag', and some reports have implied that this is the only restraint technology under discussion. In fact, this is not correct, although the air bag has often been at the centre of debate because of its dramatic mode of operation and the particular opposition it has engendered among motor manufacturers. Before analysing the political discussion over 208, it is useful, therefore, to describe the air bag and also the main alternatives in terms of their technical characteristics.

The air bag

Although the air bag is frequently represented as a novel and untried technology, its history as an automotive safety device began in the early 1950s. The first US patent was filed in 1952[1] and development work was undertaken by GM later in the 1950s. According to the Insurance Institute for Highway Safety (IIHS),[2] Ford Motor Company also began experimentation around that time with air bags and termed the results 'disappointing'.

The basic technology behind the various air bag or 'air cushion restraint' systems tends to be unchanging, although component design differs in the available models (see Fig. 1). There is a sensor fitted to the front bumper (and in some cases the dashboard also), which will operate within a time interval of approximately 1/25th of a second.[3] The next component is an energy source (most commonly sodium azide) which is connected to a system for deploying the bag, the bag itself and its housing. There is a threshold set for the sensor so that it will not activate needlessly, e.g. at low speeds or during vehicle repair work. In a collision the energy source will detonate and release nitrogen gas, which then fills the bag so as to cushion the impact of the front occupant's face and body. The gas vents from the bag as the occupant hits it and it is this venting that absorbs the energy from impact. The basic principle behind the air bag is that it can be stowed unnoticed for any period of time, it requires no active interaction by the occupant (i.e. it is totally 'passive'), it operates only when necessary and causes no impediment to vehicle control or evacuation. After operation the bag must be replaced.

By the mid-1960s, Eaton Corporation had begun cooperative R. & D. work with Ford[4] and, in 1967, Eaton announced that it had

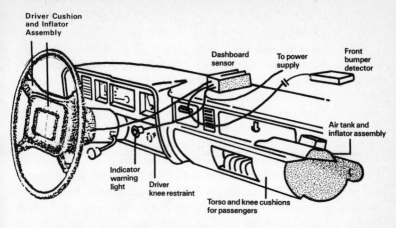

Fig. 1 Schematic drawing of air cushion restraint system (the air bag). Taken from House Subcommittee on Consumer Protection and Finance *Report on the Department of Transportation Automobile Occupant Passive Restraint Rule* (Mimeo.) September 1977, p. 46.

developed a viable occupant protection system. The basic technical uncertainties at that time included the achievement of bag deflation after impact, preventing inflation at low speeds or when otherwise unnecessary, and redesigning dashboards to stow the apparatus. One other possible drawback with the system was the problem of noise levels during detonation. Eaton claimed that levels were approximately 135 dB but that these would not have permanently damaging effects on hearing. Another potential weakness of the system was the protection given to out-of-position passengers who might strike only the edge of the bag rather than its centre.

In July 1968 the Director of the new agency (which was then known as the 'National Highway Safety Bureau' (NHSB)), Dr W. Haddon, called a meeting in order to consider the views of the US motor manufacturers and also of Eaton Corporation (at that time known as 'Eaton, Yale and Towne, Inc.'). Despite an awareness of some of the technical uncertainties still to be resolved, the Eaton representatives claimed that the technology had numerous advantages over alternative systems in terms of safety, convenience and consumer acceptability. Indeed, most of the participants appeared very receptive to the new technology and this attitude extended to include the motor industry representatives present. A GM official commented as follows:

... I would say that we have an excellent chance of building a system which would be, for practical purposes, highly reliable and reasonably free from inadvertent activation.[5]

This apparent consensus and the mood of cautious (but constructive) optimism contrast sharply with the disagreements over the air bag which were to emerge in the 1970s.

The active seat belt

Perhaps the most obvious technology to be considered as an alternative to the air bag is the active seat belt, possibly supported by 'compulsory wear' laws.[6] Legislation to the effect that all cars in the USA should have seat belts fitted had been passed in the mid-1960s although this had meant that, in many cases, only lap belts had been installed rather than lap and shoulder harnesses. However, voluntary seat-belt wear in the United States has remained at a consistently low level, with less than 20 per cent of occupants actually utilising belts, according to official estimates.[7] Various propaganda campaigns have achieved no more than minimal effect on these rates.

This situation would seem to suggest the consideration of compulsory measures but a major difficulty here is that, under US constitutional law, such legislation would have to be introduced at *state* rather than federal level. State legislative bodies have shown a distinct reluctance to pass such rulings or to become involved in the apparently inevitable discussion of personal freedom and the sanctity of human life (see Chapter 7). As a way of influencing state action, the NHTSA in 1972 proposed a standard requiring states to pass mandatory seat-belt laws or lose portions of their federal highway aid funds.[8] In 1974, following objections to this, the agency adopted an incentive grant approach – a carrot rather than a stick – to encourage legislation.[9] Despite this, as of 1984 no state had adopted a mandatory belt-use law.

The active seat belt has continued to feature in the debate over occupant restraint even after its apparent failure as either a voluntary or a mandated measure. Motor manufacturers and certain NHTSA Administrators have pushed for compulsory wear laws as a method of opposing more costly alternatives. The air bag is frequently contrasted with the active seat belt in debate in terms of effectiveness, reliability and expense. Despite the lack of progress in compulsory wear legislation and the apparent popular opposition to active seat belts, this technology has remained as a focus of discussion and most attempts at blocking air-bag legislation have included fervent advocacy of either propaganda campaigns or compulsory wear laws. As in Britain during the 1970s, the availability of this restraint system has impeded the consideration of alternatives without popular support for mandatory wear laws ever reaching the level where such legislation could be brought into action. In this way, the active seat belt has developed into a powerful blocking device for motor manufacturers wishing to oppose more stringent federal controls of occupant restraint.

The ignition interlock
The third occupant restraint measure to be considered in the USA is essentially a compromise between the active seat belt and a passive approach. The ignition interlock is a relatively unsophisticated technology to prevent a car being started with unbelted front-seat occupants. An electrical linkage between the vehicle's safety belts and the ignition system is coupled with a small number of simple sensors beneath the front seats (to detect whether a place is occupied or not). The intended effect is that the vehicle cannot be operated without full seat-belt wear.

One immediate contrast between the ignition interlock and the air bag is the speed with which it was developed. In early 1970 at least two manufacturers – both European (Peugeot and Renault) – were known to be interested in the concept of combining active restraint with a method of enforcement which could immobilise the vehicle. In July of that year the American Safety Belt Council, which represented the seat-belt manufacturers and had, therefore, a strong commercial interest in any system that included their own products, reported that it had supplied the Department of Transportation (DOT) with an ignition interlock prototype for testing on government cars. Ford Motor Company informed the DOT in early August that they also had developed an interlock device. Three months later Ford-sponsored television advertisements were extolling the virtues of the ignition interlock and disparaging the air bag. The motor company and the American Seat Belt Council also began to lobby the agency and, as will be discussed, more secretive discussions were conducted with President Nixon and White House staff. From 1971 to 1974, when the interlock device was removed from discussion, this technology played a crucial role in the debate over 208, and its political history will be examined in a later section.

Fig. 2 Automatic safety belt in Volkswagen Rabbit. As the door is closed, the shoulder belt automatically goes across the occupant. The belt is connected to an inertia reel, which allows freedom of movement but locks in the event of an emergency. A padded knee panel provides additional protection. (Sketch provided by Volkswagen; taken from House Subcommittee on Consumer Protection and Finance *Report on the Department of Transportation Automobile Occupant Passive Restraint Rule* (Mimeo.) September 1977, p. 46.

The passive seat belt

Like the ignition interlock, the fourth and final technology under discussion in the USA represents an attempt to combine the merits of seat belt wear with a system that does not rely on the voluntary participation of the occupant. In this case (see Fig. 2) the seat belt is attached to part of the car door in such a way that the occupant is automatically strapped into place when the door is closed. This apparatus has been developed by Volkswagen (VW) and was experimentally fitted to 1975 and 1976 models of the VW Rabbit (Golf) in the USA. Initial results were certainly very encouraging,[10] and in 1978 the NHTSA reported that the system was performing well as compared with active seat belts in collisions.[11]

One reason for confidence in this passive restraint technology, and also for its rapid development from invention to mass testing, is its partial reliance on the long-tried and well-tested seat belt. In fact, this system is slightly different – in that it incorporates a single diagonal belt and knee bolster (see diagram) – but its effectiveness is certainly based on accepted principles. Unlike the air bag, it is in no way a radical departure from previously available technologies. Of course, it would be misleading to suggest that the US motor industry's reluctance to accept the air bag can be traced entirely to its novel technical basis. One other reason is certainly cost, and here again the passive seat belt has a certain advantage. Whereas the passive belt was generally reckoned to add $25 to the price of an automobile in 1977, estimates for the additional cost of an air bag at that time ranged from $100 (the NHTSA's figure) to $235 (Ford Motor Company).[12] However, these disagreements over relative costs can only be understood properly in their political context and it is on this area that we will focus now.

The battle over 208

It is neither possible nor appropriate here to provide a definitive history of 208. Instead, sufficient detail will be given here to permit a basic understanding of the key debates involved. (See also *Appendix 2* for a chronology of events.) For reasons of clarity, the regulatory process will be divided into a number of chronological phases.

(1) 1967–71 : The opening rounds
As discussed in Chapter 4, the first twenty FMVSSs were issued on 31 January 1967. Among these was the initial standard 208 dealing with occupant restraint. This standard had developed out of negotiation and bargaining with the motor manufacturers during the early 1960s so that in 1967 it was relatively uncontroversial and essentially consolidated existing practice. At that stage 208 required full seat belts in each front seat if the top of the window frame was in the head impact area; otherwise a lap belt was required.[13]

Following the 1968 meeting discussed above, the first official step towards a revision of 208 came in July 1969 when an Advanced Notice of Proposed Rulemaking (ANPRM) was published inviting comments on passive restraint systems.[14] It is significant that an ANPRM rather than a Notice of Proposed Rulemaking (NPRM) was issued; the agency was assessing general opinion rather than initiating formal standard setting. Nevertheless, the notice in the *Federal Register* referred to the air bag as a 'very promising system' and argued that inflatable restraint systems should be fitted in new cars not later than 1 January 1972. This date thus became the first of a whole series of gradually receding deadlines to be proposed by the agency.

The major outcome of this notice was that a public meeting took place in August 1969. Presentations came from a wide range of interested parties[15] and a number of written submissions were also made to the agency. The vehicle manufacturers pressured strongly for an extension of the lead-time period on the grounds that they could not possibly meet the 1972 deadline. In May 1970 this date was deferred to 1 January 1973.[16] The same NPRM also established specific injury criteria with reference to an anthropometric dummy in specific crash modes.[17] With respect to these criteria, the standard was most certainly in keeping with the legal obligation to produce standards for performance rather than for design. At the same time, the specifications for this proposed standard represented a high degree of technical sophistication relative to any previous or existing legislation. The practicality of these advances would later be challenged by the manufacturers.

On 24–25 June 1970 the agency held a second public meeting at which the motor manufacturers again made strong representation and argued for more time to implement the proposed standard (which was still seen very much in terms of the air bag). At this meeting GM was the only major company to support the air bag. The previous month Edward Cole, GM's President, had argued:

The development of passive restraints for automobile occupants should be a top priority in our national efforts to reduce highway deaths and injuries. Many proposals have been made for passive restraint systems to replace the lap and shoulder belts. At this time, however, the inflatable air cushion appears to have by far the greatest potential.[18]

It is interesting that the most profitable of the manufacturers should have been the only one to support the air bag at that time. Later, under a new president, GM would fall into line with the other manufacturers. A possible explanation of the GM position is that, as the richest company, they could best afford the standard and it might even improve their market share by cutting out the small manufacturers who were unwilling or unable to make the investment required in order to comply with tougher federal controls. As a general rule, stricter safety standards increase the 'entrance fee' for any company wishing to engage in a particular market and, therefore, they strengthen existing oligopolies. This is, however, a long-term effect and manufacturers will tend to haggle over the spreading of short-term retooling and innovation costs, as in this case, and also the delaying of deadlines. There is also the possibility that any increases in unit costs may cause a reduction in demand for the products and therefore affect sales adversely.

The NHTSA, at least during its more 'dynamic' phases, has tended to assume that any increase in costs will hit all manufacturers equally and that legislation will not reduce overall sales, i.e. that the market is insensitive to price changes and that they have little effect on demand (low elasticity). Although past experience indicates that this has been the case until recently, there must be limits on demand inelasticity, especially in the bleak economic climate of the 1970s. This fear, and the general reluctance of the manufacturers to accept a strong interventionist role on the part of the government, go a long way towards explaining the industry's opposition to 208 even before one considers the particular technical aspects of the debate. The awareness of impending economic difficulties and the need to express industry solidarity perhaps account for GM's later shift towards antagonism to 208. One should also consider the hypothesis that GM may have felt that, by the mid-1970s, they had atoned for their 'sins' of 1966[19] and could safely adopt a more self-interested strategy.

Despite the stated opposition of most of the manufacturers during 1970, in November of that year the Agency issued what it considered to be a final ruling.[20] The deadline for front-seat passengers was set at 1 July 1973 and passive protection for rear occupants was mandated after 1 July 1974. However, in March 1971 an amendment to the rulemaking was announced.[21] In response to the motor manufacturers' petitions, the NHTSA revised the requirements for passive protection and allowed two options for vehicles manufactured between 15 August 1973 and 14 August 1975. The first option was full passive restraint; the second was passive protection in frontal impact only via an air bag and seat belt combination. This ruling stood until 1972 when a third option was permitted, the ignition interlock. In April 1971, Chrysler, followed by other manufactuers, began a judicial challenge of the NHTSA's passive restraint rule. Both the ignition interlock and the court review will be discussed in the next part of this chapter.

Review The strategy adopted by the agency during the 1967–71 period is worth reviewing at this point. Quite clearly, the NHTSA was determined to 'set the pace' on this issue. Although the agency did not completely ignore the industrial opposition to the air bag (and, at this stage, the air bag was the main focus of discussion), it did demonstrate a strong commitment to this technology and also a rather sceptical attitude towards the manufacturers' claims. The expressed views of agency personnel reveal confidence in the air bag as a 'technical fix' and also a belief that it was only a matter of time before this was mandated. However, important figures like Dr Haddon – who became President of the Insurance Institute for Highway Safety around this time – were also arguing for caution lest an over-rapid transition from field testing to large-scale fitting should wreck the whole programme.

The industrial opposition to the new 208 enjoyed some success, of course, in getting the deadline for implementation deferred from 1 January 1972 (as proposed in July 1969) to 15 August 1975 (as it stood in March 1971). These delays were only achieved after very determined lobbying but this lobbying was to reach an even greater pitch during the rest of the 1970s and the early 1980s.

(2) 1971–74: The interlock episode and a court challenge
As discussed earlier, by 1971 industrial opposition to 208 was running high and public opinion seemed to be at least divided over the unfamiliar gadgetry and additional costs to the consumer which the air bag represented. The public interest groups seemed equally uncertain about the technology and thus the NHTSA was left without any major political support. Ford Motor Company began to exploit this general uncertainty by running a media campaign against the device, various newspaper advertisements stressing the hazards of the air bag and focusing on inadvertent firings, failures in deployment and noise problems. The NHTSA responded with their own propaganda in rebuttal of these charges and went so far as to question publicly the motor company's motives. However, GM continued in their support for the safety technology and announced their intention of equipping one million cars with air bags – this operation to commence with the 1974 model-year.

Early in 1971 a number of petitions were submitted to the Sixth Circuit of the US Court of Appeals for a judical review of 208.[22] The eventual verdict was reached on 5 December 1972.[23] As determined by the court, the scope of the review was to decide '... whether the standard is supported by substantial evidence on the record as a whole'.[24] This necessitated a fairly broad investigation of the agency's action and an assessment of whether or not the NHTSA had transgressed its 1966 Congressional mandate. The petitioners selected three major points of contention. Judge Peck rejected the claim that 'nonexisting' technology might not be required by an FMVSS and asserted that the air bag was 'practicable' and 'safe' (terms borrowed from the 1966 Act). The judge also denied the contention that ordinary (active) seat belts offer superior protection. Peck argued that the evidence suggested that air bags were more effective and that even mandatory wear laws would produce no more than 60 per cent usage. The petitioning manufacturers were successful in one relatively minor area, the specifications of injury criteria as indicated by anthropomorphic dummies. The court upheld the claim that the dummies specified by the agency would 'not produce consistent, reliable, or repeatable test results', i.e. that they failed to meet the statutory requirements of 'objectivity'. The agency was ordered to withdraw the test specifications and rewrite them in more standardised and acceptable form. This demand was met on 28 March 1973[25] and specifications were again updated in July 1973.

Although the judicial review did vindicate the agency on nearly all the charges, the effect of the case was to slow the pace of rulemaking and ultimately to defer the application of a new 208 standard. The design and specifications of anthropomorphic dummies remain a vital technical aspect of all standards that are formulated in terms of performance rather than design. Any such standard can only be as good as its testing procedures, and criticising these arrangements has proven a very effective technique for resisting legislation. At the same time, the proposals for 208 since 1969 have been in advance of the technological sophistication of similar rulemaking in any other country of the world and this is a possible source of real regulatory difficulties. Necessarily, FMVSS 208 was in conformity with the NHTSA mandate to produce *performance* standards, i.e. it specified the forces, decelerations and injury potential of a vehicle occupant (as represented by a dummy) rather than insisting on particular forms of vehicle design and structural integrity. In principle, at least, 208 was establishing what should be achieved but not how this should be done. However, it has been argued[26] that the NHTSA was effectively moving beyond the 'state of the art' in biomechanical knowledge by setting standards in this way.

One other important aspect of the judicial review of 208 was its tacit acceptance of the capacity of a judge to assess technical argumentation and to reach a decision on the basis of competing expert testimonies. The main function of the court was to consider whether or not the standard matched the criteria laid down in the 1966 Act. This inevitably led into a technical evaluation of terms like 'objective', 'practicable' and 'safe'. The review illustrated not only the importance of the US judiciary as a branch of government but also an acceptance of the principle that experts can differ and that a 'courtroom style' adversary process is a viable means of appraising competing technical claims. Procedures of this type are a regular feature of political discussions on road traffic safety and also other technological hazards in the USA.[27] This issue will be discussed again with regard to FMVSS 301 and fire hazards.

The second topic under discussion between 1971 and 1974 that deserves our attention is the ignition interlock. As stated previously, this device was a relatively simple technology which was developed by a number of manufacturers in the early 1970s. A large amount of controversy exists over the NHTSA's final decision in February 1972[28] to allow the interlock as a third option (see above) for meeting the occupant restraint standard between August 1973 and August 1975. Various accounts suggest that the interlock was included only after Ford Motor Company had applied pressure on President Nixon and senior White House staff. This claim has been made by, among others, Ralph Nader,[29] the Insurance Institute for Highway Safety[30] and Congressman Moss,[31] former Chairman of the House Subcommittee on Commerce and Finance. In 1982, transcripts of one such meeting became available, although these do not necessarily demonstrate in themselves any covert agreement.[32]

The allegation made by these parties is that the interlock arose out of a dispute between GM and Ford over air bags. Henry Ford, it is said, was angered by GM's support of this restraint system and, in order to fight its implementation, had a number of secret meetings in conjunction with Chrysler in the White House in 1971. Ford was able to push for the ignition interlock as a cheaper solution to the occupant restraint problem largely because, it is alleged, Nixon needed Ford's contribution to the 1972 Presidential campaign. The White House then ordered Department of Transportation officials to include the interlock device as an option in its existing standard. As Congressman Moss wrote to the Watergate special prosecutor in 1975 on behalf of the House Interstate and Foreign Commerce Committee:

> . . . reports have reached the Committee from authoritative sources, including a former Administrator of the National Highway Traffic Safety Administration, that the Department of Transportation's adoption in 1972 of a standard requiring installation of so-called 'ignition interlock' safety belt devices in new cars may have been carried out partially in response to representations made by the Ford Motor Company and Chrysler Corporation to officials of the White House, including the President of the United States, and that such representations were not made a part of the public record of the Department of Transportation's development of the standard.[33]

These charges suggest a level of negotiation over the passive restraint standard which cannot be fully discussed here. However, as noted earlier, the ignition interlock did have certain advantages in terms of its simplicity and low cost, which could well have been sufficient justification for its inclusion in the legislation without any 'behind closed doors' manoeuvring. Largely because of these advantages, the interlock was seized upon by most manufacturers as a means of satisfying the occupant restraint regulations. The disadvantage of this for the proponents of the air bag was that this interim measure provided no preparation for the planned implementation of fully passive technology: no experience of the air bag was being gained nor were manufacturers developing production facilities. As it turned out, the interlock was a public relations failure for the NHTSA which did much to create a popular image of the agency as a petty bureaucracy.

In fact, the interlock was tolerated for almost exactly one year before the House of Representatives voted to make the device merely optional for the consumer by a majority of 339 to 49. The Senate also passed a similar amendment. In the course of the House debate, a large amount of criticism was voiced about safety regulation in general and any legislation that attempted to control the actions of the individual. Various references were made to 'over-regulation', 'Big Brother' and the 'un-American' nature of such federal controls. Besides these more philosophical arguments there was also a large amount of evidence to suggest that a sizeable proportion of vehicle occupants had been bypassing the device or rendering it ineffective. Although the accident statistics would later suggest that the interlock had been a very real 'success' in terms of fatality reduction, its political assessment occurred at a time when safety was seen as a less vital issue than in the mid- and late-1960s and when there was little enthusiasm outside the agency for new action. Even the public interest groups found themselves in a rather ambiguous position: they were committed to the support of any life-saving measure but were suspicious of the device's political ancestry and dubious about its public acceptability.

Overall, the ignition interlock was a massive stumbling block for the NHTSA in terms of internal morale and external credibility. There is a fair amount of evidence to suggest[34] that the ignition interlock option in the legislation was imposed on the agency from the highest level, i.e. that, despite its advantages, NHTSA officials had previously decided that it would be politically inopportune and would not aid the development of fully passive restraint. Having made the option available, they were then subjected to a massive public rejection of the device which, far from forcing the pace for passive legislation, exacerbated public and congressional antipathy to new road traffic safety legislation. The nature of the device and the mood of the mid-1970s in the USA[35] where, for the first time since 1965, a case was being argued for a moratorium or even a 'rollback' on safety legislation, acted together to provide the agency's first major public failure.

Review In analysing the development of the occupant restraint standard between 1967 and 1971, reference was made to the goal-direction of the NHTSA in terms of its selection of the air bag as the most appropriate technology. This orientation continued during the 1971–74 period, but with decreasing success. Although the judicial review caused only slight delay in terms of rulemaking, the interlock episode demonstrated the impediments and restrictions under which even the most determined government agency must operate. The political climate could only affect adversely the most publicly visible of all the proposed federal safety standards and so it was not without some justification that the Center for Auto Safety (CAS) launched a major attack on the NHTSA early in 1974. The CAS argued that the NHTSA had delayed too long over occupant restraint and that an updated 208 should be put into practice at once.[36]

What this criticism neglects is that the agency could not fulfil its 1966 mandate without external support. Congress expressed its hostility to what it considered inappropriate and unacceptable rulemaking in its vote of rejection of the interlock; the judiciary gave qualified support to the proposed standard but caused further delay; the powerful industry lobby (with only GM excluding itself) exerted itself in every way to block the legislation; President Nixon and the executive were by no means solid behind the basic principle of increased regulation. In addition, various social pressures were at work; fuel economy and air pollution had become major issues so that safety had to be reconciled with other aspects of vehicle design; the air bag was still apparently distrusted by the American public, this suspicion being encouraged by the failure of an air bag in a public demonstration in May 1972.[37] Faced with this climate of uncertainty, even GM began to seek assurance from the NHTSA as to when exactly the envisaged 208 would come into force.[38]

In the event, GM sold 10 000 air-bag-equipped vehicles by 1975 and then cut production, claiming that NHTSA's inaction had forced this decision. Others have argued that GM only fitted the device to luxury models and made little or no effort to promote the option,[39] but it remains true that the equivocation over 208 could only have had an inhibiting effect on those component or vehicle manufacturers with an interest in the air bag. At this stage, the component manufacturers could afford to await rulemaking. As the uncertainty continued into the late 1970s, companies like Eaton Corporation considered it better to terminate thirteen years of work and more than $20 million spent on research rather than remain in preparation for large-scale production any longer.[40]

(3) 1974–77: Deferment followed by action

In 1974 decisive and final rulemaking on 208 still seemed rather remote. Two government bodies in particular were monitoring the economic effects of NHTSA action (and occasionally checked rulemaking). The White House Office of Management and Budget and the Council on Wage and Price Stability had each been given the power to examine the cost (and cost-effectiveness) of all new federal regulations and to challenge the agency's inflationary impact statements.[41] Early in 1975, President Ford called for a five-year freeze on automobile emission standards and suggested that a similar approach to vehicle safety regulations was desirable.

Throughout 1975, the controversy over the air bag and passive restraint continued. At a five-day public meeting in May, over 40 witnesses were heard but the industry and public interest groups showed little sign of reconciliation, and the NHTSA Administrator, James Gregory, expressed support for passive restraint without making a final decision. On 8 August it was announced that the deadline for fully passive protection had been set back to the 1977 model-year.

In February 1976 the House Subcommittee on Oversight and Investigations, of which John E. Moss was Chairman, conducted its annual review of the NHTSA.[42] Congressman Moss in particular was concerned to examine the causes of the agency's lack of regulatory progress. In response, Administrator Gregory argued that the problems being faced were 'substantive rather than procedural' and, moreover, that further knowledge was needed in order to resolve the essentially *technical* problems posed by the occupant restraint standard. At that time, the 'technical' disagreements centred on eight basic issues:

(a) Data sufficiency: By September 1977, 12 000 air-bag-equipped vehicles[43] had travelled 480 million miles with 165 air-bag crash deployments. Did this, as the NHTSA claimed, constitute 'definitive statistical proof' or was more research (and delay) necessary?

(b) The relative effectiveness of the air bag: How did the air bag compare in terms of safety with the orthodox active seat belt? An array of conclusions about this is summarised in Table 1.

(c) Consumer cost: The 1977 NHTSA figure for installation cost was $112 but manufacturer estimates ranged from $192 to $250. Accusation and counter-accusation followed between the parties involved.

(d) Lead times: These were a constant source of controversy as the manufacturers, agency and 'public interest' groups differed over the most appropriate implementation date for 208.

(e) Product liability: This aspect of US law will be explored in Chapter 8 but, in essence, it entails the possibility of litigation against a vehicle or air-bag manufacturer in the event of a malfunction. Automobile manufacturers in particular appeared anxious lest a defective air bag should make them liable for massive damages cases; other groups argued that by refusing to accept an available safety technology the manufacturers were making themselves equally, if not more, liable.

(f) Sodium azide: Evidence emerged during the 1970s to suggest that this substance – used as a propellant – might be mutagenic and

Table 1 Effectiveness of air bag and lap/shoulder harness in preventing fatalities: estimates of NHTSA and six other studies
(per cent of unrestrained occupants whose lives would be saved by the given restraint system)

Effectiveness of air bag

Study	Air bag alone	Air bag, plus lap belt at usage rate (per cent) of:									
		10	20	30	40	50	60	70	80	90	100
NHTSA	40	43	45	48	50	53	56	58	61	63	66
GM(a)	18	19	20	21	22	24	25	26	27	28	29
GM(b)	18	19	20	22	23	24	25	26	28	29	30
Ford	37	40	42	45	47	50	53	55	58	60	63
DeLorean	47	48	49	50	51	52	52	53	54	55	56
Patrick	25	27	29	31	33	35	37	39	41	43	45
ESP	26	31	37	42	47	53	58	63	68	74	79
Average (excluding NHTSA)	29	31	33	35	37	39	42	44	46	48	50

Effectiveness of lap/shoulder harness

Study	Lap/shoulder harness at usage rate (per cent) of:									
	10	20	30	40	50	60	70	80	90	100
NHTSA	6	12	18	24	30	36	42	48	54	60
GM(a)	3	6	9	12	16	19	22	25	28	31
GM(b)	5	10	15	20	25	30	35	40	45	50
Ford	7	13	20	26	33	39	46	52	59	65
DeLorean	4	9	13	18	22	26	31	35	40	44
Patrick	3	6	9	12	15	18	21	24	27	30
ESP	6	12	18	24	31	37	43	49	55	61
Average (excluding NHTSA)	5	9	14	19	24	28	33	38	42	47

Sources: Calculated from basic estimates (for all but Economics and Science Planning) presented in DOT, *Explanation of Rule Making Action* (Standard No. 208 – Passive Restraint Amendment), Table III, p. 9. The ESP estimates for air bag alone and lap/shoulder harness are from 'Testimony by Dr. Lawrence A. Goldmuntz', Subcommittee on Consumer Protection and Finance, September 9, 1977. The effectiveness of the air bag with supplementary lap belt usage, is conservatively taken as equal to the ESP estimate for the lap belt alone, to the extent used.
Taken from: House Subcommittee on Consumer Protection and Finance, *Report on the Department of Transportation Automobile Occupant Passive Restraint Rule* (Mimeo.) September 1977, p. 47.

also carcinogenic. Concern was voiced about its possible release into the vehicle interior, about the disposal of the chemical when the vehicle was scrapped and also about exposure to the substance in the workplace during manufacture.

(g) Children: A special problem related to the protection offered to children by the air bag – especially when they were out of the normal seating position. One early test caused a child dummy to be ejected through the rear window of an automobile.

(h) Noise: This problem figured largely during early discussions (see above) but diminished in importance as the technology developed.

It can be argued in review of these eight points that, with the exception of the problem of noise, each demonstrated little sign during the 1970s of actually being resolved. Although the competing claims evolved over time, for the most part they remained relatively unchanging in their core assumptions. This situation points strongly to the suggestion that the 'battle of 208' was essentially a struggle for political dominance over regulatory responsibility rather than a primarily *technical* issue for experts alone to settle.

Faced with this unabated controversy in 1976, the NHTSA began to reveal some uncertainty about its plans for standard 208. Having issued a number of public statements in that year, it held another public hearing[44] and promised a final decision before 1 January 1977. In fact, the retiring Transportation Secretary, William Coleman, declared his verdict (in December 1976[45]) to conduct a 'large-scale demonstration program' to demonstrate the effectiveness of passive restraints. Coleman, in a long and detailed consideration of the whole issue, made his own support for passive restraint clear but argued that such a programme would encourage consumer acceptance and end doubts about the air bag.

Coleman's strategy represented an interesting and, in terms of the USA, rather novel 'middle path' between voluntary action by the manufacturers and strong rulemaking by the NHTSA. The argument was for cooperation between the government and industry so that any later standard would be an incremental rather than a radical development. The importance of public acceptability was emphasised in this approach – although the Insurance Institute for Highway Safety and the Center for Auto Safety produced contrary evidence to the effect that the public actively *sought* strict passive restraint legislation. The Center for Auto Safety also argued that the 1974 verdict on the ignition interlock had involved Congress specifically reserving for *itself* the function of assessing public reaction to restraint systems.[46]

In the event, 'Coleman's experiment' was never performed. The Carter Administration took control in 1977 and the new Transportation Secretary, Brock Adams, immediately promised to 'review most carefully' the December decision. In March, Adams annulled the agreements that Coleman had tentatively formulated with GM, Ford and Mercedes-Benz to provide the demonstration fleet.[47] Adams also announced a public hearing for 27–28 April. The new administration took even more radical action when, on 30 June 1977, fresh requirements were announced for fully passive legislation. The attitude of the regenerated NHTSA was made very clear by Adams a few months later:

I just felt in all conscience we just could not wait any longer. In his decision my predecessor . . . found all of the things required by the statute and then said, I am concerned about public acceptance and therefore will put the mandate off for a number of additional years. I felt, since statutory requirements have all been found, both by him and by myself, having rechecked it in public hearings and, in going through that enormous docket, it was time to move on it.[48]

Although there was undoubtedly a large element of truth in this personal account of Adams's action, the total effect of the new Carter Administration should also be noted, and in particular its determination in the first few months of office to appear decisive and firm in its stated purposes of pushing ahead new consumer protection legislation. The actual content of the June ruling will be considered in the next part of this account, but it is worth noting now that fully passive protection was mandated in all new cars in three main stages:

1 September 1981 – cars with 115-in wheelbase or greater
1 September 1982 – cars with 101-in wheelbase or greater
1 September 1983 – all new cars

However, this new rulemaking was by no means the end of the debate, and the various attempts at repeal will be considered in the final stage of this chapter.

Review   The years from 1974 to 1977 are difficult to review because of the sudden change in policy that occurred between January and June 1977. The three years from 1974 to 1976 revealed a certain continuity as the agency hesitated to institute rulemaking, partly under the pressure of the general economic climate and also because of the 'anti-regulation' mood in the Republican Administrations and Congress. The technical debate over 208 remained acrimonious and showed no real sign of moving towards a consensus. The air bag could have a dramatic effect in reducing deaths and injuries – or it could prove to be a costly failure, both economically and in terms of public relations for the NHTSA and government. In addition, there was little financial advantage to be gained by the manufacturers, except of course, for the air-bag producers who enjoyed little political influence over road traffic safety policy. Very little incentive existed for the motor companies to press ahead with this device, and there was the apparent disincentive of future product liability cases. In the economic and political climate of the mid-1970s, forceful rulemaking by the agency was most unlikely and Coleman's compromise arrangement may well have been a reasonable way of *appearing* to take action while not alienating any of the parties. However, it could well have been the case that such a demonstration programme would not have settled the technical and political controversy but merely deferred the political decision. The final stages of the mass test could then have been marked by fierce disagreement over the lessons to be learnt and the future policy to be adopted.

In sharp contrast to Coleman's 'cooperative' policy plan was the rapid action taken by the NHTSA and the Department of Transportation under President Carter's authority. Both Brock Adams and Joan Claybrook (the new NHTSA Administrator) had made their support of the air bag quite clear before moving into office. Although the major manufacturers had already agreed to produce voluntarily a number of air-bag-equipped vehicles,[49] this approach was rejected in favour of mandatory action (albeit on a 'phase-in' basis to assist the manufacturers).

One major consequence of this shift in policy has been to encourage the industry to utilise an alternative technology, the passive seat belt, rather than develop the air bag. The 'performance' basis of the 1977 standard meant that the passive seat belt was permissible and had a distinct advantage in terms of cost; it is, however, difficult to envisage how this system could meet any of the stricter performance requirements which were intended to follow for passive restraint. It is not without some irony that an agency action conceived in terms of air-bag innovation has had the unanticipated effect of encouraging manufacturers to rely on another technology, leaving the air-bag issue unresolved. This point must be borne in mind when making general comparisons of the 'strong, pace-setting' and 'gentle, cooperative' modes of rulemaking; what may appear to be decisive rulemaking can be less effective than a more incremental strategy.

(4) 1977–83: The regulatory war drags on
The NHTSA's ruling[50] of June 1977 was certainly not the end of the political struggle over 208. Immediately after the public announcement, two bills were introduced in the House of Representatives and the Senate which were aimed at overturning the legislation.[51] The Senate Commerce Committee and the House Commerce Committee's Subcommittee on Consumer Protection and Finance both held hearings on the standard and the opposing resolutions. These hearings saw a repetition of all the familiar technical, economic and philosophical arguments over passive restraint before the two resolutions were rejected and the 1977 version of 208 was accepted. The four major US manufacturers (including GM, who, since Cole's departure, had shown less favour to the air bag) petitioned the agency to withdraw or revise its ruling but, in December, Adams denied these claims.

In 1978, Ralph Nader challenged the standard on the grounds that the Department of Transportation had no authority to delay implementation and that the 'phase-in' requirement was illegal. The US Court of Appeals for the District of Columbia rejected this claim along with another from the Pacific Legal Foundation.[52]

In 1979 and 1980 two Congressmen in particular – John Dingell and David Stockman – attempted to have amendments passed which would effectively undermine 208 but these had only limited success. The new NHTSA Administrator, Joan Claybrook, made her support of the air bag quite clear and dismissed fears of possible product liability claims by arguing that passive restraint systems would actually *reduce* the number of such actions against the manufacturers. Claybrook's point was that people previously injured by other vehicle defects or design problems would be protected by automatic restraints and hence compensation claims would be reduced.[53]

Throughout 1980 the motor manufacturers pressed the Carter Administration for a moratorium on new safety standards, arguing the particular need for this at a time of some economic difficulty for the industry. These demands were, of course, very reminiscent of those put forward around 1974. Companies like GM saw 208 as a major target for lobbying and proposed that either the requirement for passive restraints should be dropped or at least that its implementation should be put back to start with small cars in the 1983 model-year. Despite these considerable political pressures, FMVSS 208 remained intact at the end of 1980. Starting with large cars in the 1982 model-year (i.e. from Autumn 1981), new cars were still to be equipped with front-seat passive restraints – either passive belts or air bags – to protect occupants in front and front-angle crashes up to 30 mph. However, this NHTSA resolve was transformed completely only one month later when the Reagan Administration took power with its expressed commitment to cutting back federal spending and 'liberating' private industry from state controls. The effect of this change of national leadership illustrates well the relationship between political power and matters of technological risk.

The new NHTSA Administrator was Raymond Peck and his approach to questions of regulatory responsibility and passive restraint was in marked contrast to that of Claybrook. In keeping with the political philosophy of the new Administration, Peck expressed support for making standards as 'cost-effective' as possible and for encouraging voluntary seat-belt use rather than mandatory design standards. Through 1981 fresh hearings were called on 208 as the issues were debated yet again – to the obvious disappointment of groups such as the IIHS who had now been campaigning for a decade over this issue. These hearings culminated in October 1981 when the NHTSA issued an order to *cancel* standard 208.[54] The main arguments put forward to support this decision were, first, 'uncertainty' about the public acceptability and likely usage of automatic seat belts (and it was clear by 1981 that this was the option that manufacturers would adopt rather than air bags). The second justification was the 'relatively substantial cost' of passive restraints, the NHTSA arguing that vehicle price increases of around $1 thousand million per year would have resulted. Thirdly, the agency announced its intention to encourage voluntary seat-belt use with a large-scale propaganda programme.

Of course, it should be clear from the previous discussion of 208 in this chapter that no such decision can ever be taken as final in the US regulatory system. The immediate response to the 1981 NHTSA announcement was a number of petitions for appeal. In March 1982 the Court of Appeals in the District of Columbia heard a challenge to the NHTSA ruling. At that point, the court panel had two possible courses of action: to sustain the agency action or remand the case to the agency with instructions.

June 1982 saw the regulatory battlefield change yet again as the Court of Appeals *rejected* the NHTSA decision on the grounds that the agency had not acted in accordance with its Congressional mandate.[55] In fact, the court was extremely critical of the NHTSA, arguing that it had acted 'arbitrarily and capriciously' in cancelling 208. The agency had 'wasted administrative and judicial resources' and provided an 'expensive example of ineffective regulation'. According to the court, it was:

difficult to avoid the conclusion that NHTSA's analysis ... has been distorted by solicitude for the economically depressed automobile industry — which is not the agency's mandate — at the expense of consideration of traffic safety, which is ...

Once again, however, the court decision was not a conclusion to the controversy over 208. The NHTSA now had to respond to this verdict by producing a plan of its future action over 208. From the manufacturers' point of view the 1981 NHTSA ruling had at least been successful in causing further delay in the 208 implementation date.

Throughout 1982 and into 1983 the arguments over 208 continued with little obvious sign of resolution. The NHTSA adopted a policy of arguing for delay in implementation, to allow further discussion and research and to give the motor manufacturers more time to prepare themselves. The Court of Appeals responded to this by ruling that the compliance date for all new cars should be 1 September 1983. The NHTSA's proposal for rulemaking to be reopened was thus rejected. This left the manufacturers and the NHTSA with one main option, to join in a further appeal to the Supreme Court. This appeal was made in September 1982 on three main grounds:

(a) That the Department of Transportation (DOT) had the right to revoke a safety standard when changed circumstances might nullify any safety benefits. This was a reference to the likely adoption of the passive seat belt by manufacturers in order to meet any possible 208. However, it was claimed that such devices would be disconnected by motorists and thus rendered worthless.[56] Certainly, the ignition interlock had suffered a similar fate.

(b) That implementation of 208 could have an adverse effect on public attitudes towards road traffic safety.

(c) That the Appeals Court had 'impermissibly usurped' DOT powers in setting a specific implementation date.

In November 1982 the Supreme Court agreed to review the appelate court decision. At this point the NHTSA was arguing that FMVSS 208 could not be met until September 1985 'at the earliest'. While awaiting the outcome of this review, the NHTSA pushed ahead with its plans for a large-scale propaganda campaign to encourage voluntary belt use. A decision from the Supreme Court was expected in June 1983.

The June Supreme Court decision essentially supported the Court of Appeals and found that the NHTSA decision to revoke the automatic restraint standard was indeed 'arbitrary and capricious'. The court argued that the possible disconnection of seat belts by motorists was no evidence against the mandatory fitting of *air bags*. The NHTSA should, therefore, give urgent attention to the redrafting of 208 to take this into account. However, the court was not entirely convinced that passive belt disconnection would take place on a great scale and found that NHTSA should produce more evidence on this if it wished to amend the existing standard.

In July 1983, therefore, 208 was put back before the Department of Transportation (DOT) with a view to a final ruling. By that time it was apparent that the Office of Management and Budget was taking a keen interest in the standard. Ray Peck had also resigned as head of NHTSA, and Diane Steed was his designated replacement. The arguments continued – with every sign of continuing – and 'public interest' groups such as the IIHS, Public Citizen (now with Joan Claybrook as President), the National Coalition to Reduce Car Crash Injuries and Motor Voters attacked the NHTSA in increasingly bitter terms.[57] Meanwhile, the NHTSA took the 'procedural precaution' of suspending the automatic restraint requirements of 208 by a further year. These requirements had then been under discussion since January 1967 and had been the subject of approximately 60 separate rulemaking actions.

Discussion

FMVSS 208 has been a major component of the NHTSA's strategy for reducing the number of road traffic accidents in the United States. However, protracted debate over a 14-year period (at least till the time of writing) and the necessary commitment of substantial agency time and resources were not sufficient to see the update of this standard put into practice, nor was it possible in 1983 to specify any firm date for future implementation. This in itself represents a substantial source of disillusionment among NHTSA staff and others who were eager to see the agency fulfil its 1966 mandate, but this feeling was actually exacerbated by one further factor, the shift over this period in the actual passive restraint systems under discussion. Whereas the motor manufacturers saw 208 originally in terms of the air bag, by the early 1980s automatic seat belts seemed a much more likely option for implementation, at least for the large US companies.

Automatic seat belts have obvious advantages in terms of cost. Motor manufacturers claimed in 1982 that these would add $89–150 to the price of an automobile whereas air bags would raise this by about $300.[55] Of course, pressure groups such as the IIHS would dispute these figures but the existence of a cost differential cannot be denied. The disadvantages with passive seat-belt systems seem to fall in two main areas. First, they cannot be modified to match any regulations stricter than the envisaged 30mph. Secondly, and perhaps more crucially at present, they are vulnerable to the same consumer abuse as the ignition interlock and may therefore prove useless in practice.

How then is it possible to explain the lack of progress made by standard 208 over this period? Certainly this case study illustrates well the variety of ways in which the US regulatory system can be employed to engage in a protracted struggle over an undesired measure. Although this plurality of fora for debate – including Congress, hearings, the Court of Appeals, the Supreme Court and direct lobbying of the NHTSA – could be seen as in the interests of democracy and public participation (and frequently is extolled in this way), the difficulties are also self-evident. In particular, what the case of 208 suggests is that, despite the existence of competing pressure groups, it is still possible for a single powerful group to block (or at least delay substantially) any action which it sees as contrary to its own interests. The manufacturers have enjoyed considerable success towards their goal of minimising state control over their industry. This has been true even with an 'interventionist' NHTSA such as that led by Joan Claybrook under the Carter Administration. It has, of course, been even more true with a politically conservative President in office.

The relative power of the motor industry has been revealed in a number of ways and, in general, through their greater resources for lobbying and exploring every possible means for blocking legislation. One important dimension of this power has been the use of technical expertise to give substance to the political arguments being put forward. Expertise has, in other words, been used as a 'resource' in resisting government controls. As discussed earlier, these technical arguments have taken a number of forms, from noise to hazardous chemicals, from child protection to data sufficiency. In addition, the industry has been able to deploy arguments about cost and leadtimes in a more detailed fashion than its opponents because of the privileged access to such information. In a battle which has used technical argumentation as its major weapon, the motor industry has had a consistent and undeniable advantage. Although at certain points during this 14-year period the industry has undoubtedly been on the defensive, its strategy for resisting change has nevertheless proved extremely effective.

In many ways the struggle over 208 tells the developing story of the NHTSA and its ability to act in accordance with the 1966 Safety Act. However, a later chapter will develop this further with reference to the controversy over another regulatory measure, FMVSS 301 and fuel system integrity. One aspect of 208 that has not been fully developed here concerns 'active' seat belts, i.e. those that are in regular use in many countries of the world, including Britain. New emphasis has been placed on these during the Reagan Administration, with an estimated $27.2 million being spent on propaganda during fiscal year 1983.[58] In 1983 11 per cent belt usage was reported and the NHTSA calculated that even a 1 per cent increase in belt usage nationwide would prevent 180 deaths and 3400 serious injuries annually. Despite this no compulsory seat belt wear legislation has been passed in any US state, although 29 other countries have now adopted such an approach. The contrast, then, between the debate over 208 in the USA and that over occupant protection in Britain is quite clear. In the next chapter we will examine British action on seat-belt wear in order to trace out the differences (and similarities) between the two national policy-making processes.

Appendix 2: Chronology of major events

1967, 31 January:	Original FMVSS 208 announced.
1968, 19 July:	Agency meeting to discuss air bag.
1969, 2 July:	ANPRM, proposed deadline 1 January 1972.
August:	Public meeting.
1970, 7 May:	Proposed deadline 1 January 1973.
June:	Public meeting.
3 November:	Proposed deadline for full protection 1 July 1974.
1971, 10 March:	Deadline 14 August 1975.
April:	Court challenge.
1972, 17 February:	Ignition interlock permitted.
5 December:	Court verdict.
1973, 28 March:	Agency meets new dummy standards.
1974, 12 August:	Congress rejects interlock.
1975, 19–23 May:	Public meeting.
8 August:	Deadline August, 1976.
1976, 3 August:	Public meeting.
6 December:	Coleman announces mass test plan.
1977, 27–28 April:	Public meeting.
30 June:	New implementation dates commencing 1 September 1981.
September:	Congressional hearings.
1978, 1979, 1980:	Various challenges to the rulemaking.
1981, October:	NHTSA issues order to cancel 208.
1982, June:	Court of Appeals rejects NHTSA decision.
August:	New implementation date 1 September 1983 for all new cars.
1983:	Challenges to rulemaking continue.

Notes and references

1   US Patent No. 2,649,311 for 'Safety cushions (for automotive vehicles) which are automatically inflated when there is a sudden slowing down of the vehicle'. August 5, 1952. Granted August 18, 1952.

2   IIHS *Background Manual on the Occupant Restraint Issue*, June 1978, p. 32. Available from IIHS, Watergate Six Hundred, Washington, DC 20037.

3   Kraegel, M. W. Jr. Sensible sensor in *Status Report* Vol. 14, No. 13, 21 August 1979, pp. 14–17.

4   Ford Motor Company Press Release, April 1966, p. 2.

5   This quotation is taken from the transcript of the 19 July 1968 meeting, p. 45.

6   The compulsory seat belt wear issue will be discussed at some length in the following chapter.

7   US Department of Transportation/NHTSA. *DOT/NHTSA Belt Usage Survey Results.* (USGPO, Washington, DC; 1 September 1977). By the early 1980s this figure had been reduced to 11 per cent.

8   US NHTSA. *Proposed Traffic Laws and Regulations.* Docket No. 72–11, 18 July 1972.

9   Notice of Proposed Rulemaking. *Federal Register*, Vol. 38, No. 228, 28 November 1973, p. 32818.

10 Highway Loss Data Institute (HLDI). *A preliminary comparison of results from Volkswagen Rabbits with Passive and Active Belts* (HLDI-A8), 1977. Available from HLDI, Watergate Six Hundred, Washington, DC 20037.

11 *Status Report*, Vol **13**, No. 9, 29 June 1978.

12 House Subcommittee on Consumer Protection and Finance, *Report on the Department of Transportation Automobile Occupant Passive Restraint* Rule. (Mimeo.), September 1977, p. 27.

13 For an account of this, see *Report on the Development of the Initial Motor Vehicle Safety Standards Issued January 31, 1967* (USGPO, Washington, DC; 17 March 1967).

14 *Federal Register (FR).* Vol. 34, No. 126, 2 July 1969, p. 11148.

15 Including Chrysler, GM, Ford, VW, Mercedes, Eaton, the American Automobile Association and the Highway Safety Research Institute of the University of Michigan.

16 *FR.* Vol. 35, 7 May 1970, p. 7187.

17 Crash modes: frontal barrier at 30 mph (up to 30° angle); lateral barrier at 15 mph; two complete rollovers. Injury criteria: e.g. chest acceleration not to include 40 g; force on chest not to exceed 1200 lb; head acceleration not to exceed 80 g for more than 3 ms. Other injury criteria dealt with maximum forces on the pelvis, femur and abdomen and also the general position and characteristics of the dummy.

18 Cole, E. *International Conference on Passive Restraints* 11–12 May 1970. Quoted in: Center for Auto Safety. *History of the Air Bag and Modified Standard 208: the Long (and Unfinished) Road to Universal Passive Protection of America's Motorists*, 19 February 1974, p. 5. Available from Center for Auto Safety, 1223 Dupont Circle Building, Washington, DC, 20036.

19 The reference here is to the ignominy heaped on GM during the 'Nader affair'. See Chapter 4.

20 *FR.* Vol. 35, 3 November 1970, p. 16927.

21 *FR.* Vol. 36, 10 March 1971, p. 4600.

22 Petitions were received from Chrysler, Ford, American Motors, Jeep, and the Automobile Importers of America, but not GM.

23 Chrysler Corporation *et al.* v. DOT *et al.* 472 F 2d 659 (6th Cir. 1972).

24 *Ibid.* p. 670.

25 *FR.* Vol. 38, 1973, p. 8455.

26 Mackay, G. M. in *Proc. European Motor Vehicle Symposium and the Seminar on Accident Statistics*, Vol. 1 (EEC, Brussels; 1977), p. 171. Dr Mackay is the head of the Accident Research Unit at Birmingham University. Reference is made to his work in each of the case studies in this section.

27 See Bazelon, D. L. Risk and responsibility. *Science*, 20 July 1979, pp. 277–80.

28 *FR*. Vol. 37, 17 February 1972, p. 3911. This amendment had been proposed in *FR*. Vol. 36, 1 October 1971, p. 19266.

29 Nader, R. *Washington under the Influence* (Center for Auto Safety, Washington, DC; February 1976).

30 IIHS. *Background Manual on the Passive Restraint Issue*, August 1977, p. II–17. (See reference 2 for IIHS address.)

31 Moss, J. *Congressional Record*. 93d Congress 2d Sess, 12 August 1974, p. 8136. Congressman Moss has also made available an account of an interview with Douglas Toms, former NHTSA Administrator, in which Toms supports these allegations.

32 *Status Report*, Vol. 17, No. 19, 22 December 1982, pp. 2–3.

33 Letter from John E. Moss to Henry S. Ruth, 21 March 1975.

34 To the above five references should be added the testimony of IIHS officials to the author, and also Holt, D. D. Why Eaton got out of the air-bag business. *Fortune*, 12 March 1979, pp. 148–9.

35 See Chapter 4.

36 Center for Auto Safety. *History of the Air Bag and Modified Standard 208: the Long (and Unfinished) Road to Universal Passive Protection of America's Motorists*, p. 25. (See reference 18.)

37 This demonstration was organised by the National Motor Vehicle Safety Advisory Council and, although it was later claimed that the air bag used was faulty for specific reasons, enormous adverse publicity was gained.

38 Cole, E. Letter to DOT Secretary Brinegar, 10 August 1973, quoted in Center for Auto Safety. *History of the Air Bag and Modified Standard 208: the Long (and Unfinished) Road to Universal Passive Protection of America's Motorists*, p. 21. (See reference 18.)

39 Karr, A. R. Saga of the air bag, or the slow deflation of a car-safety idea. *Wall Street Journal*, 11 November 1976, p. 1.

40 Eaton worked in cooperation with Ford Motor Company, Allied Chemical Corporation with GM. Other air-bag manufacturers are Talley Industries, Thiokol Corporation and the Hamill Division of Firestone.

41 The Council on Wage and Price Stability had consistently argued against mandatory air bags. See *Newsweek*, 19 March 1979, p. 79.

42 Hearings before the Subcommittee on Oversight and Investigations of the Committee on Interstate and Foreign Commerce. *Regulatory Reform*, Vol. IV, 94th Congress, 2d Sess. House (USGPO, Washington, DC; 1976).

43 The vast majority of these were GM cars.

44 On 3 August 1976.

45 *The Secretary's Decision Concerning Motor Vehicle Occupant Crash Protection*. DOT, USA, Washington, DC, 6 December 1976.

46   Center for Auto Safety. *Post-hearing Memorandum on Proposed Changes to Federal Motor Vehicle Safety Standard 208 to Improve Occupant Crash Protection in Passenger Cars*, 27 May 1977.

47   On 18 January Coleman had announced that GM and Ford would manufacture a minimum of 60000 air-bag-equipped cars, and Mercedes-Benz a further 2250. These would come on to the market from September 1979.

48   *Hearings before the Subcommittee on Consumer Protection and Finance of the Committee on Interstate and Foreign Commerce.* 95th Congress, 1st Sess. (USGPO, Washington, DC; 1978), p. 19.

49   By June 1977 GM had offered to produce 150 000 air-bag-equipped cars and Volkswagen and Toyota had committed themselves also.

50   *FR.* Vol. 42, No. 128, 5 July 1977, p. 34289.

51   The bills were introduced by Rep. Bud Shuster and Sen. Robert Griffin – both Republicans.

52   Pacific Legal Foundation *et al.* v DOT. 593 F. 2d 1338 (1979).

53   Claybrook, J. Automatic restraints and products liability law. *Trial*, February 1980. Reprinted in *Status Report*, **15**(4), 5 March 1980, pp. 8–11.

54   *Status Report*, Vol. **16**, No. 17, 5 November 1981, p. 1.

55   *New Scientist*, 12 August 1982, p. 414. *Status Report*, Vol. 17, No. 8, 9 June 1982, p. 1.

56   It is a necessary feature of the passive seat belt that it can be easily disconnected for the purposes of emergency rescue.

57   Joan Claybrook, for example, contrasted the 269 lives lost in the 1983 attack by the USSR on a Korean airliner with the NHTSA's 'failure' to implement a standard with the 'potential to save 9000 lives each year and to mitigate 65000 injuries'. *Status Report*, Vol. 18, No. 13, 20 September 1983, p. 4.

58   *Status Report*, Vol. 18, No. 7, 12 May 1983, p. 3.

Chapter 7

The debates over occupant restraint – II : Britain

In Britain throughout the 1970s and early 1980s there have been two major topics of public and political debate relating to road traffic safety. One, the issue of driving under the influence of alcohol, had been under discussion for at least the last 50 years.[1] The second, the main subject of this chapter, emerged as an important focus of attention from the early 1970s onwards. What these two issues have had in common is the fundamental philosophical and political question of the extent to which a society is justified in imposing limits on an individual's freedom of choice in the interests of general social welfare. It is in terms of this dilemma that both debates have been conducted, and what may at first appear to be a rather esoteric and philosophical problem has been central to political action in each area.

This point can be illustrated in regard to drunken driving by considering the controversy over the proposal in the 1966 Road Safety Bill to introduce discretionary checks by the police on motorists' blood-alcohol levels.[2] Such was the opposition to this extension of police powers that the relevant clause was dropped and replaced by the provision that drivers could be 'breathalysed' only if they were suspected of having committed a moving traffic offence or of having been involved in an accident.[3] It was in this form that the bill became law in 1967. The issue of police powers was revived by the Blennerhassett Report of 1976,[4] which argued that present enforcement methods were ineffective, that the police needed 'better tools' to continue their job, and that these must include discretionary testing authority. The debate over this issue has continued since 1976 with the Royal Society for the Prevention of Accidents (RoSPA) in particular lobbying for an implementation of the Blennerhassett proposals. The Society has claimed that about one in five road deaths are caused by excessive drinking (i.e. above the legally defined blood-alcohol level of 80 mg per 100 ml). This estimate represents some 1200 deaths per year in Britain. However, the Blennerhassett Committee's plans for increased police authority to stop motorists and administer tests have not been implemented, although the 1981 Transport Act did close certain notorious loopholes in the legislation on drunken driving.

As with compulsory seat-belt wear, at the heart of parliamentary opposition to legislation has been the perceived defence of 'individual liberty' against the incursion of state authority. Should the individual be free to act provided that no harm is being done to any outside party? Does the death toll from road traffic accidents make the arguments for 'liberty' seem misguided and trivial? Thinking more specifically about seat-belt law, other issues have also arisen during the debate. What parliamentary mechanisms are most appropriate to the discussion of this subject? What is the correct role for the elected majority on such issues? However, for most of debate it was the 'freedom vs. safety' issue which dominated. This emphasis was only to be changed somewhat in the early 1980s when the technical arguments for the effectiveness of legislation began to be challenged on statistical grounds. This controversy certainly deserves attention here, partly because of the policy implications of the discussion but also because of the issues that the dispute raised concerning the ability of Parliament to cope with technical disagreement of this type.

The background to the debate

The technology of active seat belts has a longer history than almost any other occupant protection device. 'Safety belts' were being used in aeroplanes in the first decade of the 20th century,[5] although principally for the purpose of preventing ejection rather than for crash protection. In the mid-1950s the motor manufacturers in both the United States and Britain began to make seat belts available to car buyers as an optional extra. Prior to this, very little effort had been made to transfer the device from aircraft to land transport. Certainly, the vehicle industry continued to show no great enthusiasm for their installation as standard, and consumer demand was apparently very small. The seat belts being fitted on an irregular basis to British cars in the late 1950s tended to be one of two types: the 'full harness' (two shoulder straps and a waist belt) or the 'single diagonal' (one shoulder strap only) varieties. The 'lap belt' was little used in Europe, despite its popularity in the USA.

In 1960 the British Standards Institution (BSI) introduced a 'Kitemark' scheme on a voluntary basis[6] to lay down minimum standards for seat belt construction and performance. Since 1968 the British government has made compliance with this standard compulsory so that BS 3254 has effectively become law. In the late 1970s this arrangement changed with the introduction of the EEC 'e' mark as a parallel option to the Kitemark scheme.

It was in 1961 that negotiations started between the Department of Transport and the Society of Motor Manufacturers and Traders (SMMT) on the question of the compulsory fitting of seat belts to new cars.[7] Six years later this proposal was contained in the 1967 Road Safety Act so that all cars sold after that date had to be fitted with a seat belt for the driver's and 'specified passenger's' seats. At the end of 1968 this requirement was extended to include all post-1964 cars. The slow rate at which these relatively private discussions reached their conclusion has been used by Plowden as one illustration of the Department of Transport's general lack of decisiveness:

... in Britain government has undeniably been willing to make concessions. The long delays, even after the technical problems had been solved ... show well what happens when government is reluctant simply to impose a solution.[8]

The second major legal requirement relating to seat belts is that, since 1 April 1973, all belts must be designed so that they can be released and engaged with one hand; they must also have a securing point for storage when out of use.[9] This requirement has encouraged the fitting of stalks and centre buckles to modern seat belts. Inertia reel belts have also become standard since the 1970s; reports of the actual effectiveness of these will be discussed below.

One further point of background to the seat-belt debates is to describe simply the restraining effect that a seat belt has on an occupant in a crash. The main function of a seat belt is to channel decelerative forces through the body in a relatively undamaging fashion. The head and body are not allowed to strike anything within the vehicle interior that might cause highly localised forces. The seat belt should also provide a stopping distance for the body of around 12–16 in in a frontal impact of 30 mph, thus further reducing the forces to the body.[10] Again, this contrasts favourably with the abrupt decleration often caused by impact with the vehicle interior. Later in this chapter, the statistical evidence concerning the effectiveness of seat belts in accidents will be examined.

One important final point that must be made is that 'compulsory seat-belt wear' in Britain has been seen for the most part as referring to *front seat* protection. This leaves two areas for debate: first, protection for *children* in the rear seats of automobiles; secondly, protection for *all* rear-seat passengers (adults as well as children). In fact, all British cars have been required since October 1981 to have rear anchorage points for adult seat belts. However, at the time of writing there is no requirement that adult rear seat belts should actually be fitted, nor is there any obligation on manufacturers for child-restraint anchorages to be provided. Although rear seat-belt wear for both adults and children was raised from time to time in Parliament during the early 1980s,[11] little serious debate took place.

The political debate

The history of parliamentary discussions over compulsory seat-belt wear covers a period from November 1973, when a clause was introduced in the Conservative administration's Road Traffic Bill, through to 31 January 1983, when similar legislation finally became effective. However, the debate has certainly not ended there, as a review of the law must be carried out within the first three years of its operation, i.e. by January 1986. Throughout the ten-year period prior to enactment, the seat-belt issue was a regular topic of discussion so that it was debated in each and every session of Parliament from 1973 till 1981. Although it has often been apparent that a majority of both Houses were prepared to accept legislation – for example, the Commons gave it a majority of 110 at the Second Reading in March 1976 – the opposition was (until 1981) sufficiently strong to avoid final rulemaking, largely as a result of the lack of government pressure over this issue.

Prior to 1973, a policy of publicity and persuasion had dominated British official thinking on occupant restraint. As we have seen, all cars manufactured since 1 January 1965 had belts fitted as standard and there were no real doubts raised by researchers about their effectiveness. Certainly this consensus was reflected in a 1967 White Paper on road safety[12] which stressed the importance of seat belts but without even discussing compulsory wear. In 1973, a major propaganda campaign was begun to persuade motorists to wear their belts. Such campaigns have continued since that time at an annual cost similar to that in 1973 (£805 000).[13] Their initial effect was to increase wearing rates considerably but this then levelled off to around 33 per cent overall by the late 1970s and early 1980s.

Parliamentary discussions on this issue began in November 1973 when Lord Montagu, supported by Lord Ferrier and Lord Avebury, successfully argued for the inclusion of a seat-belt clause in the Road Traffic Bill under discussion.[14] The clause survived a Second Reading in the Commons and was forwarded to Standing Committee only to be terminated by the first of the 1974 General Elections.[15] The essentially unchanged Road Traffic Bill emerged once again in mid-1974, this time to be dropped in accordance with the advice of the Labour Transport Minister, Fred Mulley, on the grounds of insufficient time to discuss the seat-belt issue when it formed only part of a 'ragbag' bill of 29 distinct clauses. Mulley promised that the issue would be put before Parliament at the 'earliest opportunity' so that it could have a proper discussion.[16] Already, then, the seat-belt issue had been delayed by both Conservative and Labour administrations without Parliament having the opportunity to offer a clear opinion for or against the proposal.

In October 1974 (following the Labour Party's second General Election victory of that year), Mulley presented a Road Traffic (Seat Belts) Bill to Parliament.[17] The timing of this gave the bill a whole new session in which to reach completion. However, the fundamental disagreements over the measure in both Houses remained unresolved and the bill was eventually abandoned. In November 1974 the Second Reading in the Commons was adjourned without a vote and no further time was found for the debate during the session. Even those Members of Parliament in favour of the legislation showed a distinct reluctance to force such a bill through Parliament, and the opposition were content to see the proposal grind to a halt and be forgotten.

March 1976 saw a new bill introduced into Parliament, this time by John Gilbert as the Labour Transport Minister. The proposed legislation would not apply to Ulster, which has its own body of road traffic law, and would have established a maximum penalty of £50 for noncompliance (the same sum as that imposed on motorcyclists who do not wear helmets). Gilbert described the 'heart' of the bill as being to insert a compulsory seat belt wear clause into the existing legislation – but also to permit the Secretary of State to make appropriate exemptions from this for certain vehicles, persons and circumstances.[18] Gilbert committed the Department of Transport (D.Tp) to carrying out consultations with various parties over exemptions only *after* Parliament had accepted the principle behind the bill. This 'negative resolution' procedure[19] became the focus of considerable criticism in debate, although it seems likely that this focus merely provided a convenient topic around which the proposal's opponents could organise themselves. Certainly, the technique of 'filibustering' was much in evidence and the bill was 'talked out' at the Report Stage with Gilbert eventually moving for an adjournment. In October 1976 the bill was further adjourned.

Thus 1976 had seen a full debate of compulsory seat-belt wear. Despite a 110 majority for the measure in the Commons, John Gilbert and William Rodgers (who replaced Gilbert as Transport Minister) were forced to admit at least temporary defeat. Responsibility for this must be placed on the measure's opponents, who marshalled a whole series of arguments to express their antipathy on the basic grounds of an individual's right to choose. However, questions can also be asked about the priority attached to the Bill by the Labour administration. Because that party was itself divided over this issue, long delays fell between the various stages of the bill's progress through Parliament whereas relatively minor pieces of legislation moved rapidly on to the statute books. What became quite evident during 1976 was the difficulty within the parliamentary system of forcing action on a problematic issue that also falls outside the usual lines. As William Rodgers later commented, '. . . we probably had the worst of all worlds – a Government Bill with a free vote.'[20]

What is also clear from the 1976 discussions was that the united opposition to the proposal was in a much stronger position within Parliament than the proponents of compulsory seat-belt wear.

The saga was to continue in 1977 when a Road Traffic (Seat Belt) Bill was introduced and voted on in the House of Lords on two separate occasions. The first bill was presented by Lord Avebury and debated fully before being defeated on its Second Reading,[21] by the very slim margin of two votes. The second bill was proposed by Lord Wigg and was debated for less than two hours before being rejected.[22] Wigg's bill was rather different from previous proposals in that it sought to make seat belts compulsory only on motorways. Both attempts at legislation were Private Members' Bills. In 1978 the Labour Government announced its intention of reintroducing a similar bill during the 1978–79 parliamentary session. This Bill passed its Second Reading with a large majority but was terminated by the 1979 General Election.

The 1979 election brought a Conservative government into office, and the new Transport Minister was Norman Fowler. Fowler's position on the proposal was always very clear: although personally in favour of seat-belt wear and appreciative of the various advantages (not least financial[23]) associated with large-scale use, he could not accept the principle of compulsion. Fowler did, however, also state that he would make no attempt to block any such proposal that was put before Parliament; he would merely join the debate as an individual MP without the added authority of speaking as Transport Minister. This was put to the test in 1979 when Neil Carmichael (a Labour MP) introduced a new Private Member's Bill on this topic. The suggested legislation passed its Second Reading in the Commons with a two to one majority[24] but, once again, was talked out at the Report stage in September 1980.

Final approval for compulsory seat-belt wear came in 1981. Lord Nugent, RoSPA's president, had introduced a Private Member's Bill to the House of Lords in the 1980–81 session, which gained a majority of 36 at the Second Reading. However, this bill was subsequently withdrawn by Lord Nugent in favour of a similar clause being inserted into the 1981 Transport Bill; this strategy was adopted on the grounds that the proposal would then be less vulnerable to Commons opposition. The clause was duly endorsed by a majority in the Lords of 40 on 11 June 1981.

On 28 July 1981, the Lords' amendment to the Transport Bill was put before the House of Commons. In the subsequent debate the arguments over personal liberty (see below) were repeated once more. One additional feature of the 1981 debates was the use made of John Adams's statistical evidence which suggested that no improvement in casualty numbers could be seen in those countries which had introduced similar laws, and indeed that compulsory seat-belt wear might even encourage more dangerous driving behaviour. These statistics and the related 'risk compensation hypothesis' will be discussed later. Nevertheless, it should be noted here that Adams's work gave new weapons to the anti-compulsion MPs. Why, after all, should individual rights be infringed if no public welfare benefits are to be gained?

What had emerged very clearly by 1981, and despite the arguments made by John Adams, was that firm support for legislation came from a large number of extra-parliamentary organisations. These included the Automobile Association, the Royal College of Surgeons (of both Scotland and England), the Royal College of Nursing, the Police Federation, the Society of Motor Manufacturers and Traders, the British Insurance Association, the Institute of Road Safety Officers and the Association of Chief Police Officers. The lobby had become very powerful and RoSPA had played a large part in organising this in an effective fashion. It had also become evident that the majority of D.Tp. staff favoured legislation as the single most practical and immediate way of reducing deaths and injuries on the British roads. The vote in the Commons was 221 to 144 in favour of the clause and, for those with an interest in British parliamentary politics, it was interesting to see the apparently ill-assorted collection of MPs who found themselves voting on the same side in this issue. For example, those who voted *against* compulsory seat-belt wear included Michael Foot, Norman Tebbit, Jo Grimond, Enoch Powell, Dennis Skinner, Francis Pym, Norman Fowler and Bob Cryer.

Immediately after the vote on compulsory seat-belt wear for adults a clause was also passed which made it illegal for unrestrained *children* to sit in the front of vehicles. Norman Fowler, as Transport Minister, then began consultation with affected parties – such as the medical profession – over exemptions from the law. These exemptions finally included local delivery drivers on their rounds, drivers while reversing and those granted a medical certificate. Certain other categories of motorist were also exempted from compulsory belt wear, for example, driving examiners when there is danger to themselves or another person, motor mechanics when carrying out certain tests, and taxi drivers. However, one cause of the delay until the eventual implementation date of 31 January 1983 was negotiation with the British Medical Association over the fee that should be charged by doctors when assessing individuals for exemption on medical grounds.

At the time of writing it is very difficult to be categorical about the percentage of motorists who are conforming to the new law. Initial reports in February 1983 suggested a very high wear rate: both the AA and RAC estimated that 90 per cent of front-seat occupants were complying. At the same time, reports from various hospitals suggested that casualties had reduced noticeably so that less eye injuries, facial lacerations and head traumas were being treated. Figures released by the D.Tp.[25] for the first five months of implementation suggested that front seat belt wear rates were around 95 per cent. Overall, casualties were down by some 7 per cent, with a fifth fewer drivers and front-seat passengers being killed or seriously injured. Of course, such evidence needs to be treated with great caution until longer-term statistics become available. A monitoring of the law's effectiveness will be conducted at least until 1985 by the D.Tp., with assistance also from Ford, BL Technology and the TRRL. With specific regard to the seat-belt clause within the 1981 Transport Act, this will involve fourteen hospitals in the UK in data collection beginning in April 1982.[26]

Mandatory seat-belt wear as a moral/philosophical issue

The principle is that this House elevates human life and practical considerations of pain and disability over pedantic obscurantism based on dubious theory. A vote for the Bill is a vote for sanity, compassion and common sense. It is, in fact, a vote for freedom and for life itself.[27]

What is involved is not a minor but a major step along the road towards the brave new world of Aldous Huxley.[28]

Discussion of mandatory seat-belt wear as a possible infringement of individual liberty has been a major theme of all political debate on this topic. The argument has taken many forms, but one common variation has been to accept the possible savings in human misery and in hospital resources but to assert that these in themselves do not legitimise state involvement in a matter for individual judgement. The philosophical problem has been to balance two principles: first, the preservation of human life and its sanctity against unnecessary suffering; secondly, the need for personal liberty. It is this problem that has transcended the party political boundaries and caused much soul-searching, but also apathy, among MPs who may well be better acquainted with the orthodox parliamentary terrain of political manifestoes and sharp boundaries between government and opposition. The development in 1980 and 1981 of a technical controversy over the effectiveness of legislation could only serve to exacerbate the problems faced by parliamentarians in grappling with this question.

The link between this philosophical quandary and other debates over technological risk should be apparent. Many issues of hazard control contain similar problems at their core – fluoridation, crash-helmet wear, planning regulations, restrictions on tobacco smoking and advertising, occupational safety legislation – although these questions may not always emerge in such a clear fashion as they have done here. When considering risk decisions as a 'balancing act' between costs and benefits, it needs to be borne in mind that these costs and benefits are not merely *economic* in character but can also involve questions of moral philosophy and human rights. However, it would be mistaken to view these problems as solely *individualistic* in nature. In the case of, for example, occupational safety, the dimension of political power cannot be ignored so that the 'rights' of managers and shareholders to make profit can come into direct conflict with the 'rights' of workers to earn their living in an environment that will not damage their health or threaten their safety. According to the perspective adopted in this book, such questions then become less an area for philosophical inquiry than for a struggle over *who* should have the dominant voice and *how* such a decision is to be made. It would be short-sighted to view the individual worker as grappling with matters of 'life versus liberty' without also considering the relative power of management and workers or the processes by which such questions are resolved at the institutional level. A parallel case for analysing the 'power dimension' could also be made for tobacco advertising or planning regulations; such issues need to be seen within the 'risk triangle' of regulated industries, regulatory authorities and those who face the physical consequences of a hazard being realised.

How then can a 'risk triangle' be applied to an issue like compulsory seat-belt wear, which seems the very epitome of an 'individual' and in no sense a 'political' issue? The answer to this lies in the previously introduced notion of 'un-politics', i.e. the idea that 'non-decisions' (or perhaps 'non-discussions') are *not* 'politically random oversights' but rather areas of 'politically enforced neglect'. What this suggests is that we need to look closely at the 'structuring' of British debates over road traffic safety in order to assess what has been apparently ignored. Compulsory seat-belt wear has been, in many ways, the *central* issue within road traffic safety policy in Britain and its characteristics need careful examination. It has focused on achieving the *active* cooperation of occupants. It relies on an existing technology which has been fitted as standard since the mid-1960s. Significantly, it has not involved the motor manufacturers in any major controversy, nor would it add any cost to new vehicles. The long-running discussion of occupant protection has been defined in purely individualistic terms without any serious examination of the possible alternatives to such an approach.

Considered in terms of what the debate has *not included*, a rather different perspective emerges. From the previous chapter it is clear that possibilities such as the passive seat belt or air bag did exist through the 1970s, yet there is very little evidence that the regulatory authorities ever analysed these possibilities seriously and certainly a discussion of these did not feed into parliamentary discussions. On those rare occasions when a Transport Minister did comment on passive restraint (e.g. John Gilbert in 1976[29]) the stance was always non-committal and tentative. The British manufacturers were just as opposed to passive technology (and over-interventionist control policies) as their US counterparts. The difference in Britain was that such topics could remain in the peripheral domain of 'un-politics' because of the lack of any countervailing pressure on the motor industry. Meanwhile, the manufacturers could study the parliamentary debates with the knowledge that their own products were safe from criticism. The British institutions have been 'impenetrable' to an open discussion of passive restraint technology because of the low emphasis which has traditionally been granted to the occupant protection framework, because of the lack of external pressure on the D.Tp. and manufacturers and because the whole topic of alternative safety policies has remained lost within un-politics. At this point the dimension of political power becomes extremely relevant to the discussion of an apparently philosophical issue. The problem for analysis is that the area of non-decision making and non-discussion becomes far less easy to explore for obvious reasons. It is because of this that a comparative perspective has been adopted here so that the gaps in one country's discussion of this hazard can be made visible by reference to political struggles in another. The comparative analysis will be developed further in the following chapters.

Mandatory seat-belt wear as a technical issue

Throughout most of the 1970s the greatest area of agreement within Parliament over this whole matter has related to the individual and societal advantages of seat-belt wear in terms of actually saving lives. As at least one Transport Minister expressed the merits of seat-belt wear to the Commons:

I emphasise that this is not the opinion of my Department alone or of any single group of experts, but is the corroborated conclusion of many careful studies in several countries. It is really no longer debatable . . .[30]

The Department of Transport's own support for this claim was, perhaps, demonstrated by its negotiations with the SMMT from the early 1960s onwards, which eventually produced legislation to compel the fitting of seat belts to all new cars. The corollary to this agreement over the merits of belt wear was also generally accepted: that, inasmuch as compulsion would increase usage rates substantially, the measure would certainly reduce the number of deaths and injuries.

In Britain this view is supported by the two major road traffic safety research centres, the Transport and Road Research Laboratory (TRRL) and the University of Birmingham Accident Research Unit (ARU). The ARU, for example, prepared a circular on this topic which was sent to all MPs before the March 1976 debate. The unit argued that mandatory seat-belt laws 'would save in the order of 1000 lives each year and totally prevent, or lessen the severity of, the injuries suffered by tens of thousands of people'. In fact, the head of ARU had also made his views known on the day of the November 1974 Commons debate. Murray Mackay, in a *New Scientist* article, attacked the 'ignorance' of those who feel that because they drive they are also experts on road traffic safety. Mackay referred to the seat-belt issue as 'the most important public health measure to be discussed for many years'.[31]

The TRRL has published a paper – by G. Grime[32] – which is generally recognised as one of the most authoritative reviews of seat-belt efficacy. Grime's conclusion was perhaps more cautious than that of the ARU but it nevertheless stated that 'very important savings' would be achieved by such a law and that seat belts reduce the risk of death by 40 per cent and of serious injury by 60 per cent. Grime also noted that 'perhaps every serious study' of seat-belt effectiveness has come out strongly in favour of their use.

It is against the background of this technical consensus that John Adams's analysis of the efficacy of seat-belt legislation must be seen. Adams's argument has been that such laws in various countries have had *no* appreciable effect in terms of reducing injury and death rates. This analysis and the related 'risk compensation' hypothesis have been controversial in the extreme and have certainly had an impact on parliamentary debates from 1979 onwards.[33]

In Adams's main paper on this subject[34] he is careful to note that the laboratory evidence for the benefits of occupant belt wear in a collision appears 'overwhelming'. However, he then proceeds to examine the statistical evidence of road fatality records from seventeen countries, thirteen with 'effective' seat-belt legislation and four (including Britain and the USA) without. The overall outcome of this analysis is that whereas road deaths fell by 17 per cent (between 1972 and 1978) in those countries with seat-belt laws, for countries *without* such laws the death rate fell by *25 per cent*. Adams proposes a 'risk compensation hypothesis' to account for these startling findings. This hypothesis states simply that 'protecting car occupants from the consequences of bad driving encourages bad driving'. A similar hypothesis has also been put forward by Sam Peltzman to explain the pattern of road deaths in the USA after the introduction of the first FMVSSs.[35]

With regard to seat-belt laws, Adams argues that, even on the most optimistic estimates, such a measure would reduce the risk of a fatal accident per kilometre travelled by a mere one-257-millionth. The 'risk compensation' notion then comes into play when the motorist perceives the measure as reducing the risk by *more* than it actually does, thus engendering a false sense of security which could itself be a cause of death and injury. Rock climbers with safety ropes, steeple jacks with safety harnesses, trapeze artists with safety nets, American football and ice-hockey players with protective clothing – all of these groups (according to Adams) take greater risks because of their safety equipment than they would ever do otherwise. Adams suggests that belted drivers act in a similar fashion and will 'compensate' for the reduction in one area of risk by increasing their chances of an accident.

Adams's work, with its detailed statistical analysis, has pointed the finger at the *ceteris paribus* assumption that has been taken for granted in all previous research into seat-belt efficacy.[36] Not surprisingly, Adams has found himself the focus for sustained attack from those involved in the pro-compulsion lobby. In 1981 his study was referred to in Parliament as an 'eccentric paper' which made a 'preposterous suggestion'.[37] A July 1981 *Times* editorial gave considerable prominence to Adams and asserted that the 'risk compensation' notion was 'no more than a hypothesis, and that the little relevant evidence in existence tends to contradict it'.[38] On the other hand, anti-belt law campaigners such as Ronald Bell made reference in the same newspaper to the statistics 'admirably analysed' by Adams.[39]

We will return shortly to the political discussion of seat-belt effectiveness but it is important to dwell a little longer on the arguments between technical experts over this issue. However, the political/technical distinction over this issue is very difficult to maintain in practice. One of the main published rebuttals to Adams came in a June 1981 letter to *The Times* written by Murray Mackay.[40] Mackay argued that Adams's analysis was 'seriously flawed' in its method and 'factually incorrect' in several instances, and its conclusions did 'not follow from the data analysed'. In particular, Mackay criticised the aggregation of all classes of road death as a basis for a sweeping international comparison. For Mackay, the effect of seat belts is likely to remain buried under the influence of various uncontrolled variables in such a broad-ranging analysis. Mackay also referred to the studies of driver risk taking which have been carried out in North America. One such investigation involved the observation of how closely drivers followed the preceding vehicle. Data on 4812 Ontario drivers was collated and compared with a similar number in Michigan, USA (compulsory seat-belt laws exist in Ontario but not in the United States). In each case, seat-belt wearing (whether voluntary or mandatory) was associated with the *avoidance* of risk.

John Adams replied to Mackay in *The Times*[41] by criticising the fact that Mackay had not published any more substantial review of Adams's work. Adams has consistently alleged that his analysis has never been refuted by anything other than assertions and that no full academic debate on his data has been conducted. In response to certain criticisms, Adams has developed his original analysis by comparing *car occupant* fatalities of countries with belt laws against those without. Furthermore, in an attempt to control for differing national experiences of the oil crisis, the fatalities for each country are divided by that country's petrol consumption. All the countries show a downward ratio in the early 1970s, but this levels off or actually turns up around the time that belt laws were introduced. For Adams, the 'obscuring-variables' hypothesis (as proposed, for example, by Mackay) needs to explain this 'extraordinary measure of coincidence';

The hypothesis requires that in every country that has passed a law, the law's enormous beneficial effect has been countered with remarkable timing, by a set of variables acting to produce a large increase in fatalities.[42]

Adams has challenged his critics to name these variables, to measure them and to demonstrate their independence from compulsory seat-belt wear. Furthermore, they need to explain why substantial increases in road deaths have not occurred in 'no law' countries.

The entrance of John Adams into the compulsory seat belt debate has certainly increased the technical, and consequently political, uncertainties surrounding this issue. Adams's complaint that his findings have often been merely dismissed rather than properly considered has been directed not just at technical experts such as Mackay but also at those involved in the political debates. According to Adams, parliamentarians in particular have often been less than impressive in coming to terms with this technical issue. As Adams observed in June 1981 with regard to the previous Lords debate on the issue:

... The view that you can prove anything with statistics had many adherents. They seemed to find a liberating insight; it freed them from the obligation to consider any statistical evidence that was incompatible with their pre-established voting intentions.[43]

This difficulty over the technical assessment of seat-belt effectiveness could be seen in most of the parliamentary debates, both since the publication of Adams's work and prior to this. Many participants in the discussions raised the possibility of harmful effects caused directly by belt usage, such as being trapped in a burning or submerged vehicle or being injured by the device itself. One member of the House of Lords argued in 1977 that the belt chafing on the skin might cause ailments, especially among women.[44] Other arguments emerged, based very often on anecdotal evidence, that it might be better to be thrown clear of a colliding vehicle rather than to be pinned into a fixed position. The experts' retort to these claims was made by the University of Birmingham Accident Research Unit (ARU) on the grounds, first, that the incidence of seat belt induced injuries is extremely low and, secondly, that a 'considerable understanding of crash dynamics and injury mechanisms' is necessary before meaningful comments can be made about such eventualities.[45] However, the case for superior understanding in such matters was weakened by the ARU's own statement in the same circular about explicitly non-technical matters such as law enforcement and civil rights. This blurring of the dividing line between the 'technical' and 'political/ethical' domains seems inevitable with such a 'trans-scientific' issue.

From the speeches made during the parliamentary debates as a whole, it is clear that a large number of parliamentarians were content to disregard the available expertise either partially or totally:

My Lords, all these percentages and statistics do not influence me at all. This is a private and personal matter for all of us and I do not think that these figures should be trotted out. Nor do I believe all that Secretaries of State and Ministers say.[46]

... let us get away from doubtful statistics which have not been proven, based ... on surveys and estimates.[47]

This line of argument, which was particularly prevalent in the House of Lords, was referred to by Lord Chesham as a

... curious rejection of a great deal of authoritative, statistical, proven, properly collected evidence ...[48]

The disregarding of the available technical expertise by certain parliamentarians illustrates well Nelkin's general proposition that:

the extent to which technical advice is accepted relies less on its validity and the competence of the expert, than on the extent to which it reinforces existing positions.[49]

The main evidence brought forward in opposition to the technical consensus was anecdotal and hypothetical, and the criticism of expertise was based, as Adams suggests, on 'lies, damned lies and statistics' accusations.

While discussing the effectiveness of seat-belt wear it is also worth considering the ARU and TRRL findings on certain types of inertia reel systems. In 1975 Murray Mackay revealed that some inertia reel devices had a slight but significant risk of malfunction. This report was corroborated by the TRRL in 1979.[50] Both sources emphasised the value of seat-belt wear, but stated that certain reels occasionally failed to lock the belt and simply allowed it to unreel. The TRRL calculated the rate of failure for specific systems to be 2 to 3 per cent.[51]

In 1977 the ARU had also drawn the Department of Transport's attention to another badly designed seat-belt system which is fitted with a pivoting arm located at the lower anchorage point. No action was taken on this matter until a young woman was killed in July 1979 while wearing such a belt. (In fact, millions of British and European cars have restraint systems of this type.) The coroner's report on the accident criticised the Department of Transport for its failure to implement the ARU's recommendations,[52] and a few weeks later the Department issued a warning about the dangers of this belt.

The ARU has also reported, following another series of tests, that several fatal accidents have involved the belt webbing being cut on the metal edge of its holder so that it offered no protection whatsoever. The British Standard on this topic had defined a sharp edge as that which could cut human flesh; only after protracted negotiation was this clause altered to match the ARU's findings.

In fact, the ARU, despite their public support for seat belts in general, have been very critical of the Department of Transport and the BSI for their failure to react to new evidence. As one of the unit's staff argued in 1979:

... the consumer is still getting a poor deal. He has a right to expect seat belts to work as intended because they all carry a British Standards Institution stamp. What he does not know is just what the standards are. In some instances they are just not good enough and the testing is not searching enough to detect faults.[53]

The ARU has a place on the BSI technical committee responsible for seat belts, but the preponderance of representation by the vehicle and belt manufacturers, coupled with the consensual nature of proceedings (there is no voting, for example[54]) means that the unit has very little power to change the existing standard. Essentially, the ARU would like to see a number of small amendments made to the existing design specifications which were developed in the early 1960s before devices like the inertia reel had been developed. The Department's reply to these criticisms has been that they consider very carefully all new evidence:

The problem is that the unit often looks at little details whereas the Department has to take a wider view, sort out the priorities, and then concentrate on the most important.[55]

It is certainly possible to question the way in which these 'priorities' are established, i.e. the consensual relationship between manufacturers and government departments which limits the possibilities for outside parties to influence policy.

Discussion

The debate over compulsory seat-belt wear in Britain certainly contrasts sharply with the wrangling over FMVSS 208 which was discussed in the previous chapter. Although the British discussions drew themselves out over a considerable period of time (approximately 10 years from the first major debate until implementation), they did at least reach a conclusion and the measure seems now to have the support of the British public. After an even longer period of discussion, the US proposals continue to languish in the middle of a well-entrenched regulatory battlefield. Whereas a commentator in the late-1970s might have seen the US political system as being superior in terms of its actual policy output, the eventual resolution of the seat-belt issue in Britain may now be judged as indicating a certain strength in that country's policy-making processes. There can be little doubt that the seat-belt law is seen by most observers as an important advance in British attempts at reducing road traffic accidents.

This comparison should, however, be balanced by the consideration of a number of points. First, the long delays involved are to the credit of *neither* nation. Britain, in passing its seat-belt law, was merely following the path already taken by a large number of other countries. Secondly, the previous discussion of 'un-politics' needs to be borne in mind; British debates over this issue have been protracted despite the fact that (unlike their US equivalents) they have not represented a challenge to the road lobby. Thirdly, the technical uncertainties about seat-belt effectiveness cannot simply be dismissed or underemphasised. Although Adams's case is far from conclusive and his evidence is a rather crude aggregation of different national experiences (including the actual rates of compliance to new laws and the individual 'accident profiles'[56] of each country), it does suggest the legitimate technical uncertainty that surrounds even such a well-tried technology. Fourthly, we have seen in this chapter how such technical uncertainties are interpreted in different ways according to the initial views of each protagonist. The work of such technical experts as John Adams or Murray Mackay has been either utilised very selectively or dismissed in favour of anecdotal evidence in order to support specific viewpoints. This illustrates well the unavoidable blurring of 'risk analysis' and 'risk evaluation' (see Chapter 2) in regulatory practice. The questions that it also raises concern the best role for technical expertise in such debates. Here, of course, we must consider an issue which is relevant not just to road traffic safety but to all matters of technological risk assessment.

Any discussion of the 'best role' for technical expertise in decision making involves a judgement as to the *criteria* according to which such expertise is to be evaluated. In the earlier part of this book it was argued that both *effectiveness* (in terms of an optimal balance between costs and benefits) and *equity* need to be taken into account here, together with the possibility that scientific evidence may be used only to *legitimate* previously desired courses of action. The full relevance of these three criteria will be explored in Part IV. Before this, two rather different illustrations of the US and British policy-making processes will be presented: fuel-system integrity and windscreen safety glass.

Notes and references

1   See Plowden, W. *The Motor Car and Politics, 1896–1970*. (Bodley Head, London; 1971), p.257.

2   See: House of Commons. *Debates*, Vol. 724, 10 February 1966, Cols 655–756.

3   House of Commons. *Debates*, Vol. 735, 7 November 1966, Cols 981–1048.

4   Department of the Environment, *Drinking and Driving*. Report of the Departmental Committee (HMSO, London; 1976). The committee was appointed in July 1974.

5   For a full account see: Nader, R. *Unsafe at Any Speed* (Pocket Books, New York; 1966), pp.86–98.

6   See Chapter 5 for a discussion of BSI Standards.

7   House of Commons. *Debates*, Vol. 636, 8 March 1961, Col. 455.

8   Plowden, W. *The Motor Car and Politics, 1896–1970* (Bodley Head, London; 1971), p.383.

9   Duckworth, J. (ed.) *Kitchin's Road Transport Law 1977* (Butterworth, London; 1977), p.16.

10 Grime, G. *The Protection Afforded by Seat Belts*, TRRL Supplementary Report 449, 1979.

11 For example, by Austin Mitchell MP.

12 *Road Safety – a Fresh Approach* (HMSO, London; 1967).

13 In fact the total expenditure by the government on seat-belt propaganda between 1971 and 1980 was £7 832 000. *Care on the Road*, February 1982, p.2.

14 House of Lords. *Debates*, Vol. 346, 15 November 1973, Cols 860–3.

15 House of Commons. *Debates*, Vol. 868, 30 January 1974, Cols 457–569.

16 House of Commons. *Debates*, Vol. 877, 26 July 1974, Col. 2120.

17 First Reading; House of Commons. *Debates*, Vol. 880, 31 October 1974, Col. 383. Second Reading; *Ibid*. Vol. 881, 21 November 1974, Col. 1639–58.

18 House of Commons. *Debates*, Vol. 906, 1 March 1976, Col. 925.

19 Lidderdale, D. (ed.). *Erskine May's Treatise on the Law, Privileges, Proceedings and Usage of Parliament* (19th Edn) Butterworth, London; 1976), p.577.

20 Rodgers, W. House of Commons. *Debates*, Vol. 921, 1 December 1976, Col. 895.

21 First Reading: House of Lords. *Debates*, Vol. 380, 9 March 1977, Col. 1033. Second Reading: Lords. *Debates*, Vol. 382, April 26, 1977, Cols 411–514. Ayes – 53; Noes – 55.

22   First Reading: House of Lords. *Debates*, Vol. 382, 2 May 1977, Col. 808. Second Reading: House of Lords. *Debates*, Vol. 383, 24 May 1977, Cols 1207–44. Ayes – 62; Noes – 86.

23   RoSPA's estimate of the likely savings to the National Health Service (NHS) provided by compulsory seat-belt wear was £130 680 000 per annum. This figure is based on 700 lives saved (each death on the road costing an average of £112 200 in NHS resources) and 11000 injuries lessened (an average saving of £4470). *Care on the Road*, February 1981, p.4. Although RoSPA's figure might well be disputed, Fowler gave every indication that compulsory wear would provide substantial savings to the nation, e.g. House of Commons. *Debates*, Vol. 9, 28 July 1981, Cols 1047–51. Fowler was quoted in 1979 as estimating the savings in medical costs as representing £5–7 million. *Care on the Road*, July 1979, p.2.

24   This took place on 20 July 1979. The actual voting was 134 to 59.

25   *The Guardian*, 5 October 1983.

26   Some detail on this is given in the D.Tp. evidence to the House of Commons Transport Committee on Road Safety, 22 March 1983 (HMSO, London; 1983), pp.40–2.

27   Ashley, J. House of Commons. *Debates*, Vol. 906, 1 March 1976, Col. 948.

28   Lawrence, I. *Ibid*. Col. 993.

29   Gilbert, J. House of Commons *Standing Committee B*, 18 May 1976, Col. 214–15.

30   Gilbert, J. House of Commons. *Debates*, Vol. 906 1 March 1976, Col. 928.

31   Mackay, G. M. Machismo on the road? *New Scientist*, 21 November 1974, p.547.

32   Grime, G. The protection afforded by seat belts. TRRL Supplementary Report 449, 1979.

33   Adams, J. Numbers in safety. *Vole*. **2** (10), 26 July 1979, pp.3–7.

34   Adams, J. The efficacy of seat belt legislation. SAE Technical Paper Series 820819. Delivered at the Passenger Car Meeting, Troy, Michigan, 7–10 June 1982. Earlier versions of this paper were circulating from the end of 1980 so that, for example, *New Scientist* published an article on Adams's work in February 1981: Hamer, M. Do compulsory seat belts save lives? *New Scientist*, 19 February 1981, p.461.

35   Peltzman, S. *Regulation of Automative Safety* (American Enterprise Institute for Public Policy Research, Washington, DC; 1975). See also: Wilde, G. J. S. The theory of risk homeostasis: implications for safety and health. *Risk Analysis*, **2**(4) 1982, 209–25. The same issue of *Risk Analysis* includes a discussion of 'risk homeostasis' presented by Paul Slovic and Baruch Fischhoff (pp. 227–34) and by John D. Graham (pp. 235–47). This is followed by Wilde's response (pp. 249–58).

36   That is, it has been assumed that laboratory studies of seat-belt effectiveness can be applied directly to mass usage without any intervening psychological variables such as changed driver behaviour or perception.

37   Moate. R. House of Commons. *Debates*, Vol. 9, 28 July 1981, Col. 1044.
38   *The Times*, 16 July 1981, p.13.
39   *The Times*, 10 June 1981, p.15.
40   *The Times*, 11 June 1981, p.17.
41   *The Times*, 16 June 1981, p.13.
42   Adams, J. The efficacy of seat belt legislation. Appendix. (See reference 34.)
43   *The Times*, 16 June 1981, p.13.
44   Lord Mouson. House of Lords *Debates*, Vol. 382, 26 April 1977, Col. 473. Lord Mouson continued, 'This may seem perhaps unduly alarmist, my Lords, but never forget that Thalidomide was originally prescribed on the National Health Service.'
45   Accident Research Unit. *Seat Belts*. Circular sent to Members of Parliament in 1976.
46   Lord Howe, House of Lords. *Debates*, Vol. 382, 26 April 1977, Col. 461.
47   Lord Balfour of Inchyre. House of Lords. *Debates*, Vol. 382, 26 April 1977, Col. 421.
48   Lord Chesham. House of Lords. *Debates*, Vol. 382, 26 April 1977, Col. 503.
49   Nelkin, D. The political impact of technical expertise. *Social Studies of Science*, **5** (1) 1975, 51–3.
50   *Care on the Road*, October 1979, p.2.
51   The specific systems at issue were the Britax Autolok Mk III and Mk IIIA.
52   *The Times*, 8 December 1979, p.3.
53   *The Guardian*, 29 December 1979, p.3.
54   See Chapter 5.
55   *The Guardian*, 29 December 1979, p.3.
56   'Accident profile' in this context refers to the distribution of road casualties between different groups: vehicle occupants, motorcyclists, cyclists, pedestrians, public transport users, etc.

Chapter 8

Legislative and judicial approaches to fire hazards

The next chapters will focus on two rather different areas of road traffic safety policy: the debate that has taken place in the United States over the prevention of automobile fires, and British/European discussions relating to 'laminated' and 'toughened' windscreen glass. The first example provides an opportunity to delve further into the practice of the US regulatory system and to consider both the legislative and judicial approaches to this form of technological risk. The second case study illustrates the British decision-making process in action but also reveals something of the significance of European (in this case EEC) activities in forming British regulatory strategies.

These examples have been chosen because each allows an exploration of the more detailed workings of the two decision-making systems. However, it is important at this stage not to generalise immediately from these case studies so as to reach conclusions about the *overall* pattern of the regulatory systems. The inevitable 'bias' in case-study selection will be balanced by a more general discussion of national policies in Chapter 10.

Fire hazards and FMVSS 301

This chapter will focus on attempts in the United States to limit the susceptibility of vehicles to fuel leakages (and hence fires) after collision. A much briefer account will also be included of British discussions over this issue. It must be noted here that fire hazards have attracted special public attention in the USA, partly because of the very controversial damages cases which will be discussed later in this chapter. Some authors have argued that only a very small proportion of road traffic deaths are actually caused by fires (see Fig. 3, for example), but the 'dread' nature of this form of hazard has been at

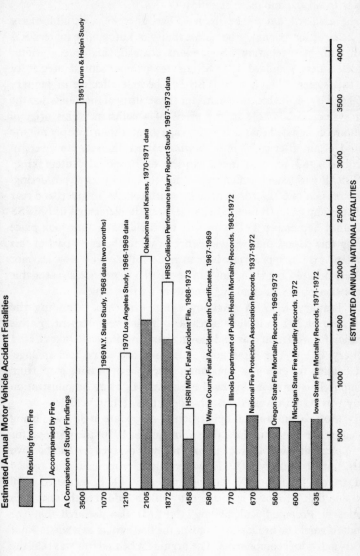

Fig. 3 Statistics from various sources for road traffic deaths caused by fires. Taken from reference 23.

least as crucial as its statistical frequency during various political debates. In addition, if one applies a time-scale of (say) ten years, then the size of the potential accident reduction from effective regulation begins to appear far more significant.

The standard that will be discussed here does not cover all forms of fire hazard; for example, the flammability of automotive materials is dealt with by a separate US standard. Instead, this Federal Motor Vehicle Safety Standard (FMVSS) relates to the structural integrity of the fuel system. The first FMVSS 301 became effective in January 1968 and it specified requirements for the security of fuel tanks and the fuel system as a whole in the event of a collision.[1] This original standard designated that no fuel leakage greater than 1 oz per minute should occur after a 30 mph *frontal* barrier impact. However, in October 1967 an 'advanced Notice of Proposed Rulemaking' (ANPRM) was issued, which stated that the agency was 'considering' the extension of 301 so as to deal also with vehicle 'rollover' and rear and side impacts.[2] In fact, no changes were implemented in FMVSS 301 until September 1975 and it is on the debates that took place during this period that we will concentrate in the early part of this chapter. It is not appropriate here to give a full blow-by-blow account of these debates, but sufficient can be written to provide a reasonable impression of US rulemaking procedure on this topic.

In January 1969 the Agency again proposed extending the provisions of 301 to include a rear-end impact requirement, on this occasion for a 20 mph rear-end moving barrier collision to take effect 1 January 1970.[3] The same notice also outlined a 'no fuel spillage' specification for cars at a 'maximum deceleration braking stop' from 80 mph. This proposal followed a Federal Highway Administration study which had revealed just this defect in certain vehicles.

By 1969–70 substantial opposition to an update of 301 was being voiced by the motor manufacturers. In August 1970[4] the proposal for the implementation of a rear impact test was delayed for another two years, until 1 January 1972. However, it was proposed by the agency that, from 1 January 1973 the impact speed would be increased to 30 mph and that a rollover requirement would be added to the test. This 'Notice of Proposed Rulemaking' (NPRM) also declared that the standard would be broadened to cover the fuel system as a whole – not just its individual components. The argument behind this was that the fuel system should be treated as a rupture-resistant network, and not simply as a collection of components adapted to a vehicle after its basic design had been completed. No regulatory action followed this new NPRM and in 1971 the NHTSA suspended the effective date of proposed rulemaking until 1 September 1976.

The arguments over 301 began to emerge more clearly in 1973. At a House Subcommittee hearing in that year,[5] the Insurance Institute for Highway Safety (IIHS) presented its own crash test research which suggested that fuel leakage could occur in medium-speed rear impacts in new cars. The tests featured six pairs of 1973 model cars of various types. In each case the fuel tanks were filled and a moving car was rammed into a stationary car at a speed between 36 and 40 mph. All the vehicles met the 1967 301 standard, but all six of those subjected to the rear-end collision leaked substantial quantities of petrol[6], and one ignited spontaneously. The IIHS tests also revealed that in five out of the six cases, one or more of the doors jammed on impact. William Haddon, the IIHS President, gave examples of various reports which had noted the alleged defects in fuel systems at that time. These included a Fairchild Hiller study,[7] a report by A. W. Siegel and A. M. Nahum,[8] the National Transportation Safety Board[9] (NTSB) investigation in 1971, a Department of Transportation[10] contract and two further NTSB investigations in 1972.[11]

On the same day that the IIHS testified to the House Subcommittee, its Chairperson, Representative John Moss, wrote to Transportation Secretary, Claude S. Brinegar, requesting a full report on NHTSA's activity on 301. The NHTSA's views were expressed in a letter to the Center for Auto Safety[12] in which the agency's Acting Administrator promised that it would issue a new ruling 'around August 1, 1973'. The Center had previously called the NHTSA's attention to a report by the National Commission on Fire Prevention and Control, which had concluded that fires in American motor vehicles caused at least 3500 deaths in 1971 and that design and materials changes could reduce this number substantially.[13]

On 3 August 1973, John Moss wrote again to Claude Brinegar, but in a stronger tone. Moss stated that the existing level of fuel system integrity was 'an indictment of both the auto industry and government inaction'.[14] On 15 August the agency announced its new measures. The only final action was to add a rollover test after the 30 mph frontal barrier collision that had been in effect since 1967.[15] At the same time, however, the agency introduced proposals for rear and lateral impacts of a type very similar to those being suggested for standard 208. The effective dates were suggested as 1 September 1976 and 1 September

1977, according to vehicle weight. Immediately after the publication of these proposals, various manufacturers began to challenge their content. The Motor Vehicle Manufacturers' Association objected to the rollover test following a 30 mph frontal barrier crash.[16] Chrysler Corporation stated that it knew

... of no feasible means which could be developed in the time frame allowed for compliance to meet the requirements.[17]

Ford Motor Company argued on a cost–benefit basis that 'the yearly benefits of compliance were estimated at just under $50 million, with an associated cost to consumers of $137 million'.[18] This argument would later assume crucial importance for the subsequent litigation involving the Ford Pinto. General Motors stated that they could not 'meet the effective dates of this amendment and we do not know when we would be able to comply'. American Motors asked for a delay in the effective date of at least one year. Opposition also came from the Recreational Vehicle Institute, Jeep Corporation, and Mercedes-Benz.[18]

As an attempt to nullify the industry's attempts at delay, a number of bills and amendments were introduced in both the Senate and House to ensure that no further extension of the effective date could occur. Early in 1974, Senator Montoya sponsored a bill requiring the NHTSA to establish new standards by 1975 and 1976 rather than the proposed 1976 and 1977. The senator argued that the ...

... magnitude of the dangers involved in unsafe fuel tanks, the existence of available technology to remedy tank deficiencies and the seeming reluctance on the part of the Department of Transportation to implement safety standards in an expeditious fashion, provided persuasive evidence of the necessity for this legislation.[19]

Congressman Moss introduced a similar bill a few months later.[20]

In March 1974 the agency responded to petitioning by introducing two separate final notices.[21] These upheld the proposed effective dates, made some minor legal changes and adopted the previously outlined specifications for angular frontal barrier crash, lateral barrier crash, static rollover (following each impact) and rear moving barrier crash. One of the proposed tests had been dropped but, essentially, the bulk of opposing arguments had been rejected.

It is worth considering at this point the nature of these notices and the form they took. As in most cases of published rulemaking in the

USA on the topic of road traffic safety, each contained a preamble dealing with the comments that had been received and justifying in some detail the final decision. For example, in one of the March notices, Ford's claim that the rollover and fuel-spillage requirements would not prove cost effective was examined in depth. Ford Motor Company had calculated that compliance with the rollover requirement would cost $11.20 per passenger car (without any profit margin being included). Ford also argued that the presented NHTSA estimate of 2000–3500 annual deaths attributable to crash-caused fires was incorrect and that a National Safety Council estimate of 600–700 was more realistic.

In response, the NHTSA rejected Ford's argument on the grounds that the 'narrow analysis' presented was based on incorrect accident statistics and a rather short-term view of the cost of a new standard. The agency also made the following comments about cost–benefit analysis in general:

Although the NHTSA uses cost–benefit analysis as a decision-making tool, it is not a perfect one, depending necessarily on extremely imprecise assumptions concerning benefits to be achieved. Granting that reasonable persons may differ on their cost–benefit projections, this agency does not consider that to be a conclusive argument against a safety requirement. On the basis of its own analysis the NHTSA is convinced that the measures provided in the standard are appropriate, reasonable, and necessary.[22]

Two points should be made about this agency notice. The first is a general characteristic of debate in the USA over vehicle safety: the NHTSA actually committed itself in public to putting forward a definite line of argument and stating the evidence on which its claim was being made. This is quite different from the same area of activity in Britain, where most argumentation remains confidential in the interest of 'flexibility'. The Department of Transport prefers not to publicise its reasoning, presumably on the grounds that this might impede future changes in policy.

The second important feature of the 301 standard is the *technical* evidence involved and its frequently contradictory nature. The sharp contrast between Ford Motor Company's use of the NSC estimate of 600–700 directly attributable deaths and the NHTSA figure of 2000–3500 has already been noted. In fact, as Fig. 3 shows, there has been an enormous variation in the estimated annual fatalities both directly resulting from fires and being merely accompanied by fires. To this should be added the analysis prepared by Peter Cooley of the Highway Safety Research Institute at the University of Michigan.

Cooley made explicit note of the methodological problems involved in assessing the relationship of vehicle fires to human injuries and fatalities. He outlined five possible ways of categorising fire-associated deaths:

(1) Deaths which were in no way the result of the fire.
(2) Deaths as a result of impact injuries where minor burns also occurred.
(3) Deaths where the medical condition was worsened by burns.
(4) Deaths from impact *and* burn injuries.
(5) Deaths solely attributable to fire.[23]

According to Cooley, categories 3, 4 and 5 should be considered as fire-associated deaths. What is quite clear, however, is that apart from the statistical problems of sampling and accuracy, there is also a large scope for imputation and intuition in the categorisation of any particular accident. For example, physicians and data gatherers may well differ in their individual assessment of the three types of fire-associated death; especially when their major concern may not be with the preparation of statistically reliable information. In this situation, the motor manufacturers exploited the technical uncertainty to the maximum extent.

As an example of the use of empirical confusion for lobbying purposes it is possible to examine the activity of one US manufacturer, Ford Motor Company.[24] Ford, it would seem, were not perturbed by the original 301 standard, which dealt only with frontal collision. In fact, a Ford memorandum which was later leaked to the Center for Auto Safety suggests that the company conducted at least 250 crash tests involving fuel tanks. The results of these have never been made public. However, it is alleged that they demonstrate that frontal collision standards were already attained, but not those for rear impact.[25] Ford did have a particular problem with one vehicle, the Ford Pinto. This was scheduled for production in August 1970, by which time the total investment was to be $200 million. The positioning of the Pinto fuel tank seemed likely to cause difficulties in reaching the performance level of an updated 301 (see Fig. 4). At this point, Ford began to argue for a delay in the implementation of the standard by asserting that there was a lack of evidence to support the measure.

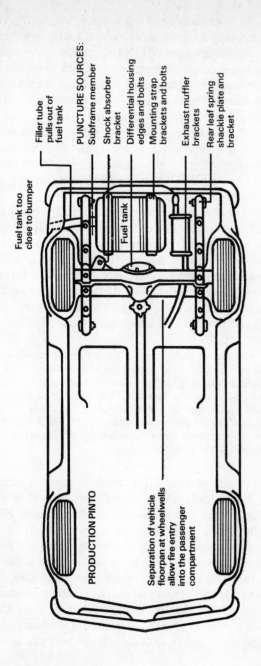

Fuel tank too
close to bumper

PRODUCTION PINTO

Separation of vehicle
floorpan at wheelwells
allow fire entry
into the passenger
compartment

Filler tube
pulls out of
fuel tank

PUNCTURE SOURCES:

Subframe member

Shock absorber
bracket

Differential housing
edges and bolts

Mounting strap
brackets and bolts

Exhaust muffler
brackets

Rear leaf spring
shackle plate and
bracket

Fuel tank

Fig. 4 The Ford Pinto. Taken from reference 28. Drawing by Byron Bloch, Auto Safety Design Consultant, West Los Angeles.

The first argument made by Ford was that, statistically, vehicle fires were an extremely minor problem which barely deserved NHTSA attention. Accordingly, the NHTSA spent some time analysing the existing data and commissioning new research work. Corroborating evidence for the revised standard came from studies like that of Cooley, which argued that each year in the USA there were 450–650 fire-associated fatalities in motor vehicles. Cooley estimated that the update of 301 would prevent 40 per cent[26] of these deaths once all vehicles were in compliance, i.e. approximately ten years after the standard's introduction. The suggested saving in annual fatalities would then be 180–260 or, in terms of cost–benefit analysis at $200 000 per life,[27] $36–52 million.

This evidence still allowed Ford to put forward two other lines of argument: first, that rear-end collisions were comparatively rare, and secondly, that it was collision *impact* and not fire that was causing the majority of fire-associated deaths. The NHTSA eventually rejected these arguments but there was certainly a fair delay before the agency could feel sufficiently confident of its footing to put its full weight behind the proposed FMVSS. In regard to Ford Motor Company, one critical account described its lobbying methods as follows:

There are several main techniques in the art of combating a government safety standard: (a) make your arguments in succession, so the feds can be working on disproving only one at a time; (b) claim that the real problem is not X but Y . . .; (c) no matter how ridiculous each argument is, accompany it with thousands of pages of highly technical assertions it will take the government months or, preferably, years to test. Ford's large and active Washington office brought these techniques to new heights and became the envy of the lobbyists' trade.[28]

There may well be some justification for this indictment of Ford (especially in the light of the 'Ford Pinto Affair' which will be examined later) and also perhaps of the 'weak-kneed NHTSA', as described by Dowie. Nevertheless it is true that the agency found Ford's technical arguments very challenging. They did point to real gaps in knowledge and could not be simply dismissed as mere 'delaying tactics' if the NHTSA was to retain any 'regulatory credibility'. Indeed, those NHTSA officials who were directly concerned with 301 have since described themselves as 'walking on eggs' during that period when the evidence seemed both controversial and contradictory.[29] It might have been a major *faux pas* to issue a final standard which the industry could later reveal to be shakily based and 'unreasonable'.

Following the issue of an updated 301 in March 1974,[22] further opposition presented itself: a court challenge was prepared. American Motors asked the US Court of Appeals for the Sixth Circuit to review the rulemaking. However, this relatively small manufacturer was alone in making the appeal and the lack of support from the other companies, coupled with an assessment that the action would be unsuccessful, encouraged American Motors to withdraw its litigation in September. Meanwhile, the other manufacturers filed formal petitions with the agency to lower the requirements and gain a later effective date. As it stood, the first stage would commence in September 1975 with rear impact specifications starting in September 1976. However, these petitions were largely unsuccessful and only minor amendments were made in the standard.

At this point it may be useful to summarise just what this revision of FMVSS 301 actually involved. As it stood in October 1975 – and no major changes have occurred since – the main test requirements were as follows for passenger cars manufactured on or after 1 September 1976:[30]

(1) frontal barrier crash at 30 mph;
(2) rear barrier crash at 30 mph;
(3) side (lateral) barrier crash at 20 mph;
(4) rollover.

For each of these tests, specific limits for fuel spillage were prescribed. For barrier crashes these were 1 ounce by weight until vehicle motion had ceased, then 5 ounces in the following 5-minute period, then no more than 1 ounce during any 1-minute interval in the subsequent 25-minute period. Of course, 301 also laid out far greater detail about general test conditions and techniques for the conduct of each category of collision or rollover.

Following this final ruling, a number of applications for exemption were considered, the bulk of these coming from small 'specialist' companies, e.g. Vintage Reproductions[31] and Marathon Electric Vehicles.[32] The majority of these claims were granted, but usually for a limited period only. A more important exemption case related to a General Motors product, the 1977 Chevrolet Chevette. General Motors disputed the apparent failure of the vehicle in DOT tests but eventually decided (in November 1978) to recall all 1976 and 1977

Chevettes so as to remedy the problem.[33]

A more recent case of apparent fuel system defects has related to the Toyota Corona. The IIHS has lobbied the NHTSA to initiate a recall and has produced evidence from both its own tests and an accident in which three women were killed.[34] The IIHS repeated this request for action in June 1980 and claimed that five deaths and one serious burn injury could then be related to Toyota Coronas as well as some other Toyota vehicles with similar fuel systems.[35] In 1981, the NHTSA responded to the IIHS and announced its intention to drop investigations into the Toyota vehicles on the grounds that analysis to that point did not indicate 'sufficient likelihood' of a safety defect.[36]

Perhaps the obvious final point on which to close this initial part of the discussion is with a consideration of the actual *effectiveness* of standard 301. However, as Chapter 7 has already noted, and as will be argued once again in Chapter 10, such assessments of effectiveness are rarely as straightforward as might be expected. This remains true even after (at the time of writing) a time lag of over seven years since the implementation date. In fact, the NHTSA argue that the standard has reduced the rate of fires by 43 per cent in crashes of 'major crash force levels' and by 23 per cent in 'low-to-moderate crash force levels'. In terms of casualties, the agency estimates that 301 has saved 400 lives each year and prevented 520 serious injuries. The estimated cost of compliance with the revised 301 is calculated as $8.50 per car (which takes account both of manufacturers' costs and those in extra petrol consumption due to a slight additional weight factor).[37]

Court review and judicial involvement in fire hazards

As Levine and Cornwell[38] and numerous other political commentators have noted, the judicial branch is an integral part of the United States system of government. It is not surprising, therefore, to find that the courts have become involved in a range of issues relating to road traffic safety. We have already seen (here and in Chapter 6) that the judiciary can conduct a 'review' of rulemaking so as to establish whether the NHTSA is acting in a manner that conforms to the Constitution and existing statutory requirements. The judiciary has also been engaged in two other areas of law relating to automobile safety: the civil law of torts and product liability. It is the latter area that has represented the more important judicial influence on manufacturing and design practice in the USA.

The product liability law in the USA makes a manufacturer liable for 'defective conditions unreasonably dangerous to the user or consumer'. In a 1968 test-case, the court spelled out the basis of liability:

While all risks cannot be eliminated nor can a crashproof vehicle be designed under the present state of the art, there are many common sense factors in design, which are or should be well known to the manufacturer that will lessen the injurious effects of a collision, the standard of reasonable care is applied in many other negligence situations and should be applied here.[39]

What is initially required for a test to be brought against a manufacturer is for someone to be injured by a vehicle incorporating a certain (perhaps unusual) design feature. The injury must then be shown to be directly attributable to the feature. Of course, the injured person must also find an informed lawyer (preferably a specialist) to pursue the case. An enormous advantage in such a claim is the testimony of some 'insider' or 'whistleblower' who has been involved in planning and discussion over the design feature, i.e. someone who can demonstrate that the manufacturer had some awareness of the danger, but chose to ignore it. Manufacturers are aware that precedents in meeting damages claims can prove very expensive, and will therefore fight each and every claim most resolutely – or else settle out of court. Once a feature has been judged to be below the standard of 'reasonable care' then design changes are unavoidable. In this way, product liability cases can provide a useful, although inevitably retrospective, way of forcing vehicle design changes and thus serve as a partial alternative to NHTSA standard setting. It should also be noted that the number of product liability cases has in general increased in the United States. In 1974 some 1579 such claims were filed in federal courts, and the figure for 1980 was 7775.[40] Among these cases motor vehicles have been a particular focus of attention.

It is impossible to estimate the cost to manufacturers of product liability suits in recent years. Settlements are often made out of court and on the condition that the sum paid to the plaintiff is not revealed. However, one authoritative summary of automobile design liability cases[41] lists 62 (involving seven major automobile companies) that relate to fuel system integrity alone. Examples of recent verdicts in the USA include the following[42]:

a US District Court jury in Boston awarded a $1 049 000 judgment against Ford Motor Company following an accident involving a 1972 Ford Mustang (damages awarded in April 1982).

A Los Angeles judge awarded $1 183 322 to the family of a man killed in an accident involving a British Leyland Jaguar XJ6 (verdict in November 1979).

$3.15 million was awarded in Detroit to the family of a young man who died when his petrol tank exploded in a 1977 crash. The car involved was a 1975 Mercury Montego manufactured by Ford (verdict in November 1981).

A suit brought against General Motors Corporation and involving a 1976 Opel concluded in a settlement of $17.5 million (settlement reached June 1982).

In the general context of FMVSS 301 and fire hazards, one especially important damages case has involved the Ford Pinto. The lobbying strategy adopted by Ford to oppose 301 has already been discussed. It was also noted that this manufacturer was having particular problems with the fuel tank design of the Pinto. However, these problems became even greater for Ford *after* the vehicle was deemed to have complied with the existing standard and was released on to the market.

The court action at the centre of the 'Ford Pinto Affair' was that of Richard Grimshaw who at one point was awarded $128 million by the Santa Anna Superior Court in 'punitive damages'.[43] On appeal by Ford this sum was brought down to $2.8 million 'compensatory' and $3.5 million 'punitive' damages. Prior to the Grimshaw case, the first damages award against Ford for the Pinto amounted to $3.3 million in a Florida court in 1975 following an accident in which a Pinto's fuel tank had exploded. In 1976, an Alabama jury awarded $1.2 million to the plaintiff in a nearly identical Pinto crash. One year later, a Virginian court ordered Ford to pay $625 000 in a similar case. It was at this time that the Grimshaw case commenced — more than five years after his accident on 28 May 1972.

The incident at the centre of the case occurred when Richard Grimshaw, then thirteen years old, was given a lift in a new Pinto by a friend of his family, Mrs Lily Gray. As they headed across southern California the Pinto stalled and was hit in the rear by a following vehicle at a speed of 28 mph. The petrol tank ruptured and a spark ignited the mixture. The vehicle was soon enveloped in flames. Lily Gray died in hospital two days later as a result of her burns, and

Richard Grimshaw suffered 90 per cent burns and lost his nose, left ear and four fingers. He has since undergone more than fifty operations and he remains severely scarred.

The difference between the Grimshaw case and those that went before it was that the lawyers were arguing for 'punitive' damages, i.e. convincing the jury that Ford had 'consciously and wilfully' disregarded public safety. For such a verdict to be given, there was clearly a need for a reasonable amount of very damaging evidence to be produced. Ford's main defence was that the Pinto had always met or surpassed government safety standards (of course it is only since September 1976 that the 30 mph rear-impact requirement has been in force). This statement was not challenged by the prosecution, but other submissions were made. A large amount of this evidence was presented in *Mother Jones*[44] in September 1977:

> Fighting strong competition from Volkswagen for the lucrative small car market, the Ford Motor Company rushed the Pinto into production in much less than the usual time.
> Ford engineers discovered in pre-production crash tests that rear-end collisions would rupture the Pinto's fuel system extremely easily.
> Because assembly-line machinery was already tooled when engineers found this defect, top Ford officials decided to manufacture the car anyway – exploding gas tank and all – even though Ford owned the patent on a much safer gas tank.
> For more than eight years afterwards, Ford successfully lobbied, with extraordinary vigor and some blatant lies, against a key government safety standard that would have forced the company to change the Pinto's fire-prone gas tank.[45]

In all the testimony that followed during the case, including various expert statements (among them the one made before the trial by Dr Ball, former safety chief of the NASA space program, that 'the release to production of the Pinto was the most reprehensible decision in the history of American engineering'),[46] one piece of evidence was particularly crucial in turning the case against Ford. This was a 1972 Ford internal memorandum which presented a cost–benefit analysis of improving the Pinto's safety.[47]

The analysis assumed that 180 people were likely to be burned to death in one year in Pinto accidents, and calculated the benefits of saving these lives (at a value of $200 000 per life) plus 180 serious burn injuries (at $67000 per injury), plus 2100 burned vehicles ($700 each). The total of $49.5 million was balanced against the cost to Ford of complying with the updated 301 at $11 per car and truck. With sales of

11 million cars and 1.5 million light trucks, that would cost $137 million, with 'benefits' of only $49.5 million. This led Ford to reject any improvement in the Pinto fuel tank, even though a heavy rubber bladder inside the gas tank could have solved the problem for an estimated $5.08 per car.[48] The human 'benefits' calculations were taken from the official NHTSA figures for 1972 and this whole argument was put to the NHTSA in opposition to the 301 update. Ford later met the new September 1976 standard by fitting an extremely cheap (approximately $1) plastic baffle on to the differential housing, which prevented the fuel tank from being perforated by four protruding bolts (this was the basic cause of fuel tank rupture – see Fig. 4).

It is worth considering Ford's use of cost–benefit analysis a little further. The cost of $11 for improving the tank's integrity was the company's own figure and the basis of its calculations. Could the manufacturer be blamed for not utilising a technological solution of which it was unaware? Under US law the answer to this is 'probably not'. The crucial evidence that emerged was that Ford was indeed aware of the $5.08 rubber bladder device *before* the Grimshaw accident occurred. A Ford confidential report revealed that a test rear-impact crash was carried out on 2 December 1970 on a car with a bladder fitted. The tank ruptured, but the fuel did not leak. On 15 January 1971, another successful test was carried out.[49] Without the publication of this secret memorandum, Ford might well have been able to argue that it had exercised 'reasonable care' and would certainly not have been open to punitive damages charges.

The part played by cost–benefit analysis in influencing governmental and industrial activity must also be considered. Ford's calculations of the value of a human life were based on a 1972 NHTSA study. Later in that year, the agency demonstrated how the figure of $200 000 had been arrived at. The major component was for 'future productivity losses', a total of $173 300. The second largest, although considerably smaller category, was 'victim's pain and suffering', $10 000. Other components with lesser values included 'insurance administration', 'property damage', 'legal and court' and 'medical costs'. It is immediately clear that there must be a large subjective element in any such calculation. How is 'victim's pain and suffering' ever to be satisfactorily quantified? No account is taken of pain and suffering to the family of the victim: what is the cash value to a child of a mother or father? At the same time, while recognizing these weaknesses, proponents of cost–benefit analysis argue that *implicit* values are continually put on these factors in deciding any future course of action; why not make these *explicit* and therefore open to debate?

Although cost–benefit analysis was a popular tool for the agency in 1972, by 1974 it was arguing that the technique was necessarily based on 'extremely imprecise assumptions'[50] and indeed at that time the NHTSA also rejected Ford's calculation on the Pinto as a 'narrow analysis' based on only short-term costing and incorrect statistics (see above). A major weakness of cost–benefit analysis is that for practical purposes its use has done nothing to quell disagreement when the studies have been made public; the parties to the debate have shown themselves well capable of producing conflicting analyses based on different sets of assumptions. The general distrust in the USA which public interest groups tend to have for manufacturer-prepared cost figures must also be noted here. In this area, of course, the industry has unique access to information and is generally reluctant to release relevant data.

Cost–benefit analysis was rejected by Congress in 1966 as a prerequisite to motor vehicle safety standard setting. Later, the Motor Vehicle Information and Cost Savings Act of 1972[51] introduced a requirement for cost–benefit studies relating to bumper standards. United States Government bodies like the Council for Wage and Price Stability and the Office of Management and Budget have also requested the Department of Transportation to supply cost assessments of all its actions along with their intended benefits. However, the Pinto court actions have, more recently, had the effect of discrediting any policy that can be justified only by analyses of this type. What has tended to happen since the mid-1970s is that the technique has become a part of the rhetoric used in lobbying activities, but it is not relied upon as the final determinant of decision making. The presentation of cost and benefit statistics has become merely a part of the battery of arguments used by lobbyists in presenting their case to the NHTSA and to public hearings. It is an important aspect of such debates in the USA that the parties tend to put forward detailed technical cases rather than manifestly political or moral arguments. In regard to court actions, it would appear that cost–benefit analyses do not provide manufacturers with sufficient defence against damages cases although such calculations can be used as supporting evidence. Altogether then, by the late 1970s, cost-benefit analysis had been generally accepted as an analytical technique, but with the status of one bargaining strategy among many others.

In 1979 Ford Motor Company was also facing a charge of 'reckless homicide' following another Pinto crash on 10 August 1978 (before the major recall) in which three young women died from burn injuries.[52] A criminal indictment against the company charged it with three counts of reckless homicide for knowingly selling a vehicle with a petrol tank that was 'inclined to rupture' in a rear-end collision. The maximum penalty for this offence is $10 000 for each count, but these fines would have been far less important than the symbolic precedent of a manufacturer being found guilty of a criminal offence and the effect this would have on future sales and new litigation. In fact, Ford was found not guilty of 'reckless homicide' and 'criminal recklessness' but the case raised many points about the suitability of criminal (as opposed to civil) litigation being brought in this context. Representatives of Ford have argued that such trials can only be damaging to the company (regardless of their outcome) and that they tend not to appreciate the inevitability of *some* 'balancing act' being conducted between costs and benefits. In addition, such cases tend to be emotionally charged and particularly susceptible to sensationalist reporting.[53] Overall, one can suggest that US damages cases over vehicle safety illustrate well the many tensions and complexities of assessing technological risk.

British judicial involvement of this type has been far less common. Although the Unfair Contract Terms Act of 1978 has effectively prevented manufacturers or proprietors disclaiming liability or responsibility for faulty products and unsafe services, this law has not been widely applied to road traffic safety cases. Under present British law, the equivalents to US 'product liability' are breach of warranty or implied warranty, failure to exercise reasonable care, or straightforward negligence.

The British Safety Council has been especially concerned with the workings of the law in this area. This organisation is very critical of the whole field of vehicle defect monitoring as it operates in Britain, but it sees legal action as being largely ineffective in the present situation. In the first place, there is general public ignorance of the present law so that the vehicle owner or injured party is unaware of the procedures that should be followed. The citizen will also find it difficult to discover whether the accident in question is merely an isolated case or rather the latest in a long sequence of occurrences. Manufacturers are naturally unwilling to disclose such information or to reveal details of previous research and testing relating to the design defect. There is, in addition, a distinct shortage of technical experts who are capable of linking an injury to a specific feature of the vehicle and also prepared to give evidence in court.[54] More fundamentally perhaps, the 'common sense' of road traffic accidents in Britain encourages the injured party to concentrate on human error as the underlying cause rather than to consider areas of engineering and vehicle design. There is some evidence that the present spate of product liability cases in the USA only came *after* the 'conceptual shift' of 1965–66.[55]

There are two specific changes in British law which could at least affect product liability cases of this type. The first would be the implementation of the Pearson Commission report of 1978, and the second the passing of an equivalent EEC proposal on 'Liability for Defective Products'. Each of these would make a manufacturer strictly liable for the safety of its own products and this would cover both defects arising out of errors in the production process and also those that are 'designed in'. The effect of this in Britain would be to shift the burden of responsibility on to the manufacturers for proving that their products were *not* defective, rather than forcing the injured party to prove negligence.

Discussion

It is quite clear from the above account that the apparently technical question of fuel system integrity and procedures for testing has become a subject for lobbying and the mobilisation of political power on a very large scale. This serves to underline once again the argument that the assessment of technological risk needs to be seen in its social and political context.

In addition to this, one can pick out other features of the US handling of this technological risk. Closely linked to the 'politicisation' of standard setting, there is the *adversarial* manner in which the debates have been conducted. Large industrial companies like Ford have stated their, at times, open opposition to 301, but these views have been matched by oppositional groups such as the Insurance Institute for Highway Safety, who have expressed their case in an equally forthright fashion. A classic pluralist account of this 'pressure-group battlefield' might suggest that the state – largely in the form of the NHTSA – has played the part of neutral mediator or referee between these colliding standpoints. However, such a role for the state cannot simply be assumed. On the one hand, it could be argued that the long delay before an update of 301 came into implementation suggests large concessions by the NHTSA to the interests of the motor manufacturers. Alternatively, the case could be made that the strengthening of 301 suggests an agency which was prepared to force the industry into taking an undesired course of action. This is an issue to which we shall return in Chapter 10. Before concluding this section it is important to offer a brief comparison with the equivalent British area of regulatory activity.

The British situation is complicated by the existence of three different sources of regulation. First, there is the Economic Commission for Europe (ECE), a subsidiary body of the United Nations; secondly, there is the European Economic Community (EEC), and thirdly, there is a British 'Construction and Use Regulation'. The strictest standard to have emerged from these national and international authorities is the ECE regulation[56] which followed the establishment of the updated 301 in the USA. This in itself represents an interesting phenomenon and one which has manifested itself in other cases than this – the tendency for countries to mimic US standards so as to ensure that barriers to trade are avoided. When one is considering relatively fundamental design features (rather than 'bolt-on' modifications), it becomes inevitable that manufacturers wishing to export to the United States will build vehicles that already conform to existing standards for safety (and, indeed, emission controls). The economic pressures for 'harmonisation' – especially when the industries are seeking to develop 'world cars' – have become important in ensuring a 'filter-down' effect from the USA to European, Japanese and other manufacturers.

The rear-impact test specified by the ECE standard is for 35–38 km per hour (approximately 22–24 mph) with a moving barrier which weighs 1000 kg. The US standard that we have discussed requires a *30* mph collision with a moving barrier of *1830 kg*, a substantially more stringent performance level. This means that, despite the 'filter-down' effect, a car which narrowly gains ECE approval will have no chance whatsoever of meeting US requirements whereas a vehicle built to FMVSS specifications will pass the European tests comfortably. In this situation, potential exporters to the USA need to construct vehicles that exceed the demands of existing European standards. Perhaps of greater concern to most Europeans, however, is the implication of a lower level of safety enforced in countries like Britain. Although manufacturers might argue that the US requirements go beyond what is 'reasonable',[57] there has been little or no public debate over this and certainly none of the 'public interest' lobbying that we have observed in the USA. The lack of broader participation in such issues has left the arguments over what is 'reasonable' to be interpreted by default in terms of the common perceptions of the motor industry and government officials.

There can be little doubt that British and European regulatory authorities have given relatively low priority to the topic of fuel system integrity. The major justification put forward for this is the small proportion of accidents which actually involve vehicle fires. The British Department of Environment (D.O.E.) has argued that only 54 people died in 1973, for example, from vehicle fires.[58] A 1973 study by the Accident Research Unit at the University of Birmingham reported that only 0.29 per cent of vehicle collisions (excluding those involving pedestrians or bicyclists) resulted in vehicle fires.[59] One might add that the respected Cooley study (discussed earlier) suggested that the updated 301 might only save 180–260 fatalities out of an annual total (at that time) of approximately 55 000 deaths in the United States (i.e. at best 0.5 per cent). However, the 1983 NHTSA report discussed previously has disputed such figures. Furthermore, even if one takes the relatively low statistics provided by the D.O.E. for vehicle fires as a cause of death, there is still the need to balance these annual fatalities against the economic costs of design changes such as those enforced through 301 in the USA. Whereas it is self-evident that costs need to be balanced against the potential fatality reduction, the *manner* in which such 'balancing acts' have been made in Britain and the European institutions (such as the EEC and ECE) is certainly open to challenge. At the very least, a careful and open consideration is needed in Britain of the lessons to be learnt from the implementation in the USA of FMVSS 301.

One other aspect of the US discussions over fire hazards which represents a sharp contrast with British policy making regards the involvement of the judiciary – especially through product liability cases. The relevance of such cases in the present context lies in the 'feedback' nature of judicial involvement; a court's determination that a vehicle's design does not meet the necessary standard of care cannot be ignored by manufacturers and car designers. Accordingly, product liability cases serve as a back-up to federal standards: they can concentrate on weaknesses in existing regulations, provide a detailed investigation of current practices and make information public that might otherwise remain confidential. Furthermore, the discussion of what is, or is not, an 'acceptable' level of risk can be transferred away from the legislature and manufacturers to be conducted, instead, in a rather different institutional location. The very existence of such a court network allows greater opportunities for the democratic control of hazardous technologies, especially in regard to the monitoring of Congressional activity and the resolution of any major weaknesses in existing procedures.

At the same time, product liability can be rather uneven and unpredictable in its effects. It must be considered that the Ford Pinto was in full compliance with all federal safety standards at the time of its manufacture. The company's cost–benefit analysis was condemned in court and yet this technique is used frequently by other manufacturers and regulatory agencies. Indeed, there seems little alternative to *some* type of cost–benefit analysis being conducted, whether formally or informally. Faced with the horror of an actual accident (as opposed to the hypothetical and nameless deaths of a risk-analytical exercise) juries seem naturally inclined to see those harmed as the victims of a corporate conspiracy. The unavoidably complex nature of any decision over 'acceptable risk' is ignored in the face of real human suffering and trauma. It is not surprising, therefore, that manufacturers have a strong distaste for such proceedings. Litigation was developed even further when Ford Motor Company was faced with a *criminal* charge of 'reckless homicide'.

There are also problems relating to evidence for product liability cases. There is a need for technical expertise to be presented before a lay audience and this may cause difficulties of comprehension and interpretation. Attorneys may well be working on a 'percentage' basis (i.e. contingency fees) so that there is a strong incentive to manipulate the evidence in order to mount a compelling argument for compensation. This may pose particular problems for the manufacturer. In the emotionally charged atmosphere that usually surrounds these cases, any adverse evidence will appear as proof of guilt, and large quantities of favourable test results can be dismissed as biased research. The general effect on sales of such cases must also be taken into account: such losses as a consequence of 'bad publicity' can outweigh even the largest damages claims. Moreover, the 'bad publicity' effect may persist despite the eventual dismissal of product liability claims.

Of course, oppositional groups would argue that this represents merely a brief reversal of the usual position where manufacturers have the monopoly of technical resources and can challenge the NHTSA to substantiate its case in a not dissimilar manner. Product liability cases are in effect a temporary transferral of the 'burden of proof' from the agency to the regulated industry. What such cases certainly do constitute is a separate forum for debate over the effectiveness and equity of national safety controls. However, court review does not make federal standard setting in any sense redundant. Product liability cases serve as a useful 'safety net' when standards prove weak or ineffective. They can also help to assess whether statutory duties are being performed. Nevertheless, each of these judicial activities depends on the prior existence of a specialised standard-setting authority. The point therefore needs to be stressed that Britain does not have such a system of 'dual authority' and may thus be at a distinct disadvantage in terms of the equity and effectiveness of policy making.

Notes and references

1   *Federal Register (FR)*. Vol. 31, No. 234, 3 December 1966, p.15221. See also: U.S. Department of Commerce, National Traffic Safety Agency, *Report on the Development of the Initial Federal Motor Vehicle Safety Standards issued 31 January 1967*. USGPO, Washington, DC; 17 March 1967).
2   *FR*. Vol. 32, No.200, 14 October 1967, p.14282.
3   *FR*. Vol. 34, No. 16, 24 January 1969, pp.1174–5.
4   *FR* Vol. 35, No. 169, 29 August 1970, p.13799.
5   US Congress. House Subcommittee on Commerce and Finance *Hearings*, 29–31 May 1973. (USGPO, Washington, DC; 1973).
6   In fact one of the vehicles was the Ford Pinto, although the IIHS were not at that time aware of any difference between it and the other vehicles.
7   Fairchild Hiller Experimental Safety Car Study, Phase 1, *Final Report*. DOT Contract No. FH 11–6820, 26 August 1968.
8   Siegel, A. W. and Nahum, A. M. Vehicle postcollision considerations in *International Automobile Safety Compendium* (SAE, New York; 1970).
9   *NTSB–HAR–71–3*, 20 January 1971.
10   Johnson, N. B. An assessment of automotive fuel system fire hazards. Dynamic Sciences, *Final Report*, DOT FH 11–7579, December 1971.
11   NTSB–HAR–72–1, 15 March 1972. *NTSB–HAR–72–4*, 6 July 1972.
12   Quoted in *Status Report*, Vol. **8**, No. 13, 25 June 1973, p.1.
13   US National Commission on Fire Prevention and Control. *America Burning* (USGPO, Washington, DC; 1973).

14   Quoted in *Status Report*, Vol. **8**, No. (17), 10 September 1973.
15   *FR* Vol. 38, No. 160, 20 August 1973, p. 22397.
16   Standard 301. *Docket No. 73–20*. Notice 1 ; 010 15 October 1973.
17   *loc. cit.*; 007, 4 October 1973.
18   *loc. cit.*; 014, 15 October 1973.
19   *Status Report*, Vol. 9, No. 3, 6 February 1974, p.2.
20   See *Status Report*, Vol. 9, No. 12, 18 June 1974, p.8.
21   *FR* Vol. 39, No. 56, 21 March 1974, pp.10586–88 and 10588–90.
22   *Ibid.* p. 10587.
23   Cooley, P. Fire in motor vehicle accidents. *Proc. Fourth International Congress on Automotive Safety*, 14–16 July 1975. (USDOT, Washington, DC; 1975), p.105.
24   Evidence for this has been taken from a variety of sources – notably Dowie, M. Pinto madness. *Mother Jones*, September/October 1977, and interviews with NHTSA officials and pressure group members.
25   *Status Report*, Vol. 8, No. 23, 20 December 1973, p. 7.
26   Cooley, P. Fire in motor vehicle accidents, p. 122. (See reference 24.)
27   For 1972–75 $200 000 was the official NHTSA figure for the value of a human life. This had been determined by an agency report in 1972. NHTSA, *Societal Cost of Motor Vehicle Accidents*. Preliminary Report. (USDOT, Washington, DC; 1972).
28   Dowie, M. Pinto madness. *Mother Jones*, September/October 1977, pp. 9–10 (reprint).
29   Interviews at NHTSA, March 1979.
30   *FR.* Vol. 40, No. 200, 15 October 1975, pp.48352–55.
31   *FR.* Vol. 43, No. 33, 16 February 1978, p.6865; *FR.* Vol. 43, No. 121, 22 June 1978, p.26814. Exemption granted until 1 March 1981.
32   *FR* Vol. 43, No. 123, 26 June 1978, p.27630; *FR.* Vol. 43, No. 205, 23 October 1978, p.49339. Exemption granted until 1 September 1980.
33   See *Status Report*, Vol. 13, No. 7, 31 May 1978, pp. 9–10. Also: *FR.* Vol. 43, No. 95, 11 May 1978, p. p.20292. *FR.* Vol. 43, No. 106, 1 June 1978, p.23780. *FR.* Vol. 43, No. 113, 12 June 1978, p.25400. *Status Report*. Vol. 13, No. 16, 17 November 1978, p.9. *FR.* Vol. 43, No. 231, 30 November 1978, p.56123.
34   *Status Report*, Vol. 14, No. 17, 28 November 1979, p. 1.
35   *Status Report*, Vol. 15, No. 10, 25 June 1980, p.2.
36   *Status Report*, Vol. 16, No. 2, 9 February 1981, p.10.
37   *Status Report*, Vol. 18, No. 2, 1 February 1983, pp. 2–3.
38   Levine, E. J. and Cornwell, Jr. E. E. *An Introduction to American Government* (Macmillan, New York; 1968), pp. 125–6.
39   Larsen vs. General Motors Corporation. 391. F 2d. 495 (CA 8 1968).
40   Wheeler, M. E. Product liability, civil or criminal – the Pinto litigation. *The Forum* (American Bar Association). **17**, Fall 1981, p.258.
41   Goodman, R. M. and the Center for Auto Safety. *Automobile Design Liability*. 2nd Edn. (The Lawyers Co-operative Publishing Co., New York, and Bancroft-Whitney, San Francisco; 1983).
42   Thee examples are taken from the *Automotive Litigation Reporter*. Published twice monthly and available from Andrews Publications, Inc.

Edgemont, PA. 19028.

43 *The Sunday Times*, 12 February 1978, p.1.

44 *Mother Jones* is a monthly American magazine published by the Foundation for National Progress. It is named after a pioneer US socialist, Mary Harris 'Mother' Jones (1830–1930).

45 Dowie, M. Pinto madness. *Mother Jones*, September/October 1977, p.1.

46 *The Sunday Times*, 12 February 1978, p.4.

47 Ford Motor Company internal memorandum: *Fatalities Associated with Crash-induced Fuel Leakage and Fires*. Reproduced in the following accounts: Dowie, M. Pinto madness. *Mother Jones*, September/October 1977, p.6. *The Sunday Times*, 12 February 1978, p.1. CIS. *Ford – anti report*, p.43. Available from CIS, 9 Poland Street, London W1.

48 The jury of the Grimshaw case used the same figures to calculate that Ford had saved $100 million by not installing a safer fuel tank, therefore any award of less than that sum would not be 'punitive'.

49 Dowie, M. Pinto madness. *Mother Jones*, September/October 1977, pp. 8–9.

50 *FR* Vol. 39, No. 56, 21 March 1974, p.10587.

51 Public Law 92–513. 92d Congress. S. 976. October 20, 1972.

52 McCann, H. Where does blame begin? *Detroit News*, 28 January 1979, p.1.

53 Wheeler, M. E. Product liability, civil or criminal – the Pinto litigation, pp.250–65. (See reference 42.)

54 See: British Safety Council. *Second Report to Members of Parliament on Vehicle Defects*, April 1979.

55 Little, J. W. Modes in standard setting; judicial versus legislative, in *Proc. Fourth International Congress on Automotive Safety*, 14–16 July 1975. (USDOT, Washington, DC; 1975), p. 389.

56 UN ECE. Agreement concerning the adoption of uniform conditions of approval and reciprocal recognition of approval for motor vehicle equipment and parts, Regulation No. 34. *Uniform Provisions Concerning the Approval of Vehicles with Regard to the Prevention of Fire Risks*. E/ECE/TRANS/505, 25 July 1975. See also: EEC Council Directive 70/221/EEC. *Official Journal of the European Communities* (OJ), L76, 6 April 1970, p.23.

57 Rogers, K. Saab story in perspective. *Care on the Road*, December 1979, pp. 4–9.

58 Department of the Environment. *United Kingdom Fire and Loss Statistics, 1971* (HMSO, London; 1974). *Idem. Road Accidents. Great Britain 1973* (HMSO, London; 1974).

59 Gloyns, P.F., Mackay, G. M. and Chatterjee, S. *Project Report on Post-collision Vehicle Fires*. Accident Research Unit, University of Birmingham. (Mimeo.), April 1975. This report also contains an excellent review of the literature on vehicle fires and a useful bibliography.

Chapter 9

Windscreen 'safety glass' : technological uncertainty in Britain

The cases of FMVSS 301 and 208 have permitted an exploration of the US regulatory system and, in particular, a consideration of the realities of post-1966 rulemaking. The example of 'safety glass' allows a similar discussion of British procedures although, as we shall see, European developments are central to such an analysis. The specific controversy examined here has centred on an assessment of the merits of two main varieties of glass, laminated and toughened. It is worth while at this stage to provide a brief description of their characteristics.

Laminated glass was the first of these products to be developed. Prior to the innovation of this glass,[1] motor vehicles were fitted with plate glass, which had some manifestly dangerous properties. A frequent consequence of a collision between road vehicles was the ejection of the screen from its frame, causing a shower of sharp splinters and, consequently, a number of injuries to both motorists and pedestrians. Glass-related injuries were, in fact, one of the earliest road traffic safety problems to emerge.

At the 1906 Motor Show a part-time inventor exhibited a laminated screen based on a 'glass sandwich' of two sheets of plate glass separated by a celluloid filling and balsam. The design aroused little commercial interest at that time but, in 1912, the Triplex Safety Glass Company was formed to market a similar idea. Triplex still produce laminated screens today and, although manufacturing techniques and design features have changed considerably, the basic concept of a 'glass sandwich' remains unaltered.

From the 1930s onwards, toughened windscreen glass began to appear. The heat tempering of this product gives it its impact resistance properties, and the fact that it consists of only a single sheet means that it can be sold at a considerably lower price than its main rival, the laminated screen.

The Traffic Act of 1930 effectively banned the use of plate glass in windscreens by compelling new private vehicles to be fitted with 'safety glass' by 1 January 1932, and all cars to conform by 1 January 1937. Later legislation specified that safety glass should be used for all car windows. Safety glass is defined as follows by British law: 'a glass which, after fracture, gives fragments which are less liable to cause severe cuts than those of ordinary glass'.[2]

Since the 1930s, laminated and toughened screens have remained the only two means of compliance with the law. By 1934 Triplex were selling more 'toughened' than 'laminate' and the disparity in sales in Britain has increased ever since. A 1961 survey of car windscreens[3] suggested that, for cars registered before the end of 1946, toughened glass outnumbered laminate by a ratio of 3:1. For the later dates of registration, the ratio increased to 8:1. One estimate for 1975 was that 90 per cent of vehicles on the British roads had toughened windscreens.[4]

The major reason for the popularity of toughened screens is lower cost. Estimations of price difference vary according to whether one takes the price of standard fitting by the manufacturer or individual replacement charges. The TRRL estimate[5] is that a laminated screen should be about twice as expensive as a toughened one, but this assumes mass fitting rather than the current situation. At present the replacement cost of a laminated windscreen is roughly three times that of the toughened variety. Against this cost difference must be weighed the fact that, according to the TRRL, toughened screens are replaced on average twice as often. This is attributable to the tendency of toughened glass to shatter entirely when cracked by, for example, a piece of grit thrown up by forward traffic. This characteristic is not shared by a laminate; in most cases the breakage will be limited to this immediate area of impact and, very often, no loss of vision or inconvenience will follow.

The cost advantages of toughened screens have meant that the majority of British cars have been fitted with these by the manufacturers. The traditional exceptions to this have been luxury vehicles, e.g. Rolls-Royce, Bentley, Aston Martin, Jaguar and the most expensive models in various mass-produced ranges. However, there has been a tendency in recent years for car manufacturers to move over to laminated glass throughout their model range so that the Volkswagen–Audi group fit these screens as standard, as do Volvo and Saab. General Motors have announced that they will fit laminated screens to all Vauxhalls and Opels from 1982 onwards. Altogether, in 1983–84 around 65–75 per cent of new cars in Britain are fitted with laminated screens. At the same time, BL have altered their previous policy by reverting to toughened glass windscreens on certain models of the Metro and Acclaim which previously had laminated screens. They justify this switch on the grounds that customers would prefer their money to be spent on more visible additions to the vehicles, for example a higher quality of interior trim.[6] This issue of the relationship between safety and cost has been at the nub of the windscreen debate in Britain and the EEC.

The major case that has been put forward for the fitting of laminated glass rests on the claim that it is superior in terms of occupant protection. The two varieties of windscreen rely on rather different principles for their safety characteristics. Toughened glass has a high resistance to breakage and will only shatter into relatively blunt fragments, i.e. the fracture planes will be of approximately 90°. Laminated screens are designed so that on impact the fractured pieces will be held in place by the interlayer and the edges of the glass are not exposed. Various modifications can be built into individual brands of windscreen glass, but basically the characteristics and general principles of damage resistance remain the same for each variety.

The technical controversy over windscreen glass surrounds the assessment of the relative effectiveness of these two design principles. This question has divided the two main British research groups, based at the TRRL and the Accident Research Unit of Birmingham University. Indeed, the Department of Transport's recommendations – supporting the continued use of toughened screens – have been at odds with the bulk of European and US opinion, and this has been reflected in the discussion of this question within the EEC. A major concern of this case study will be to discuss the relationship between the available technical expertise and the views put forward in negotiations on this issue by government officials.

Another important theme of this case study is the inaccessibility to the 'outsider' of the British policy-making processes. One facet of this problem is the difficulty of gaining satisfactory information about the lobbying activities of various groups. In the USA the openly adversarial operation of the political system forces pressure groups to make their positions on a specific issue publicly known and it is normal practice that this position will be reinforced by the production of appropriate documents and the marshalling of corroborating evidence

– including technical reports. Likewise, it is customary for the appropriate agency of the government to prepare its own case and publish an assessment of the petitions that have been received. In Britain, however, many groups, including the government, prefer not to make their stance on particular issues generally known and, provided the topic does not emerge as a major controversy, they are able to lobby and bargain with a high degree of confidentiality and without the necessity of justifying individual actions to the general public. Consequently, as in the case to be examined here, it can be very difficult for the outsider to these processes to pinpoint the origin of specific arguments or to clarify the role of certain pressure groups, e.g. the vehicle manufacturers, who are directly concerned with a specific area of policy making.

This problem of access to information must be acknowledged, although every effort has been made to utilise all available sources. At the same time, this feature should not be seen as an isolated phenomenon, but rather as an integral part of the British political system. The informal cooperation that often exists between British civil servants and industry officials does not lend itself to the continuous preparation and publication of policy statements, which may have the effect of diminishing each party's flexibility. The relationship is not seen as an open battle, but rather as a partnership in which the government is anxious to identify with the manufacturers' concerns and achieve agreement without confrontation. This two-sided relationship is considered legitimate because of the government's claim to be the custodian of public interest. Hence 'public interest' pressure groups of the type found in the USA are seen by both government and industry officials as superfluous in many contexts.

Political debate in Europe over windscreen glass: the Council directive

The main forum in which the British assessment of the relative merits of toughened and laminated glass has been argued is the EEC. The issue forms part of the general European trend towards the elimination of technical obstacles to trade covered by Article 100 of the EEC Charter; the specific area of type approval for motor vehicles was the subject of a 1970 Council Directive.[7] The Council directive relating to windscreen glass proposed the compulsory fitting of laminated glass in all EEC countries. It developed as an idea from 1969 onwards and was then discussed by various representatives of the separate national administrations and by the transport ministers of member countries. In drawing up the specifications for a draft directive, the Commission consulted with one established advisory body, the Working Group on the 'Elimination of technical barriers to trade, motor vehicles' and one specially created technical body, the Study Group on 'safety glass'. Government officials and industry representatives predominated in the membership of each of these groups. Although some disagreement seems to have existed within these bodies (the proceedings are kept secret) the Commission decided that the proposal merited submission to the Council of Ministers for formal appraisal. In fact, the Commission submitted two documents to the Council. The first was a general discussion of the issues involved[8] and the second a detailed draft directive complete with precise specifications for testing procedures.[9] It is this 1972 proposal for mandatory fitting of laminated glass which still awaited adoption in 1983.

The discussion document included an assessment of each type of safety glass and made a very strong case for the superiority of laminated glass (and, more specifically, one variety of laminate – high penetration resistant glass (HPR)). The major conclusions of the report were that, first, laminated HPR glass prevents loss of visibility and the consequent dangers of this when a screen is struck by an external object. Secondly, laminated glass reduces damage to vehicle occupants in a collision, in terms of both head impact and eye injury. In support of these conclusions, the Commission cited seven technical reports which had considered the relative safety of each glass.

There is not the space here to review these research reports in any detail. It should be noted, however, that the studies were drawn from different nations and that the techniques used also varied widely. For example, a Wayne State University project was based on laboratory dummy testing so as to calculate the risk of brain damage in a 50 km/h impact with a fixed object, and also to estimate the extent of lacerations to vehicle occupants.[10] A rather different investigation by the Accident Research Unit at the University of Birmingham and the Trauma Research Group of the University of California used British and US field data of actual collisions to contrast the two glass types.[11] Despite these differences in style and national setting, each of the reports came out in favour of laminated windscreens on safety grounds.[12]

These seven studies are, in fact, very representative of world-wide opinion on the merits of both types of windscreen glass. In line with these findings a number of countries have mandated the use of laminated glass: USA, Canada, Sweden, Finland, Denmark, Russia, Czechoslovakia, Brazil, Switzerland, Italy, Belgium and Norway.

On the question of economic considerations, the Commission report argued that there were no major difficulties. All the large glass manufacturers in the EEC (at that time a total of ten) had a licence to produce laminated windscreens. However, official statistics revealed that 72.5 per cent of EEC cars were fitted with toughened glass by the vehicle manufacturers, i.e. 5 800 000 vehicles out of a total yearly production of 8 000 000. Clearly a substantial lead time would have to be allowed for the glass industry to switch its production capacities. The report argued that the average increase in the total cost of a vehicle would be 0.6 per cent which, according to the Commission, should not prove prohibitive.

The Commission concluded its report by emphasising the importance of the measure and advocating two deadlines. The first, for cars capable of travelling over 130 km/h, was 1 October 1974. For all other cars, the directive's proposed implementation date was 30 September 1976. As a final comment, the document noted the position of two countries which were then about to join the European Community. By Norwegian law all cars registered after 1 January 1971 had to be fitted with laminated screens, so no objection could be anticipated from that quarter. However, the Commission was aware of the hostility of one potential newcomer:

For its part, the United Kingdom has raised several doubts on the conclusions of the studies summarised in the present statement of intent and indicates that it would be useful to them to undertake several complementary studies.[13]

In fact, British 'complementary studies' had been going on for some time at the TRRL and these will now be examined. It should be noted that, as a British commentator pointed out in 1972, the Department of Environment's cost–benefit analyses suggested that even a 100 per cent effective laminated glass screen would not be acceptable. The D.O.E.'s calculation seemed to be that, even if laminated screens could lead to the disappearance of *all* car windscreen injuries, the cost of switching from one screen to the other would still outweigh the benefits by a factor of 3.[14]

This analysis estimated the cost of implementation in Britain as being £15 million. The British opposition to the directive was not based on this argument alone but also on a programme of research which had been carried out at the TRRL over a period of more than ten years. In the 1970s the TRRL studies stood alone against the international assessments of the greater safety of laminated glass. An extensive literature search has failed to discover any major research team which has supported the laboratory's pro-toughened line in recent years. This isolation certainly merits investigation.

TRRL investigations of windshield performance

The earliest report on this question prepared by the research arm of the Ministry of Transport (then known simply as the Road Research Laboratory) appeared in 1961.[15] The author, R. D. Lister, compared the characteristics of both glass types in regard to the effect of impact with the occupant's head in a collision. The laminated glass being produced at that time consisted of two plate-glass sheets held together by a polyvinyl butyral interlayer (modern laminates do not use plate glass). Changes have also been made in the thickness of the interlayer used (see below) since that time. Lister tested the force required to shatter each type of windscreen and examined the consequent glass splinters. The overall conclusion was in favour of toughened glass screens. Although Lister noted that toughened glass has a greater propensity to shatter when hit by small pieces of stone, etc., this was dismissed as being 'troublesome' but not a 'serious cause' of accidents. The TRRL have in fact continued to argue that the sudden loss of vision caused by a shattering toughened windscreen is not a hazard of any proportion. Another study by the laboratory, reported on in 1979 by the Under-Secretary of State for Transport, concluded that out of 2130 accidents which had been investigated, only three had followed windscreen failure.[16]

The next major paper on windscreen safety to emerge from the TRRL was published in 1968.[17] Again, this gave strong support to toughened glass. In fact, the study concluded that occupants in the front seats of cars with laminated screens ran a three to five times greater risk of being injured by glass than those in vehicles with toughened screens. This study was essentially complementary to

Lister's earlier report. Although in agreement over their conclusions, Lister's results had been based on laboratory testing whereas this paper relied on a statistical analysis of 640 accidents which had occurred between 1955 and 1964.

Following the 1968 report, a number of other TRRL studies on this theme appeared,[18] but the next substantial comparative assessment was not published until 1975.[19] This report set out to update the 1968 analysis by including a new type of laminate which had made its appearance in 1965–66 but which had not been included in the 1968 study. This type, known as high penetration resistant (HPR) glass, had an interlayer of 0.76 mm (0.03 in) rather than the earlier 0.38 mm (0.015 in). The effect of this change was roughly to double the head velocity required to rupture the interlayer and this could be expected to reduce the number of glass-related injuries. It is generally accepted that less injuries will occur if a screen does not fracture. The occupant is then contained within the vehicle and is prevented from injuring her/himself on external fixtures like the bonnet or roadside; the obvious dangers of flying glass splinters are also eliminated.

The Grattan and Hobbs study was a statistical analysis based on 920 seriously injured occupants seen between 1965 and 1975. Of these occupants, 20 per cent had been injured by the windscreen. This paper was slightly more cautious in its conclusions than earlier RRL reports based on the 0.38 mm interlayer screen, but it nevertheless came out in favour of toughened windscreens. Grattan and Hobbs argued that, although the number of cases investigated which involved laminated-glass-related injuries were small (a total of fifteen), it was possible to conclude that the risk of head injury was greater with HPR laminated glass than with toughened glass. The paper also presented the *type* of injury caused by each glass type. The commonest injury of a severe nature (i.e. 'more severe than minor') was facial laceration. Just over one-third of the toughened-glass-related injuries consisted of lacerations of over 1-in length; 50 per cent of laminate-linked injuries were lacerations of this type. The other windscreen-related injuries noted were concussion, which was more closely linked with HPR laminated than toughened screens, and, less frequently, fracture to a facial bone or eye injury.

A further source of information about the TRRL position in regard to windscreen glass is the leaflets issued by the laboratory in 1975.[20] The 1975 leaflet began with the statement that 14 per cent of the 44 000 car occupants in Britain who are killed or seriously injured each year suffer head injury owing to head impacts with the windscreen. A comparison of the relative merits of each glass type followed under a number of specific headings: 'Fracture by road stone' (laminated appeared as superior), 'Accident injury' (very little real difference), 'Reduction of injury' (seat-belt wear seen as the way forward) and 'Cost effectiveness' (strongly favouring toughened screens). The cost-effective argument was used by the Department of the Environment and the Department of Transport on more than one occasion and it is worth examining its basis although, in fact, the cost-effectiveness analysis presented in this leaflet is about as unproblematic as any such exercise could be. The argument is as follows. Given the TRRL evidence that 'Both screens probably produce similar overall medical costs resulting from accident injury' and that 'the universal (i.e. British) use of laminated screens would probably result in an increased overall cost of £10 000 000 per year', it is not sense to make laminated screens compulsory on the grounds of either injury reduction or cost. It was also asserted that mandatory seat-belt laws would diminish the importance of windscreen safety as an issue in any case (because of the reduced number of head impacts with the screen).

The 1976 TRRL leaflet[21] was similarly based on a comparative analysis. It examined first of all the characteristics of each in regard to fracture during normal usage (i.e. with no collision involved); in this area laminated is clearly superior. The analysis continued with a comparison based on three different scenarios: minority use of seat belts (as was then the case); majority use of seat belts (as would presumably occur under mandatory seat-belt laws); and vehicle redesign. At present, laminated glass is seen as causing a higher percentage of facial lacerations and concussion. The cost-effectiveness analysis used in 1975 is added, making a very strong case for toughened glass. With regard to mandatory seat-belt use, the TRRL position was that windscreen-related injuries would no longer be a cause for serious concern.

The leaflet went on to argue that, even without majority seat-belt usage, vehicle redesign could 'substantially reduce lacerative, concussive and eye injuries related to windscreens'. This conclusion is especially interesting because it represents one of the few occasions when a *passive* approach to road traffic safety has been advocated by an official British source. A number of specific vehicle design features were proposed. One of these was modification of the fascia and leg restraint area to prevent occupants from being levered down on to the windscreen. At present the occupant's legs are normally retained by the vehicle interior so that the body pivots around this area and the head travels *down* the plane of the screen rather than hitting it at 90°. The effect is for the head and face to collide with a deep 'column of glass crystals' with obvious results. Another design suggestion was for lower windscreen edges to be recessed so as to conceal pieces of glass retained in the windscreen surrounds. This feature is now included in the British Leyland Princess model.

The overall conclusion of the 1976 pamphlet was as follows:

The general use of seat belts and the design of improved layouts of fascias around toughened screens should so reduce injury that the choice between toughened, HPR laminated and thin toughened/laminated screens could be made almost entirely on cost and convenience grounds rather than on injury considerations.[22]

The 'thin toughened/laminated' screen referred to represents an attempt to combine the strengths of both types of screen. It utilises toughened glass for the outside layers and a 0.76-mm HPR interlayer. This design can be seen in the Triplex Ten-Twenty screen once fitted as standard to the Rover saloon range and the Princess 2. Triplex claim that this unique design can reduce facial lacerations by up to 99 per cent.[23] More will be said about the Ten-Twenty later.

It can be seen from this account that the TRRL has consistently taken a pro-toughened-glass line since the 1960s, despite changes in the design of laminated glass. This view has been shared by Department of Transport officials and various ministers so that, for example, the Under-Secretary of State for Transport could claim in 1979 that there was 'insufficient justification' for any legislation that made laminated glass compulsory.[16] Of course, this view has been arrived at not only through consultation with the TRRL, but also by discussions with the glass and vehicle industries. Certainly, the government laboratory's technical assessment alone has not decided the case, but it has undoubtedly been influential and the Department of Transport has not hesitated to use the TRRL reports as support for their case against the EEC directive on windscreen glass.

While considering the TRRL research findings, the confrontation within Britain between this group and another research team which is partly sponsored by the Department of Transport should be noted. Dr G. M. Mackay of the Accident Research Unit (ARU) at Birmingham

University has, along with other members of the group (notably Dr P. Gloyns, now a Director of Vehicle Safety Consultants Ltd), been the major critic of the TRRL's assessment of windscreen safety in Britain. Two of Mackay's papers have already been noted.[24] The 1975 TRRL publication made frequent reference to this disparity of opinion and attempted to account for it in terms of sample bias and faulty methodology on the part of Mackay. In 1978, Mackay published his own critique of the TRRL studies,[25] focusing on the 1975 paper as this was the only one of the series of reports which compared toughened glass with the newer HPR type of laminate.

Mackay made a number of critical points about the 1975 TRRL study. He pointed to the striking difference between these results and those of other research workers. He also questioned the validity of the methodology used by Grattan and Hobbs. In particular, Mackay claimed that the TRRL researchers had actively sought out laminate-injured individuals so as to 'balance' the sample. The TRRL was additionally criticised for studying only those who had been injured by a collision and were in-patients in a hospital. The 1975 study was also based on a small sample of laminate-fitted vehicles — only 37 for a ten-year data collection period. Overall, Mackay reached the following assessment:

... the TRRL study concluded that the risks of head injury both of the lacerative type and the concussive type were greater for HPR laminated than for toughened glass windscreens. This conclusion is at variance with all other recent studies, but the methodology of the sampling of cases mentioned above, provide reasons for this unusual finding.[26]

Certainly, Mackay's critique of the TRRL research makes a powerful case for the superiority in safety terms of laminated glass. The Accident Research Unit has also continued in its advocacy of HPR laminate since 1978 and, furthermore, has argued that legislation would remove the financial handicap in terms of vehicle price to the individual manufacturer in fitting such screens. In contrast, the TRRL has consistently rejected the case for laminated glass although it can be seen that, as in the 1976 leaflet, their argument has shifted away from opting for toughened glass because of its technical superiority and towards the assertion that both types of glass are similar as regards safety, but can be easily differentiated on the grounds of cost-effectiveness. However, even this change in the TRRL case still leaves a large disparity between that group and the bulk of world-wide research.

One of the major problems for the technical assessment of road traffic safety is the establishment of a valid 'proof'. There are two basic methodologies to be used by any attempt at achieving this. The first, as in Lister's 1961 report, relies on *laboratory experimentation*. This is also the principle behind 'performance' testing as practised in the USA. One specific type of accident is simulated and then studied in very close detail so as to gain a large amount of information about the causation and consequences of one particular incident. If necessary, an attempt at replication can be made under the same carefully controlled circumstances. The whole intention of this approach is to discover the structural characteristics of a particular event and then generalise from this to all similar events.

The second methodology that can be utilised relies on an *epidemiological* style of reasoning. This approach is quite different from the laboratory-based technique and attempts to gather data about whole populations of events rather than single occurrences. The epidemiological approach has been used extensively by the ARU and also by the TRRL, although the statistical validity of the latter's sampling may well, as Mackay argues, be open to question.

The two methodologies can be complementary in certain circumstances but neither is capable of producing an absolute proof. There is always scope for questioning the general validity of any laboratory test: in what sense does the test correspond to a real accident; how are the injuries to be assessed; if dummies are used, how lifelike are they? Likewise, epidemiological studies can be criticised for sample bias and general methodological weaknesses. In this situation of technical uncertainty – which is very similar to the circumstances of many assessments of technological risk, e.g. toxic chemicals or radiation hazards – there is a wide margin for disagreement, and also for those parties that have a financial stake in a particular issue to utilise this uncertainty for their own benefit.[27] The social interests that have been operating in the case of windscreen glass will now be examined. However, it should be stressed at this stage that the approach that will be adopted in this chapter is not based on a 'conspiracy theory' of industry officials deliberately selecting out only that evidence which is suitable to their case, or of research teams 'selling out' to outside interests. The argument is rather that a 'constitutive' theory of knowledge production should be adopted in which the relationship between technical expertise and its social context is seen as being more complex than a use/abuse model would suggest.[28]

Political debate in Europe: discussions of the directive

Following the appearance of the Commission's proposal for a directive on safety glass, the President of the Council of the European Communities requested the European Parliament to deliver its opinion. Before Parliament debated the issue, however, it was sent to four existing committees for discussion, all four committees consisting of members of the European Parliament. On 9 October 1972, the proposal was referred to the Legal Affairs Committee, the Committee on Regional Policy and Transport, and the Committee on Social Affairs and Employment. On 21 December of that year it was also submitted to the Committee on Economic and Monetary Affairs. The directive was approved by all four committees and the findings were announced in April 1973.[29]

The first parliamentary debate on the issue took place in May 1973.[30] Bermani (Legal Affairs Committee) and Seefeld (Regional Policy and Transport Committee) put forward a strong case for the directive, and no real opposition was heard. The debate was brief and totally favourable to the proposal. However, little political action followed the enthusiasm given to the measure in both committee and parliamentary debate stages. In December 1973 the Council on Industrial Policy of the EEC resolved that a decision on safety glass would finally be made by July 1974 at the latest.

By February 1974, at least the Socialist Group was beginning to voice concern over the lack of EEC activity on mandatory laminated windscreens and an oral question to the European Parliament was put by Seefeld and Bermani. The question is worth quoting in full as it clearly portrays their assessment of the situation.

In connection with the proposal for a directive concerning safety glass for use in motor vehicles on which the European Parliament delivered a favourable opinion on 7 May 1973, the Commission is asked,

1. When can the Council be expected to adopt the proposal?
2. Is it true that differences exist among Member States?
3. Which Member States are opposing the introduction of this proposal?
4. What grounds do these States advance against the adoption of the directive?

5. What does the Commission intend to do to ensure that its proposal is adopted?[31]

In particular, Seefeld attacked the Committee of Permanent Representatives (CREP) for blocking the proposal by suggesting to the Commission 'at the last minute incomprehensible amendments'. The German delegation to CREP had put forward a proposal that technical specifications for both types of glass should be improved and that motor manufacturers should still be given the choice between he two. CREP have the power to block any measure by asking the Commission to work out a new proposal or indicating to the Commission that an existing proposal will not be passed by the Council of Ministers. The members of CREP are civil servants who represent the countries of the EEC. Seefeld's argument was that CREP was far more concerned about industrial interests than about road traffic safety.

The reply to Seefeld and Bermani was made by Gundelach on behalf of the European Commission. Gundelach stated the Commission's determination to have the directive passed by the Council of Ministers but pointed out that Germany and Britain were against the proposal. Bermani followed Gundelach's speech with an even stronger attack on the way in which 'commercial interests' were 'being put before personal safety'.

It is fair to say that Bermani's and Seefeld's speeches accurately reflected the mistrust of CREP and the Council of Ministers which was present in the minds of many of the politicians involved in this issue. The Parliament had passed the proposed directive unanimously but now it was being blocked at a later stage in its legislative progress. In fact, the next major European debate on the issue was not until January 1976, by which time the opposition to compulsory laminated glass usage was proving itself insurmountable. Of course, a major source of this opposition – according to some accounts *the* major source – was the British Department of Transport. One document that goes some way towards clarifying the British stance on safety glass is a 1975 House of Lords Select Committee report on the proposed EEC directive.[32] This document is unusual in the context of British regulatory activity over road traffic safety because it did allow the views of the major concerned parties to be put on public record.

The select committee report divided into four sections. Each consisted of evidence given by a particular individual or group that was directly involved in the discussion, i.e. the Department of Environment, the glass industry, Dr G. M. Mackay, and the TRRL. As a preface to the evidence, the committee noted that discussions of the directive within the European Council were unlikely to be resumed in the near future.

Before the Select Committee the Department of Environment defended their position on windscreen safety by using the TRRL reports to question the performance of HPR laminated glass. The officials estimated that the proposed EEC directive would cost Britain around £20 million a year and this would certainly not be cost effective. In addition to this familiar argument, the Department of Environment produced a second reason for their opposition to the proposal. The D.O.E. case was that there was insufficient production capacity in Britain to produce laminated screens at the required volume without a long lead time for the glass makers. This argument is one that has been repeatedly used by motor manufacturers in the United States to delay impending legislation. It is interesting in this case that the argument was being made, not by glass manufacturers, but by the government department responsible (at that time) for road traffic safety. In fact, the testimony of the glass industry showed only enthusiasm for the directive. The glass manufacturers appeared totally convinced of the superiority of HPR laminate and, for example, the Pilkington Group (90 per cent of whose windscreen output was toughened glass) stated:

. . . because of the overwhelming evidence on the safety issue, we believe that this legislation will have to be supported, and that we will have to make a substantial investment in plant and machinery, and this we are willing to do.[33]

Pilkington actually estimated that the 'substantial investment' involved would amount to £25 million but considered that this would be acceptable if it were spread over a period of approximately five-and-a-half years. Furthermore, the glass makers argued that the compulsory fitting of laminated glass would add only £10 to the price of a new car. The glass manufacturers' views were largely echoed by the motor manufacturers' representatives, who supported laminated glass on safety grounds and argued that an EEC directive would ensure that all companies acted together and thus would avoid any price handicap. However, the testimony of the glass industry representatives concluded on a fascinating point when they were asked why, in their opinion, the Department of Environment's judgement was so different from their own.

The explanation is largely that the Road Research Laboratory has its own view, as part of their general accident investigations, which is confined to an area close to the Road Research Laboratory. They have had great difficulty in finding a significant number of injury accidents with the new type of laminated screen over several years, and have only found a few examples, because laminated windscreens are so rarely fitted as standard, and toughened screens are generally fitted.[34]

The next witness, Dr G. M. Mackay, was included in the hearings only at the strong insistence of the glass industry representatives. That the glass manufacturers should want Mackay's pro-laminated screen evidence to be heard leaves little doubt about their own support for the EEC directive (provided, of course, sufficient lead time was allowed).

At the hearing Mackay reviewed his own research findings and argued very strongly in favour of the directive. By this time, the Select Committee had become very aware of the fundamental disagreement that existed over the issue.

Our difficulty . . . is trying to resolve something on which the Department of Environment has one view and the EEC has another, the EEC's view being very similar to yours.[35]

In the final session, three TRRL representatives were questioned. By this time, the Select Committee had heard a pro-HPR case being made by the glass industry and Dr Mackay directly, and by the Consumers' Association, the SMMT and the motoring organisations in written evidence. The TRRL spokesmen proceeded by re-emphasising their own technical assessment that laminated glass causes slightly higher injury rates. At this point, Lord Hinton of Bankside expressed the committee's very real confusion:

I am finding that the evidence is so conflicting that I hardly know where to start . . . We have got two who give one story and another one who gives a completely different story. I am at the moment simply finding this extremely puzzling.[36]

The Committee did, however, express citicism of the very small data base on which the TRRL findings were produced. Out of the 555 injuries in toughened-screen-fitted vehicles only 123 injuries could actually be related to the screen. For the HPR laminate sample only 15 cases of screen-related injuries were seen.

The Select Committee did not reach any final conclusions, but its report did serve to pinpoint the basic arguments being propounded. Until this time, the issue had received very little public attention in Britain. In October 1975, however, the BBC 1 peak-time programme 'Nationwide' featured the safety glass debate in controversial terms.

The television broadcast focused on two popular former sportsmen, Colin Milburn and Gordon Banks, who had been badly injured by toughened glass screens. It was claimed that the HPR screen is undoubtedly superior to toughened glass on safety grounds and that an irrefutable case existed for the proposed EEC directive to be put into practice. The broadcast traced the directive's progress through the EEC system and concluded that it had been blocked by one delegation. It was argued that, whereas the German representatives had originally opposed the proposal, that country had now agreed to support the measure (in fact, all German motor manufacturers now fit laminated glass as standard on a voluntary basis). In the broadcast's terms:

That left—yes—Britain as the country that secretly blocked that safety law that could have saved drivers all over Europe from permanent injury.[37]

The 'Nationwide' team then asked the Department of Environment to justify its position. The D.O.E., of course, pointed to the TRRL findings and claimed that the research centre's views were widely shared.

We asked by whom. They wouldn't tell us. So we looked for some research centres somewhere in the world that like them favoured toughened glass. We found none. As far as we can see, the Department of Environment Road Research Laboratory is on its own.[37]

The programme further alleged that the D.O.E.'s stance was closely linked to the British motor industry's reluctance to accept government controls over vehicle design, a point to which we will return.

In December 1975 the EEC Committee on Regional Policy and Transport prepared a report on its own initiative as an attempt to hasten legislative action on windscreen glass.[38] The document criticised the laggardly progress of the proposed directive and urged the Council of Ministers to adopt it as soon as possible. In making this recommendation the Committee had the full support of the Committees on Economic and Monetary Affairs and on Public Health and the Environment. Very little new evidence was produced except for a survey of European motor and glass manufacturers.

The survey was conducted by Seefeld, the committee's 'rapporteur', who simply wrote to each company asking for their opinion on the issue. Of the 43 manufacturers who replied to Seefeld's enquiry (12 of which were makers of glass, the rest of motor vehicles), only two actually stated that they were opposed to HPR laminated glass as such (Vauxhall of Britain and Audi of West Germany). Another six companies claimed that they had commercial reasons for opposing laminated glass. Of course, it should be noted that the 23 firms which expressed themselves 'in favour of HPR' were not necessarily in favour of the use of compulsion to achieve this.

If the eight British-based manufacturers[39] are now examined, a number of points about the industry's views on safety glass legislation can be perceived. The only glass manufacturer represented – Pilkington – expressed advocacy for HPR glass, and it was supported by just three small 'specialist' car manufacturers, Lotus, Morgan and Rolls-Royce. The 'big four' companies – Leyland, Chrysler, Vauxhall and Ford – gave no opinion, except for Vauxhall which was actively opposed to laminated glass. The smaller companies, who presumably were less concerned about price rises in their already expensive vehicles, had commenced fitting laminated glass as standard and were therefore unconcerned about the EEC proposal. Of the larger companies, Chrysler and Vauxhall were fitting only toughened glass, and Leyland and Ford offered laminated glass as an optional extra.

The major outcome of the Regional Policy and Transport Committee's report was a new debate in the European Parliament in January 1976. Seefeld opened the discussion with a speech that reflected disillusionment with EEC procedures. Seefeld argued that the strong support of Members of the European Parliament (MEPs) for compulsory fitting of laminated windscreens had been 'disintegrated' by 'commercial considerations and vested interests:

My appeal is therefore to the governments, to the people who, on whatever grounds, are postponing the decision and do not appear to realise the implications of their indecisiveness.[40]

Seefeld's speech was endorsed by members of the Christian–Democratic Group and by the European Progressive Group. However, a British representative of the European Conservative Group (Mrs Kellet-Bowman) spoke in favour of delay and stated that her group was 'not convinced' by the evidence on safety. The more fundamental argument of the Conservative Group was that the consumer should be given a 'freedom of choice' and not be dictated to by national or international legislation. This sentiment has, of course, been a common strand of political philosophy underlying many of the discussions over regulatory activity in Britain and the United States. The policy adopted in this case by the Conservative Group was for its members to abstain from any vote on the proposed directive. It was also apparent from the British Conservatives that the SMMT had a rather equivocal stance on the proposal and that the large motor manufacturers were arguing for delay.

Since 1976 it has become apparent that the issue of windscreen safety is likely to drag on within the EEC for some time. In addition, 1983 finally saw the introduction of compulsory seat-belt wear to Britain which, following the TRRL's logic, would appear to weaken slightly (though certainly not totally) the case for mandatory fitting of laminated glass. One clear consequence of this has been the economic costs paid by glass companies such as Triplex (part of the Pilkington Group). Brief mention was made above of the Triplex Ten-Twenty windscreen and it is worth commenting here on the recent history of that product.

In the mid-1970s Triplex announced its plans to develop the Ten-Twenty and, by the early 1980s, the company had spent some £20 million on preparing for mass production of the screen.[41] Triplex were working on the assumption that there would be a market of around a million screens a year by the 1980s, a market which would be partly created by the envisaged EEC directive. Ten-Twenty was about 1.7 times as expensive as HPR laminated glass but it was argued that it would offer a far greater degree of occupant protection. The problem faced by Triplex was that of achieving the long production runs necessary for the economic viability of the screen. British Leyland showed some interest in the product and it was fitted as standard to the Rover SD1 (and, later, to the Princess and Dolomite Sprint), but other large motor manufacturers such as Ford, Vauxhall and Talbot rejected it – mainly on the grounds of cost. By the 1980s it was apparent that sales would be insufficient to merit the maintenance of production facilities and Triplex withdrew the Ten-Twenty from the market. Perhaps as a final blow to Triplex, a study from the Accident Research Unit in Birmingham suggested that, although the Ten-Twenty did have certain advantages in terms of occupant protection, when fitted to the Rover it might not be as effective as had been suggested. The problem seemed to be that the bonnet catch on the Rover was 'pre-fracturing' the screen before it was struck by vehicle occupants. The unit also questioned the method of bonding the screen to the frame in some cars.

The story of Ten-Twenty glass is certainly illustrative of the political uncertainties that have surrounded laminated glass since the early 1970s. Of course, the predicament of Triplex is also symptomatic of the position in which component manufacturers can easily find themselves when dealing with the powerful motor companies on which they depend. In Chapter 6 a similar series of events in the United States was described when air-bag manufacturers were forced to withdraw from the market as a result of regulatory vicissitudes and industry's reluctance to adopt this safety technology. It can often appear at the inception of a proposed regulation that the market for a component is virtually guaranteed. However, the history of road traffic safety policies in both Britain and the United States strongly suggests that this 'guaranteed market' can either evaporate or its creation can be so long delayed as to put component manufacturers into extreme financial difficulties.

In the 1980s, the issue of laminated glass has certainly not disappeared although EEC activity remains unlikely. In 1982, the Parliamentary Advisory Committee on Transport Safety (PACTS) recommended the fitting of HPR glass to all cars[42] and calls for compulsion were supported by the Labour Party in its document on Transport Policy.[43] The Accident Research Unit has also maintained its support for HPR laminate. In the 1982 Foley Memorial Lecture Dr Mackay argued that toughened glass causes at least four times as many facial lacerations as laminate. According to Mackay:

In this country, toughened glass windscreens still probably damage or destroy the sight of about 1800 eyes each year. In contrast, eye injuries from laminated glass occur in negligible numbers.[44]

However, official opposition to compulsory fitting remains. In 1982, the Secretary of State announced that there was 'insufficient evidence' to justify such a move but that she was prepared to keep the topic 'under review'.[45] As Chapter 7 discusses, 1983 saw the introduction of compulsory seat-belt law to Britain and this seems very likely to reduce windscreen-related injuries. Nevertheless, the case for laminated glass is still being put forward by organisations such as PACTS on the grounds that (a) some front-seat passengers will still be unbelted despite the law (perhaps 10–15 per cent); (b) that other car occupants need to be considered – especially those in the rear seat. PACTS argues that, at the additional cost of only £8 per new car, a mandatory specification of HPR laminated windscreen must be more than worth while.[46] One can add to these points the fact that serious eye injuries can still be caused to belted passengers by shattered fragments of toughened glass screens. Evidence to this effect was emerging during 1983.[47]

Discussion

Two preliminary points should be made about the case study presented here. The first is that the resolution of safety-glass policy in the USA has merely been touched upon from time to time in this chapter, and never discussed in any detail. This is partly a deliberate strategy to provide scope for studying the British policy-making process in greater depth. However, it should also be noted that, in contrast to many other areas of political action on road traffic safety, there has been almost complete consensus on this particular issue in the United States. Laminated glass has been accepted by all the parties to the political process and toughened glass has never been in mass use. Perhaps because of this historical commitment to one product, no rivalry has developed between the two types, and laminated glass was incorporated with very little debate (and then only on relatively minor points) into the original federal motor vehicle safety standards.[48] Certainly, no technical controversy has arisen over the merits of safety glass, and all the major research reports have supported the continued use of the modern HPR windscreen. The only US debate in recent years over windscreen glass has concerned the NHTSA's persistent refusal to authorise use of a windscreen (known as the 'Securiflex') manufactured by Saint-Gobain Vitrage. This screen incorporates an anti-lacerative film of clear plastic to protect occupants. In 1983, NHTSA granted General Motors permission to test 2500 cars fitted with Securiflex. A successful trial should encourage the agency to amend FMVSS 205 (which dates from 1968) so as to accommodate the design.[49]

The second point that must be made is that this case study has been concerned almost exclusively with the *British* assessment of the risks, costs and benefits of windscreen glass. Some of those involved in the EEC debate would argue, in contradiction to the 'Nationwide' broadcast discussed earlier, that Britain has not always been alone in opposing the Council Directive. This may well be the case, but the real concern of this chapter is with just one nation.

What is perhaps most intriguing about the debate over the mandatory fitting of laminated glass is the relationship which it implies between the concerned parties. We have seen that the TRRL/Department of Transport stance on windscreen glass has been consistent – at least since the early 1960s – in its opposition to laminate. At the same time, an evolution has occurred in the reasoning behind this antagonism. The argument put by Lister in his 1961 paper was that toughened glass was superior according to both safety and cost criteria. This conclusion was supported by the 1968 study. The introduction of new (i.e. HPR) types of laminated glass seems a major factor in producing a more cautious analysis in the 1975 TRRL report. However, the basic advocacy for toughened glass on safety grounds continued. In addition, the Department of Transport had been arguing since 1972 that even a 100 per cent effective laminated glass would not merit mandatory fitting because of its insufficient cost–benefit justification.

From the mid-1970s onwards, the cost-effective argument has been increasingly stressed by the Department of Transport. Modern types of laminated glass, notably the Triplex Ten–Twenty are not regarded by the Department of Transport as being totally devoid of safety advantages, but the government officials have argued (a) that the cost of mandatory fitting would be too high,[50] (b) that the production capacity is not available and therefore glass would have to be imported,[51] and (c) that alternative, passive measures are available. As noted above, this was one of the rare occasions when passive design improvements have actually been advocated by government sources in Britain. The British Government has used all these arguments in EEC debate to block the mandatory introduction of HPR glass.

Lined up against the TRRL/Department of Transport case is an impressive array of technical evidence to suggest that the safety benefits of HPR glass are considerably greater than the Government would allow. It would appear that the 1975 TRRL study of windscreen glass, which has remained of central importance to the Department of Transport's case against the directive, relied on a rather small number of laminate-related injuries – indeed only fifteen of any severity. This appears extremely insubstantial for a report which has had crucial political significance and which has been opposed by the bulk of international opinion. In Britain, the major technical opposition has come from the Accident Research Unit, a group which has also been funded by the Department of Transport. The major problem for the ARU has been the lack of any appropriate public medium by which to question the Department of Transport's actions and draw attention to the case for the mandatory fitting of laminated glass.

It is at this point that the lack of any effective public interest group network in Britain manifests itself. Such groups, at least as they operate in the USA, would be likely to seize on the British Government's political vulnerability in this matter and give it maximum critical exposure. In fact, the BBC and RoSPA have given coverage to the issue but neither has been able to sustain any external pressure on the Government. The Department of Transport has simply ignored outside disparagement and has not been drawn into a public controversy.

One of the most interesting aspects of this case study is the relationship between the glass and motor manufacturers and the Department of Transport. The glass industry has argued in favour of laminated glass on technical grounds and advocates compulsory fitting, provided sufficient lead time is given. Indeed it can be argued that compulsory fitting of laminated glass could have strong economic advantages for glass makers by replacing a relatively cheap item with a rather more expensive (and possibly more profitable) product.

The opinion of the British motor manufacturers has been less explicit. Although the SMMT has generally expressed itself in favour of the EEC directive, there would seem to be a certain amount of disagreement within the industry. Vauxhall in particular made its opposition clear. At the same time, the industry is generally hostile to government intervention of this type and, as a matter of general stragegy, would not want to establish an undesired precedent. It should be noted, however, that in the late 1970s individual manufacturers such as Ford and British Leyland stated their support for laminated glass publicly, and openly recommended the compulsory approach to this. As a Ford spokesman maintained in 1978:

There is no doubt in our minds that laminated glass is desirable on safety grounds . . . Industry must gear up for the universal use of laminated glass for screens eventually – laminated is the inevitable way to go.[52]

A similar argument has been put forward by BL:

. . . laminated glass, or Ten–Twenty glass, is the best answer and legislation would remove the financial handicap which must inevitably be borne by any manufacturer who opts for it.[52]

It is in the context of viewpoints such as these that the Department of Transport's reluctance to accept the EEC proposal must be considered. In some ways it would appear that the D.Tp. is more concerned about the possible adverse consequences of the move than the industries most affected. The contrast with the regulatory style of the NHTSA in the United States could hardly be more clear. The Department of Transport in no way sees its task as 'forcing the pace' of safety innovation; its chosen role is rather to encompass all the 'best interests' of concerned parties (including the public) and to proceed in an incremental and consensual manner. Throughout both Conservative and Labour political rule, the Department of Transport's regulatory philosophy has remained unchanged in its dependence on a *laizzez-faire* approach to windscreen design. In adopting this stance the Department of Transport has also succeeded – largely because of the lack of a strong public interest lobby – in removing matters of vehicle safety from the political agenda, and has maintained them instead within a small and very closed community of major parties to the discussion. The 'un-politics' of windscreen safety should be seen, therefore, as a reflection of a more general regulatory style and, in particular, of a relationship between the regulator and the perceived needs of the regulated. At the heart of this relationship there is a reluctance from the state to dictate to the business sector how to conduct itself in matters of safety.

As a final comment in this chapter, the position of the TRRL should be noted. As a government laboratory with an especially close link with the Department of Transport, obvious pressures exist that constrain the research programmes selected and the funds that are made available. What is perhaps most surprising about the TRRL's research on windscreen safety is that there should have been such little response to the various criticisms of this work that were made in the 1970s. Despite repeated reference to the inadequacies of the methodology used in the 1975 study and the obvious isolation of the TRRL's technical assessment, the laboratory has not responded with new studies or a sustained critique of the rival views. Of course, it would be unfair to blame the technical personnel for this situation: the TRRL is now under severe financial constraints and is, in many ways, struggling for its survival as a viable unit. It might be added that, given the Department of Transport's stance on this issue, investigations into windscreen glass safety are unlikely to be granted priority within the shrinking TRRL budget. The case of laminated versus toughened windscreen glass provides us, then, with a clear example not only of the British regulatory philosophy concerning road traffic safety but also of the relationship between political power and technical expertise that can develop in this area.

Notes and references

1   Plate glass was fitted to motor cars in Britain from the first decade of the 20th century. Earlier vehicles had no windscreen at all.
2   British Standards Institution. BS 857:1954. *Safety Glass for Land Transport.*
3   Milsom, B. M. *Distribution of Toughened and Laminated Glass Windscreens in Cars.* Road Research, Note RN/4028, BMM, August 1961.
4   Fourteenth Report from the Select Committee of the House of Lords on the European Communities R/1927/72. *Harmonising Safety Glass Fitted in Motor Vehicle Windscreens,* p. iv.
5   TRRL leaflet, *LF 578 (Issue 2),* May 1976, p.3.
6   *Care on the Road,* January 1983, P.1.
7   EEC Council Directive 70/156/EEC *Official Journal of the European Communities (OJ),* L42, 23 February 1970.
8   Draft Council Directive on the Harmonisation of Member States. Legislation Concerning Safety Glass to be Mounted on Motor Vehicles. *Working Document* 144/72, 15 September 1972.
9   Proposal for a Council Directive Concerning the Standardisation of the Laws of Member States Relating to Safety Glass Intended to be Fitted to Motor Vehicles. *OJ* C119 16 November 1972, p.21.
10 Patrick, C. H., Trosien, K. R. and Dupont, F. T. Safety performance comparison of 30 MIL HPR laminated and monolithic differentially tempered windshields. SAE. *International Automobile Safety Conference Compendium,* 1970, pp.1113–33.
11 Mackay, G. M., Siegel, A. W. and Hight, P. V. Tempered versus HPR laminated windshields; a comparative study of United Kingdom and United States collisions. *Proc. 14th Stapp Car Crash Conference,* 17–18 November 1970, Michigan, pp.369–87.
12 The other five technical reports in published form were: Breitenburger, G. and Rodloff, G. Windshield and internal safety. *ATZ,* (11), 1970. Research conducted at the University of Vienna. Francois J., DeVos, E. and DeLombaert, C. Ocular accidents caused by breaking of windshields. *Ann. Ocul. (Paris)* **204** (1), 1971, pp. 49–54. Research conducted at the University of Ghent. Holland, G. Eye and eyelid injuries from windshields and means to prevent them. SAE *International Automobile Safety Conference Compendium,* 1970, pp.

1187–94. Research conducted at the University of Dusseldorf. Mackay, G. M. Injuries from glass in motor vehicles. *2nd Conference on Motor Vehicles and Motor Engineering*, Society of Engineers, Sopron, Hungary, October 1971, pp. 61–71. Renard, G., Bregeat, P. and Offret, G. The windshield; an eye hazard. *Bull. Acad. Nat. Med. (Paris)*. **154** (26), 1970, pp. 698–702. The authors were ophthalmologists at the Cochin Hospital and the Hotel-Dieu de Paris.

13 European Parliament *Working Document* 144/72, 15 September 1972, p. 25.

14 *New Scientist*, 12 October 1972, p. 86.

15 Lister, R. D. Safety glass for windscreens. *Automobile Engineer*, **51**(9), 1961, 341–7.

16 *Care on the Road*, February 1979, p.2. (J. Horam was the Minister).

17 Hobbs, J. A., Allsop, R. E. and Starks, H. J. H. *Injuries Produced by Motor Car Windscreens*, RRL Report LR 152, 1968.

18 Grattan, E., Clegg, N. G. and Hobbs, J. A. *Toughened Glass Windscreen Injuries in Car Occupants.* RRL Report LR 282, 1969. Harris, J. *Impact Tests on Toughened and Laminated Windscreen Glass.* RRL Technical Note TN 355, December 1968.

19 Grattan, E. and Hobbs, J. A. Windscreen glass injuries to the head in front seat occupants of cars and light vans. Preprint of paper presented to the *5th International Conference of the International Association for Accident and Traffic Medicine and the 3rd International Conference on Drug Abuse of the International Council on Alcohol and Addiction*, London, 1–5 September 1975.

20 TRRL leaflet, *LF 578*, 1975.

21 TRRL leaflet, *LF 578 (Issue 2)*, May 1976.

22 *Ibid.* p.4.

23 Kay, S. E., Osola, U. J., Pickard, J. and Brereton, P. A. Triplex Ten–Twenty. *ATZ*, September 1977.

24 See also Mackay, G. M. Incidence of trauma to the eyes of car occupants. *Transactions of the Ophthalmological Societies of the United Kingdom*, **XCV**, Part II, 1975, pp. 311–14.

25 Mackay. G. M. *Injuries from Windscreens – a Review of Some Recent Literature.* University of Birmingham Department of Transportation and Environmental Planning, Departmental Publication No. 53, 1978.

26 *Ibid.* p.16.

27 Many excellently documented examples of this strategy as employed by the chemical industry in the USA can be found in Epstein, S. S. *The Politics of Cancer* (Sierra Club Books, San Francisco, 1978).

28 See Chapter 2.

29 European Parliament. *Working Documents* 13/73 16 April 1973.

30 *OJ. Debates*, No. 162, 7 May 1973, p. 14.

31 *OJ Debates*, Oral Question No. 175/73, 12 February 1974, p.84.

32 Fourteenth Report from the Select Committee of the House of Lords on the European Communities, R/1927/72. *Harmonising Safety Glass Fitted in Motor Vehicle Windscreens*, 4 March 1975 (HMSO, London; 1975).

33   *Ibid.* p.9.
34   *Ibid.* p.15.
35   *Ibid.* p.18.
36   *Ibid.* p.24.
37   Transcript '*Nationwide*', 8 October 1975, p.4.
38   Committee on Regional Policy and Transport. Draft report on safety glass for use in motor vehicles. *EEC Working Documents* 397/75, 3 December 1975.
39   The eight manufacturers were Pilkington (Triplex's parent company), Leyland, Chrysler, Ford, Vauxhall, Lotus, Morgan, Rolls-Royce.
40   *OJ Debates*, No. 198, 15 January 1976, pp. 183–4.
41   See: *Care on the Road*, May 1982, pp. 4–5.
42   *Care on the Road*, August 1982, p.12.
43   *Care on the Road*, November 1982, p. 24.
44   Mackay, G. M. Reducing car crash injuries: folklore, science and promise. The First Foley Memorial Lecture, 29 September 1982. Available from Pedestrians Association, 1 Wandsworth Road, London SW8 1LJ.
45   *Care on the Road*, June 1982, p.2.
46   PACTS. Evidence to the House of Commons Select Committee on Transport Inquiry into Road Safety, March 1983.
47   *Care on the Road*, October 1983, p.1.
48   US Department of Commerce. National Traffic Safety Agency. *Report on the Development of the Initial Federal Motor Vehicle Safety Standards Issued from January 31, 1967.* (USGPO, Washington, DC; 1967), pp. 76–7.
49   *Status Report.* Vol. 18 No. 1, 18 January 1983, p.1.
50   The 1975 estimate was £20 million.
51   Lords Select Committee. R/1927/72, p.10.
52   *Care on the Road*, August 1978, p.1.

Part IV

Chapter 10

State management of road traffic hazards

If a car's lifespan is ten years, then one in three will kill somebody.[1]

Since the first motor-vehicle death in the United States, about 2 340 000 persons have died in motor vehicle accidents through the end of 1980 . . . If the current annual trend in motor-vehicle deaths continues, the 3 000 000th motor-vehicle death will probably occur in the early 1990s.[2]

This book has presented a large amount of background material relating to national approaches to road traffic safety in the USA and Britain. The emphasis throughout Parts II and III has been on general policies and, in particular, on the relationship between these and the broader theme of 'risk and the control of technology', which is the overall focus of this book. In Part IV the main concerns of the earlier chapters will be considered with a view to drawing together some of the issues raised. Of special concern here will be the questions of 'effectiveness and equity', which were introduced in Chapters 1 and 2.

As outlined in Chapter 1, there were a number of reasons for selecting road traffic safety policies as an example of regulatory practice; the economic significance of the industries in question and their symbolic importance, the magnitude of the public health problem involved, the apparently 'taken-for-granted' nature of road deaths. However, the justification for using *any* such example needs to be borne in mind, i.e. the importance of getting away from the empty abstractions (for example, of the 'how safe is safe enough?' variety) which often dominate discussion of technological risk. It has been argued here that decisions over hazard control can only be understood in their proper social and economic context and that this context should include a full analysis of the parts played by technical experts, the state, outside organisations and, finally, the general public. The analysis in Parts II and III has dealt with these four groups with a view to contrasting their operation in two countries.

If the argument about the importance of considering matters of technological risk in context is to be validated, conclusions need now to be drawn about both 'risk and the control of technology' at the general level and about 'road traffic safety' at a more specific focus. The underlying purpose, then, of Part IV is to demonstrate how a study of the sort conducted here can shed light on each of these problem areas. Accordingly, Chapter 10 will conclude the analysis of road traffic safety policies and Chapter 11 will reflect upon the value of 'technological risk' as a concept and as an aid to future policy making.

Detail in Part III has been provided in the form of a number of case studies of the two national regulatory strategies in action. From the USA the main examples have been the still unresolved debates over FMVSS 208 and occupant protection (Chapter 6), the successful lobbying to strengthen FMVSS 301 so as to reduce the number of fire-related deaths and injuries (Chapter 8) and, more briefly, the requirements for laminated safety glass as specified by FMVSS 205 (Chapter 9). Within Britain, principal attention has been paid to compulsory seat-belt wear legislation (Chapter 7), fire hazards (Chapter 8), and the arguments over windscreen 'safety glass' (Chapter 9). Part III has also raised the whole issue of product liability (in Chapter 8), which has assumed some considerable importance in the United States but has not played such a major role in Britain.

The specific topics of Part III can best be summarised and reviewed by considering these examples within the broader framework suggested by Chapter 2.

Technical expertise

In Chapter 2, an approach to understanding technical expertise was advocated which rejected the existence of a division between the practice of scientific work and the socio-political context in which that work is performed. Science is viewed as a labour process which can only be interpreted with reference to those social influences that shape the direction and form of knowledge production. This is not to suggest that some crude correlation can be established between the goals of dominant social groups and the emergence of 'expedient knowledge', but rather that socio-economic interests permeate the scientific labour process and serve to facilitate certain types of research work rather than others. This relationship between expertise and its context is especially important in the case of 'risk analysis' (defined in its broadest sense to include not only the 'science of road traffic safety' but also examples like major hazards, toxic substances and occupational hygiene). 'Risk analysis' is, by definition, a problem-oriented activity and is therefore dependent on wider society for the establishment of its goals and direction. As was observed in Chapter 4, changing regulatory philosophies can have a profound effect on the form taken by 'risk analysis' – in this case as federal authorities, pressure groups and manufacturers required new forms of expertise to sustain their arguments. Scientific work in the area of technological risk will inevitably be sensitive to the contingencies of its social climate and can be expected to develop accordingly. This does not deny the value of technical expertise in these matters but suggests that such evidence needs to be treated with special caution by policy makers and pressure groups.

The second major characteristic of the approach to technical expertise discussed previously is its presentation of science as being differentiated in its practice and possessing an internal diversity in which separate professional groupings operate very often with different intellectual orientations and conceptualisations of a given problem area. This is in contrast to those approaches to science that suggest that as an institution it is cognitively and organisationally homogeneous.

In Chapter 3, the technical expertise that relates to road traffic safety was divided into three relatively distinct specialty areas: traffic engineering, human factors and occupant protection. These three are distinguished by the intellectual orientation of their practitioners (this orientation being largely influenced by the disciplinary approach which dominates each specialty), the organisational and administrative separation of the specialties and the resources made available to each by funding bodies. Historically, the three specialties have evolved quite separately and this cognitive and professional separation shows very little sign of achieving reconciliation.

The heterogeneous nature of the technical expertise relating to road traffic safety should be considered in the context of the social settings in which it has developed, in this case the USA and Britain. In particular, the consequences of each specialty in terms of policy recommendations need be taken into account and examined with regard to the socio-economic interests of various groups and organisations which are directly or indirectly involved in road traffic safety as a political issue.

It was argued in Part II that the traffic engineering approach has supported further road-building projects by providing a justification for these in terms of increased safety. In serving this function, the specialty has directly and indirectly promoted the interests of the road lobby, that is, those industries that would ultimately profit from increased expenditure on highways (namely the road construction, oil, road haulage and motor industries). It is not surprising then that these industries should have actively encouraged the development of this approach via direct sponsorship and lobbying for further government funding in the area.

In sharp contrast to the traffic engineering approach, there is the occupant protection specialty, which historically has been neglected by both industrial organisations and governments. The general recommendation for policy which emerges very clearly from this specialty is that vehicles should be designed so as to provide the maximum collision protection for occupants and other road users. This conclusion has been firmly resisted by motor manufacturers in both the USA and Britain (with certain exceptions such as Rover) on the grounds that 'Safety doesn't sell', the argument being that the design modifications suggested by this specialty increase the cost of vehicles substantially while diminishing the consumer appeal of the motor industry's products.

The third specialty area, human factors, provides an interesting case because the assumption that the vast majority of accidents are directly or indirectly attributable to human error has been extremely influential over government policies in Britain till the present time, and also in the USA to a lesser extent. It has been argued earlier that the persuasive force of this concept is linked to its ideological role of blaming the road user rather than the machines that actually cause the damage, i.e. the vehicles themselves. In this way, attention has been diverted away from the design of road vehicles for crashworthiness and from the political measures which might be introduced to ensure these design modifications. Accordingly, it is in the perceived interests of the motor manufacturers to encourage the growth of human factors along with traffic engineering while neglecting the occupant protection framework. The evidence for this claim can be obtained from an examination of the emergence of the three specialties and particularly the underdevelopment of occupant protection until the 1960s, when various groups in the USA outside the motor industry began to appreciate the implications of the specialty for future policy. The determination with which motor manufacturers have fought against regulatory measures based on occupant protection, and the public statements made by industry representatives on this subject, provide strong evidence to suggest the connection between the support of certain branches of technical expertise and the perceived self-interest of powerful economic groups such as the motor manufacturers.

In Chapters 4 and 5 the relationship between technical approaches to road traffic safety and national regulatory policies was discussed in the light of these arguments about the ideological importance of each specialty. At this 'macro' level of policy making, the technical principles of each approach have been of great importance, and pressure groups have utilised particular branches of expertise so as to employ technical rather than manifestly political arguments to support their respective cases. In this way, scientific knowledge has served as a 'resource' for social action which confers authority and legitimacy on the claims of an interest group. However, the 'resource' analogy is rather misleading in its implication that whereas scientific expertise may be used to influence political debate, the expertise itself is actually constituted in a social and political vacuum. The discussion here and in Part I has argued against this view in favour of a more permeable division between risk analysis and social interests.

The utilisation of technical expertise as a resource for political debate has been discussed both in Part II (at the macro level of national 'risk philosophies' for the control of automobile technology) and in Part III (at the micro level of specific measures within this broader national philosophy). At the macro level in Britain, the dominance of the traffic engineering and human factors specialties over political action has been noted. This hegemony has been linked to the consensual relationship between government officials and industry representatives and also to the lack of any powerful public interest groups seeking to force the consideration of the 'alternative expertise' represented by occupant protection. These aspects of the political structures will be examined further in the following section, but at this point it is important to note the significance of technical expertise in justifying the existing institutional mechanisms without the necessity of raising manifestly social arguments over 'who should decide what is safe?' or 'what type of policy actually serves the public interest best?' In this way, risk analysis can serve a crucial legitimising function by establishing and maintaining the issue of road traffic safety as a basically technical rather than a socio-political problem. Accordingly, policy is perceived to be the rightful domain of experts rather than of political activists.

In the United States, a similar approach dominated national thinking until the mid-1960s when, as described in Chapter 4, a whole series of political initiatives based on the occupant protection framework reached their culmination and revolutionised policy making. The close linkage between the technical assumptions of the specialty approach and their political consequences was absolutely explicit when some of the major exponents of occupant protection (such as Haddon, Nader and Moynihan) later became extremely influential over the form and practice of the 1966 legislation. The 1966 Safety Act embodied the principles of this specialty and in so doing provided the basic terms of reference within which the many debates over specific standards have taken place.

The years 1965 and 1966 in the USA saw a political outburst over road traffic safety which included a series of strong attacks on the motor manufacturers and a questioning of industry's right to decide for itself what risks should be accepted by the American public. Concern was expressed about the need for greater democratic involvement in decision making of this type and it was widely accepted that stricter external controls were required over the motor industry if public welfare was to be adequately protected. Since the late 1960s, the issue of road traffic safety has assumed decreasing importance on the US political agenda, and a process of institutionalisation has occurred whereby 'public interest' and 'industrial' pressure groups have settled into a relatively stable relationship with NHTSA officials. Parallel to this 'depoliticisation' has been the increasing tendency for debate to be conducted in technical language – a process which Habermas has termed 'scientisation'.[3] Lobbying and public hearings routinely take the form of competing cost–benefit or cost-effective analyses rather than ostensibly political arguments. The 'scientisation' of debate in both the USA and Britain has been illustrated in Part III by a number of specific cases of regulatory action.

The discussion of FMVSS 208 in the USA provides an excellent example of the deployment of technical expertise in order to develop an essentially political and economic case against rulemaking. The motor manufacturers have been successful in delaying the standard's implementation by arguing that further research work is needed on a number of specific points. However, an examination of the wide gulf that exists between the manufacturers and public interest groups on these points suggests strongly that 'more information' alone will never reconcile the technical differences because of the entrenchment that already exists based on the competing social and economic perspectives deployed by these groups. The uncertainty which, as argued in Part I, inevitably surrounds the assessment of a technological hazard prior to general release (and often even after) has been exploited by the various sides to the debate for their own political purposes. Accordingly, technical expertise does not function as the final arbitrator of what is true or false; it is employed selectively (and sponsored in a similar fashion) so as to justify particular arguments. In this situation, appeals for further research or for a cool and dispassionate technical analysis serve a useful bargaining purpose in what is essentially a *political* struggle.

Although the use of technical expertise as a political resource has been analysed in particular detail during Chapter 6, a similar process has also been found in Chapter 8 in regard to US rulemaking. In that case study, the delaying tactics employed by Ford over FMVSS 301 were the focus of discussion.

In addition to the deployment of expertise to influence the rulemaking process, the use of scientific knowledge in the US courtroom must also be considered. The enlisting of expert witnesses in this context to defend public or private interests represents a relatively new role for the scientific worker, which involves subjection to cross-examination and legal scrutiny of a type that not all scientists find especially agreeable. It may be the case that the appearance of experts in this forum permits the implicit interests served by certain branches of knowledge to become explicit. At the very least, judicial inquiry will encourage a broader awareness of the fact that scientific experts can indeed differ and that these differences of opinion may be related to the social relations within which the relevant research has been conducted. The judicial system as it operates in the USA is forcing an increasing number of technical experts to defend their views in front of an often hostile lay audience. This experience may well serve to encourage an increased critical awareness of the political significance of technical expertise, an awareness which is just as necessary for scientists themselves as for the general public and policy makers. However, the growing role for technical experts in judicial and quasi-judicial situations (e.g. at a British public inquiry) deserves serious study and would be a useful focus for future research in this area.[4]

In Britain the debate over windscreen glass (Chapter 9) represents another clear example of the 'scientisation' of debate. Perhaps the most interesting source of expertise in regard to that particular issue has been the TRRL, which has steadfastly opposed the bulk of research on the relative merits of laminated and toughened glass. It was argued earlier that this stance must be understood in the light of the D.Tp.'s general non-interventionist stand on matters of vehicle and component design. In particular, the D.Tp. has been concerned with the economic consequences of the compulsory fitting of laminated windscreens and this economic assessment has diminished the perceived need for the sponsorship of a large-scale TRRL study of contemporary windscreen performance. Accordingly, the D.Tp. has used the TRRL studies (in order to argue that no lives are actually being lost or injuries caused as a result of the failure to compel the use of laminated glass) while drawing upon economic arguments as the final criteria for choice. On this occasion, the technical evidence over windscreen safety produced by the TRRL is being used to ward off any major public criticism until such time as a final decision is made either to accept or decisively reject the proposed EEC legislation. The expertise provides a defence from potentially damaging accusations, e.g. that the D.Tp. is knowingly permitting damage to human beings, and so justifies the delay in rulemaking which the Department considers necessary.

In many ways, the debate over mandatory seat-belt wear in Britain (Chapter 7) is somewhat different from the other case studies discussed in Part III in that it does not involve the proposed application of a technological fix but rather a behavioural modification based on an already available technology. However, what has emerged since 1979 is yet another technical controversy, this time focusing on the work of John Adams and his statistical analysis of the actual effectiveness of seat-belt laws. A number of conclusions can be drawn from the technical arguments over this issue, not least concerning the 'noisy' nature of such statistics, so that it becomes extremely difficult to link together cause (in this case seat-belt wear) and effect (a reduced casualty rate) given all the other changing variables such as the vehicle population, new traffic laws and the consequences of the mid-1970s fuel crisis (see below). The Adams controversy also illustrates well the close relationship between such technical arguments and their political background. Adams's analysis was seized upon by those parliamentarians who were opposed to compulsory seat-belt laws whereas the pro-compulsion lobby dismissed the findings apparently without any full consideration of their empirical basis. The debate was equally heated between experts and was on occasion conducted through acrimonious exchanges in *The Times* rather than the more conventional scientific channels. Quite clearly, the argument over seat-belt effectiveness was heavily loaded, both for experts and politicians and this was a severe impediment to the full and informed discussions which might have been better suited to this issue. At the same time, the part played by values should not be overlooked here, so that, once again, expertise was used as a resource to support the amalgam of social views and concerns which fell into each of the 'pro' and 'anti' lobbies over seat-belt compulsion.

The other important aspect of the part played by technical expertise in the seat-belt debate is its basic structuring towards *active* rather than *passive* forms of occupant protection. The evidence is inevitably misleading unless presented within a discussion of the broad array of possible protective measures, such as, for example, those under debate in the USA which are passive in design (i.e. they do not require the active and repeated cooperation of the vehicle occupant). At this point, the technical evidence which was *not* presented becomes as important as that which actually was. The explanation for this 'blind spot' may be found by returning to the earlier discussion of British policy in general and its failure to consider vehicle redesign as a fruitful safety measure, this failure in turn being linked to the consensual nature of the political system and the absence of a strong public interest group network which might seize on this alternative strategy.

The role of the state

In Parts II and III, evidence was presented by way of characterising the administrative and political procedures for the control of road traffic safety in the United States and Britain. Two related features of the national systems that deserve particular attention are the consensual/adversarial style of decision making and the degree of openness/closedness that operates in each case.

A broad contrast can be drawn between the political conflict involving the NHTSA, manufacturers and public interest groups as it has taken place in the USA and the rather less strident terms in which similar negotiations have been carried out in Britain. The greater availability of information to the general public in the USA about potential rulemaking has also encouraged a more widespread participation in decision making, whereas in Britain only a limited number of groups and individuals have been consulted before proposals for new legislation emerge. Taken together, these two features suggest that the debate over road traffic safety in the USA has been rather more public than its British counterpart.

The type of conflict that has occurred in the United States has been illustrated by the case studies relating to FMVSS 208 and FMVSS 301. In both examples the agency has found itself at the centre of a protracted dispute in which it has come under political pressure not only from lobby groups and the general public but also from Congress, the executive branch and the judiciary. One frequent outcome of these disputes has been an extensive delay between the initial development and proposal of a standard by the NHTSA and its actual implementation. This, often lengthy, adjournment has repercussions in terms of the casualties that would presumably have been avoided had application been more rapid and also in terms of the economic costs of the uncertainty faced by vehicle and component manufacturers. One aspect of this is the case of certain air-bag suppliers in the USA who have opted to withdraw from any future market rather than risk further losses. Of course, FMVSS 208 has provided an especially vivid example of the 'regulatory battlefield' that can develop in the USA over the control of technological risk. Despite the intentions of the NHTSA to 'force the technological pace' and innovate a stringent standard for occupant protection, a stalemate has been reached so that the original FMVSS remains and there was little sign in 1983 of a new standard being put into practice. The contrast with Britain is also very clear where an *active* means of compulsory occupant protection has been achieved and has immediately been applied to almost the entire vehicle population. Even the adoption of the proposed FMVSS 208 in the mid-1980s might leave it open to consumer abuse (in the form of passive belt disconnection). Should the problem of widespread disconnection be avoided, there will still be an appreciable delay until the new 208 applies to a sizeable proportion of vehicles (because, unlike the British law, the updated standard could refer to *new* vehicles only).

The second major criticism that can be made of the US system is that the cumbersome decision-making process encourages rigidity. The inevitability of a protracted political struggle over any amendment to an existing standard ensures that it is often difficult to alter a requirement in the light of new technical evidence or changes in the character of the vehicle population. It is also almost impossible to maintain the overall coordination of safety measures with other important areas of vehicle regulation, e.g. fuel economy or emission control.

In sharp contrast to the United States, the operation of the Department of Transport in Britain has been geared towards the reduction of conflict through informal and formal consultation with 'interested parties' *before* the publication of a new proposal. In this way, a consensus is achieved between government officials, industry representatives, established pressure groups (such as the motoring organisations) and also other government departments. Discussion of the major aspects of an issue will take place but the views expressed during this will not, in most cases, be made public. The intention behind this style of approach is that later controversy may be avoided and the measure will therefore pass easily into law. The basic procedure then is a free exchange of views between recognised parties but with more widespread debate being discouraged and little being published by way of explaining the rationale behind a decision. This is certainly open to criticism on the grounds that it excludes any broader participation and may well engender an excessively cosy relationship between regulators and the regulated. The difficulty for an external observer in attempting to identify the major influences over D.Tp. policy when so little information is made public has been partially illustrated by the British assessment of the relative merits of laminated and toughened windscreen glass. In that case, the D.Tp.'s relative isolation in not supporting laminated glass brought it under attack by the mass media. However, the Department remains open to such indictments while it continues to avoid any greater public accountability. Although outside bodies may well not agree with the reasoning behind a decision, the publication of the underlying arguments and an invitation to greater participation would at least ensure that the various policy alternatives could emerge and be given adequate discussion. In the present situation, the lack of information about the policy-making process may well encourage outsiders to adopt a rather more conspiratorial view of that process than is perhaps strictly justified.

What immediately becomes clear in any discussion of state activity (and it should be emphasised here that we are considering the 'State' in the terminology of Chapter 2 and not as the individual 'state' within the United States of America) is that it is impossible to consider this without also examining the network of pressure groups which structure its activities and respond to its actions. In the present analysis of attempts at regulating an especially powerful economic sector, it is important to explore the links between state officials (as in the D.Tp. or the NHTSA) and industry representatives. Something has been said earlier about the character of these relationships in the two countries but this narrow comparison has tended to stress the points of *difference* (e.g. in terms of consensual/adversarial style or degree of openness/closedness) rather than the broader areas of *similarity*. This can be rebalanced here by a brief consideration of the actual *output* in policy terms from the two nations.

A number of arguments may be put forward to support the proposition that US regulatory authorities have enjoyed a much greater independence from industrial pressures against regulation than their British counterparts. The success in 1966 of the Safety Act represented a defeat for the manufacturers by its insistence on a strong federal role in the design of motor vehicles. The creation of a single-focus agency whose major reason for existence was the development of stricter safety standards[5] could be viewed in similar terms. The social movement surrounding Ralph Nader and his *Unsafe at Any Speed* brought public criticism down on General Motors and, by association, the other manufacturers. The availability of information to the public and the campaigning of groups like the Insurance Institute for Highway Safety or the Center for Auto Safety have also been counterbalances to the power of the industry. President Carter even appointed Joan Claybrook, a known consumer advocate and former associate of Nader, to the post of NHTSA Administrator.

However, it needs to be pointed out that these very visible successes for regulatory authorities and public interest groups have not always been matched by the development of actual performance standards. As discussed in Chapter 4, the initial set of FMVSSs were prepared in extreme haste and, very often, attempted to consolidate existing practice rather than enforce innovations. Despite the fact that NHTSA has achieved its goal of improving upon these preliminary standards in such cases as fuel system integrity (301) and also side-door strength (214), there are many other cases where the federal standard has been little altered since 1968. The last ten years of ferocious lobbying have produced few sustained victories for consumer groups and FMVSS 208 stands as a symbol of the motor industry's ability to block undesirable courses of action. It has been at the very centre of the arguments for improved passive restraint and yet nearly two decades of hard bargaining have produced few enforced modifications to American automobiles.

Additional factors behind the success of the motor industry in withstanding external safety controls have been the broader political and economic background of the 1970s and 1980s. More specifically, long periods have occurred when American politics have been dominated by the neo-liberal arguments for 'deregulation' and an ideology which has opposed the more interventionist safety policies of the late 1960s. One such period fell in the mid-1970s; a second was introduced by the Reagan administration of the 1980s. Agencies like the NHTSA could hardly remain immune from such pressures – especially given the practice of political appointments to the leadership of NHTSA and the Department of Transportation. The effect on NHTSA morale of a declining budget and a reluctance by its senior officials to be forceful in the pursuit of the agency's original goals could only be to inhibit regulatory output. This ideological perspective needs to be understood together with the immediate economic climate in the USA during the late 1970s and early 1980s. The much-publicised financial plight of companies like Chrysler and Ford was an important check on the Carter administration which might otherwise have been more supportive of the NHTSA's mandate. Manufacturers have exploited this situation fully by asserting that the agency has imposed a massive burden on the consumer, increased the rate of inflation and substantially weakened the long-term stability of the US motor industry and its ancillaries. Taken together, these *ideological* points, which oppose the very principle of state involvement in vehicle design, and *economic* arguments, which present a more pragmatic case against external controls, have protected the interests of industrial capital against substantial challenge on the issue of safety.

For Britain the analysis of state involvement in road traffic safety seems more clear-cut with the D.Tp.'s general philosophy being based on an 'identity of interest' between regulator and regulated. The D.Tp.'s non-interventionist posture was also especially apparent in the discussions over windscreen glass when sectors of the glass industry presented arguments for compulsory laminate. However, the overall reluctance of the motor industry to accept state standards has been clear and there has been little disagreement over this during various discussions in Britain. The political role played by technical expertise has also been vital (as discussed earlier) in shaping the emphasis of road traffic safety policy towards driver education and road improvements rather than vehicle design modifications. It should be noted, however, that the British consensual approach has at least allowed the acceptance of a measure for occupant protection (i.e. compulsory seat-belt wear) whereas the US system stagnates in a series of court challenges and air-bag tests. The 'partnership' between the motor manufacturers and the state has not been without some success even if such developments as seat-belt laws, recall campaigns and stricter vehicle testing have tended to follow the line of least industrial resistance. In terms of the overall output of the policy-making process in Britain it is perhaps ironic that the 'filter-down' effect of US standards has tended to enforce similar modifications to British vehicles. In order to limit the commercial barriers to trade imposed by FMVSSs, bodies such as the EEC and ECE have attempted to produce comparable European design requirements. Accordingly, although there are differences between vehicles for the British and US markets in such areas as windscreen glass, fuel system integrity and protection from side collision, the effects of commercial pressures towards harmonisation and the slow pace of US rulemaking have kept the 'international crashworthiness gap' relatively small. Nevertheless, the existence of any gap whatsoever is surely a legitimate cause for public concern and deserves further investigation and debate.

The analysis here has suggested that there has been a powerful industrial influence over national standard setting in both the USA and Britain. Although the precise form of the state–industrial capital linkage has been different in each context, the underlying structure has been similar. This case can be established more clearly if one considers that there are a number of assumptions about transport policy that have underpinned debates about road traffic safety but have rarely been discussed in explicit fashion. Put in its simplest terms, neither the NHTSA nor the D.Tp. have seriously challenged the centrality of the *automobile* within the national transportation systems. Although, for example, the US manufacturers have often been under attack for their reluctance to accept design changes, they have not been forced into a consideration of alternative modes of travel, e.g. public transport, which might lessen road traffic accidents in a more dramatic fashion by removing the hazard of automobiles *at source*. There is a far greater degree of risk attached to travel by automobile than for example, by train or bus.[6] In Britain during 1979, buses and coaches travelled some 52 000 000 000 km with a loss of three drivers and 31 passengers. The same distance when travelled in Britain by car will kill on average 329 car occupants. The relative risk of being killed on a journey by car is, therefore, ten times greater than that of being killed on a bus. When a similar comparison is made for trains, the relative risk for cars is four to five times greater. It should be noted that trains and buses are also less injurious in terms of pedestrian casualties. For the same distance travelled, cars will kill or seriously injure two-and-a-half times as many pedestrians as a bus or coach, and six times as many as a train. Overall, therefore, it is difficult to avoid the conclusion that transport by bus or train has important advantages in terms of safety over car travel.

Of course, such simple comparisons tell us very little about the feasibility of a large-scale alteration in transportation systems and they certainly tell us nothing about the social acceptability of the alternative modes of travel. However, they do suggest very clearly that the automobile is open to challenge in terms of its intrinsic safety. What can also be seen in the present context is that the discussions about road traffic risks that have been presented in this book depend upon certain accepted notions of 'transport technology' which have not been the subject of sustained public debate. In this way, the NHTSA and its 'risk philosophy' have tended to divert attention away from these basic and more divisive issues and operate instead only in the terms of the existing status quo. The Department of Transport has had a broader ambit but it has not been conspicuously eager to challenge the importance of the motor car within British society. This is an important point in any analysis of state regulatory activity over technological risks: to limit rulemaking activity to the evaluation of the risks of a specific technology may well be to ignore the basic technological alternatives that exist. Risks need to be seen in the context of the technologies to which they are linked; in the end it may be more appropriate to evaluate 'acceptable technologies' rather than limit attention to 'acceptable risks'. The direction of debates over road traffic safety in Britain and the USA has been such as to ignore these more fundamental points about technological choice; the 'un-politics' behind this has represented perhaps the major success of the motor manufacturers in avoiding a more radical scrutiny of their actions and strategies. The structuring of debate so as to accept without challenge a model of transportation in which the automobile assumes central status is reflected also in the form of public interest activity found in the two countries.

Pressure group organisations

The significance of industrial lobbying within state standard-setting organisations has been discussed at some length throughout this book. However, there has been a striking difference between the two countries in terms of the part played by public interest groups. Whereas in the USA a large number of such groups have made demands on the agency and manufacturers, in Britain only a limited number of organisations (as discussed in Chapter 5) have come into existence and these have not focused on road traffic safety to a similar extent. Although this difference may well be a general feature of the two political systems as they operate in many other contexts, the comparative 'visibility' of road traffic safety as an issue must also be taken into account. The evolution of public concern over road traffic accidents was traced in Part II and a number of factors were suggested to account for the emergence of the topic to prominence in the United States in 1966.

There is a clear disparity in the number of public interest groups which have been formed in the two nations, and a certain qualitative difference can also be discerned. This leads us back to the discussion of 'acceptable transport technologies'. Lobby groups in the USA have, generally speaking, accepted the part played by the private motor vehicle in the transport system, and have concentrated their efforts on improving safety without any demand for radical policy reforms, e.g. towards public rather than private transport technologies. Equally, although 'public interest' groups have been highly critical of the automobile industry and its power over the NHTSA, they have not advocated a major restructuring of the US political and economic system. In contrast to this, the more energetic public interest groups in Britain, e.g. Friends of the Earth (FoE), Transport 2000 or the Socialist Environment and Resources Association (SERA) have argued that they would not be content to see modifications made within the existing transport system if these would only reduce the *rates* of road traffic accidents and not the *absolute numbers* (given the rising vehicle population in both nations). Their case is for a restructuring of the British transportation network in which the private car would play a severely diminished role. Such groups in Britain have, in many cases, argued the need for a more fundamental social change than could ever be achieved by the lobbying of a government department and, accordingly, their demands for participation in the policy-making process within the D.Tp. have been rather less than those made by similar groups in the USA. Furthermore, the British state has been more successful than that of the USA in incorporating the views of those 'establishment' groups whose overall assessment of the present transport system is most similar to their own. This has reduced conflict with organisations like RoSPA and assisted in the marginalising of groups like SERA and FoE. In this way, the potential challenge to the common views of state officials and industry representatives has been severely attenuated.

The discussion so far in this chapter of technical expertise, pressure groups and the state has argued the view that the relationship between the motor industry and regulatory authorities has generally served to protect the long-term interests of capital. This is not to suggest that significant reforms have not been won, e.g. the 1966 Safety Act or specific standards such as 301; hence the significance of the concept of 'relative autonomy' as argued in Chapter 2. However, over a period of two decades, the industry has succeeded in limiting the debates over road traffic safety to an assumption of the continued role of the automobile. In Britain, the strategies suggested by traffic engineering and human factors have diverted attention away from the vehicle itself. The US focus on occupant protection is potentially more challenging but has been successfully parried and blocked without any long-term public relations damage to the industry. What this present discussion has ignored so far is the part played in these developments by the bulk of the British and US populations: a factor which was termed in Chapter 2 the 'social assessment of risk'.

Social assessment

One of the original motives behind the selection of road traffic safety as a case study was a curiosity concerning the apparently taken-for-granted nature of the hazard: Lord Rothschild's statement to this effect was quoted in Chapter 1. What we have discussed so far reveals that the relationship of the general population to the politicians, civil servants and pressure-group members who claim to be acting 'in the public interest' on specific issues is certainly a complex one. In the USA during the mid-1960s, road traffic safety was perceived to be an important political issue and various opinion polls and other, more qualitative, indicators such as letters to Congressmen and newspaper articles, made it clear that there was a strong national demand for firm regulatory action to curb the power of the motor manufacturers and to produce reforms along the lines advocated by Nader, Ribicoff and Kennedy. The problem, however, is the manner in which the social assessment of a hazard is to influence decision making in more recent years when road traffic safety (as in the USA) has been replaced on the political agenda by other issues or (as in Britain) has never been seen as a major political question at all.

The first point that must be made is that the above implicit portrayal of the British or American public as a vast amorphous and homogeneous entity is extremely misleading. Rather than view the 'public' as sharing a 'social assessment', it is far more accurate to consider a variety of 'publics' possessing an array of 'social assessments' of road traffic safety. These 'publics' can then be seen as a number of overlapping social groups divided according to such factors as class, race, occupation, gender and geographical location. Each of these groups is likely to adopt a distinct perspective on the hazard in question.

A major feature of the social assessment of road traffic safety is that it is in the nature of this hazard not to select any particular occupational, geographical or class-related group as its victims (although see also the discussion of pedestrian safety which follows). However, certain biases do exist in the prevalence of road traffic accidents, so that those who live near major roads or spend more of their time travelling in motor cars may suffer disproportionately. Nevertheless, these biases have not been sufficient to encourage the growth of a large number of specifically safety-oriented pressure groups based perhaps on accident sufferers or those especially exposed. For other types of technological risk, e.g. occupational health and safety, an already existing organisational base can be found for those affected to voice their concerns and argue a common case for political action, in this instance the trade union movement. The organisational base may in other cases be a clearly identifiable local community or a minority whose interests are being especially affected, e.g. fell walkers or a political association. In contrast, road traffic accidents affect individuals who may have no social or political connection other than being resident in a particular nation. This amounts to a general problem for public participation in the regulation of consumer products and widely dispersed environmental hazards. Although it is true that the US system encourages the growth of loosely based consumer pressure groups much more than is the case in Britain, the common difficulty in organising the population at times other than those of special concern over an issue remains. Meanwhile, there is a very real tendency for those pressure groups that claim to represent the 'public interest' to become increasingly isolated from the general population without ever being accountable for their aims and policies. Such a development is certainly not a desirable one for any political system which claims to be democratic.

The low level of expressed public concern over road traffic safety in the late 1970s may be accounted for in a number of ways. One immediate point is that the actual rates of accidents have remained relatively constant during the decade and have indeed shown a slow decline. The emergence of concern over fuel economy following the oil crisis of the mid-1970s, and also over the question of air pollution from vehicles, has attracted attention away from matters of safety. A most pressing problem in both Britain and the USA has been the financial state of the national economies and, in particular, the motor industry.

As an additional factor closely related to these points, there has been the part played by the scientisation of debate. Regulators and pressure groups in both countries mount their campaigns via technical rather than explicitly political challenges. In many ways, of course, this policy is itself a response to the changed political climate and in particular the inability of public interest groups and regulators to mobilise large-scale support from the population as a whole. Accordingly, the form of debate has been shifted to one where the motor manufacturers can employ their large resources to their own greatest advantage. There is a certain circularity, however, in the effects of this resolution of debate into a number of technical issues; the presentation of technical evidence may well be a response to the lack of public interest in road traffic safety policy in both nations, but the conduct of discussion in these terms serves only to depoliticise the issues further and remove them even more from general concern. The frequently abstruse nature of the debates renders them largely inaccessible to the wide population and thus imposes large checks on the possible extent of public participation in decision making. In this situation, it becomes inevitable that certain groups will appoint themselves as intermediaries between the regulators and the citizenry, although, as was discussed earlier, these intermediaries may never be subject to public scrutiny.

One further factor that seems to be linked to the public perception of any hazard is the degree of *powerlessness* that exists: to what extent can potential or actual victims hope to eradicate or improve the hazardous situation with which they are faced? The realisation that there are feasible alternatives which can significantly reduce the physical risks tends to increase public awareness as specific demands are made and a sense of purpose is achieved. One such example was portrayed in Chapter 4. Improved knowledge about occupant protection permitted the establishment of a channel for public pressure and campaigning. It is very possible that the adverse economic climate of the 1970s and 1980s has led to a loss of faith in this approach. In Britain, occupant protection has not been presented seriously to a general audience so that the 'common sense' of road traffic safety has remained in the mould of driver error and safe roads. It is very clear that in this context information *is* power, as any consideration of policy alternatives needs a basic understanding of just what directions are available and worthy of discussion. In Britain and the USA the distribution of this information has not always been in the commercial interests of those most concerned.

Throughout this book, road traffic safety has been discussed in terms of three main approaches: occupant protection, traffic engineering, and human factors. An argument has also been presented concerning the more fundamental issue of transportation systems and the effect that a radical alteration in these would have on the whole topic of safety (by substantially reducing the number of road vehicles and relying, for example, upon mass transportation networks such as public buses). However, an important perspective on this whole issue can also be gained by including here a brief description of a newly emerging approach that considers one group of road accident victims whose interests have often been ignored.

Pedestrian protection

Pedestrian injury research is a relatively new avenue for technical expertise in this area and it has not yet made a political or public impact. Nevertheless, as with other branches of the 'science of road traffic safety', it has very clear policy implications. Research by Ashton, for example, has suggested that a reduction of around 33 per cent could be achieved in the number of pedestrians injured after being struck by the front of a car.[7] Such a reduction would require specific improvements in vehicle design.

During the 1960s as the occupant protection approach emerged in the USA a number of accident analyses included the consequences for pedestrians as well as occupants of a major or minor collision. However, more specific research into pedestrian injury seems only to have been conducted since the 1970s into such basic matters as *what* injuries are sustained by pedestrians and *how*.[8] According to Ashton and Mackay of the Accident Research Unit (ARU), such studies were begun in England and West Germany in the mid-1970s and in the United States during the late 1970s. For example, the ARU had investigated some 700 pedestrian accidents by 1979 and similar projects were undertaken at Berlin Technical University, in France and under NHTSA sponsorship in the USA (this latter study involving an examination of some 2000 pedestrian accidents). As well as investigations into real-world accidents, data on pedestrian injury patterns have also been accumulated from experimental testing and mathematical modelling. Taken together, this evidence has provided an improved understanding of such factors as the location of pedestrian–vehicle impact, the action of pedestrians during and immediately after impact, the pattern of consequent injuries and the relationship between these factors and impact speed.[9] It is generally accepted, for example, that, with current car designs, pedestrians struck at less than 25 km per hour will on average sustain only minor injuries; below 50 km per hour the probability of survival is high but above 55 km per hour death is the most probable outcome. Of course, such generalisations need to take careful account of the wide variations in the population in terms of their physical ability to survive any collision; the proportion of those who actually die following a non-minor injury slowly rises from around 5 per cent in the 5 to 15-year-old category, to 25 per cent for the over 80 year olds.

Although statistics such as the above are obviously important in themselves, the main policy implications of pedestrian protection emanate from the attempts that have been made to correlate current vehicle design to pedestrian injury causation and then to consider how such designs might be improved. As with occupant protection, the notion is to accept the inevitability of accidents and to concentrate on how the consequences of such accidents can be minimised. This seems especially relevant when three main groups account for a large proportion of pedestrian accidents: young children, intoxicated adults and the elderly. Certainly, researchers in this area – who very often have a background in occupant protection – have not been slow to recognise the practical potential of their work. As Murray Mackay has argued regarding the engineering application of such research:

Numerically the case is strong, technically it is feasible, morally it is right, but politically, so far, it generates profound disinterest.[10]

In terms of their potential for injury reduction, aspects of the vehicle structure that have attracted particular attention are the bumper height (this influences the location of leg fractures), bumper lead i.e. the distance by which the bumper is further forward than the bonnet front edge (this influences whether physical damage is caused primarily by the bumper or bonnet), and bonnet height (which influences the pattern of pelvic and thigh injuries). Secondary vehicle contact can also be crucial. This is typically in the form of head impact against the bonnet (or possibly the ground, depending on the location of the initial collision). The exact site of head contact with the vehicle is very important. It has been claimed that impact against the windscreen frame is more likely to cause serious injury than contact with the bonnet. The ideal is, of course, to strike a relatively soft and 'forgiving' part of the vehicle structure. However, the management of secondary impact is made difficult by the variation in possible impact speed.

What clear design changes follow from such studies of pedestrian collisions? The argument put forward by groups like the Accident Research Unit is for a compliant front structure to the vehicle which would reduce the likelihood of non-minor leg and pelvic injuries but also 'grip' the pedestrian so as to ensure that head contact would be with the bonnet. The elimination of stiff areas around the bonnet, such as the joints with the wings and scuttle, could also have an effect in terms of injury reduction. Another argument that can be drawn from this research is for a lower bumper height. The present US bumper standard seems to have been established with a view to occupant protection and reduced repair costs rather than pedestrian safety. Bumpers should avoid striking a pedestrian at adult knee height ('the pedestrian legs are struck by the worst possible structure at the worst possible anatomical site'[10]) but this seems to illustrate the lack of attention that has been paid to the safety of pedestrians, who do not even have as much influence as car buyers over the structures with which they may collide. One other straightforward design point follows from a concern with pedestrian protection: that it would be extremely beneficial to provide 2 in of crush distance for the bumper, bonnet edge and bonnet surface. Ashton's claim that feasible vehicle redesign could reduce serious pedestrian injuries by a third is based upon just this type of measure. Ashton and Mackay have also argued that the benefits of pedestrian protection are at least as great as those for occupant-focused modifications. The point that must be made here is that pedestrian protection has so far attracted little public or political attention and that few groups – other than the researchers themselves – have attempted to make the present knowledge of accident causation available to a wider audience.

The development of pedestrian protection and its policy implications are very relevant to the previous discussion of social powerlessness. Logically, of course, it is impossible to separate the category of 'pedestrian' from other terms like 'driver' or 'vehicle occupant'. There is a sense, therefore, in which all car buyers have a vested interest in pedestrian protection as they are likely to become 'pedestrians' themselves once engaged in everyday activities such as shopping or crossing a road. However, relatively disadvantaged groups in society – the old, the poor, the very young – will not have the same access to private modes of transportation. These groups, especially the elderly and very young, are also most at risk from pedestrian accidents. Their weakness in political terms, together with a prevailing view of road casualties as a combination of 'human error' and 'Act of God', have permitted the significance of vehicle design as a contributory factor in accident causation to pass without serious debate. Pedestrian safety has remained in the shade of un-politics for reasons which must be related to the patterns of political power within road traffic safety.

Effectiveness

The discussion so far of 'social powerlessness' and its relationship to the control of technological hazards is central to one of the themes of this book, the equity of decision-making processes. This theme has been explored extensively throughout this and the previous chapters and there has been special emphasis on the 'un-politics' of regulation. The question of 'who decides and how?' has accordingly been answered not only in terms of the official bodies who are manifestly responsible for policy making, but also with regard to the 'politically enforced neglect' of certain options for reducing road traffic deaths and injuries. These options are exemplified by the lack of regulatory attention to the pedestrian protection specialty just described. However, what must also be considered at this stage is the actual *effectiveness* of those policy options that have been adopted in the two countries. Given the differences of emphasis discussed in Parts II and III, what consequences have there been for fatality and injury reduction?

Table 2 contains a collection of data relating to the years 1970–80. It should be pointed out that such statistics are inevitably subject to variation according to the classification systems and data collection methods employed. For example, how many days after an accident can someone die and still be counted as a 'road traffic victim'? As an illustration of this the figure for deaths in the USA during 1977 can be compared; the US National Safety Council have assessed this as 49 510, the International Road Federation as 48 700, and the Government Statistical Office in Britain as 45 422. The organisations in question will usually explain their choice of figure and no criticism of their operation is intended here, but a simple note of caution when making international comparisons is justified. This is all the more true when data for 'persons injured' (see Table 3) are studied, as the definition of 'injury' is even more open to variation than 'fatality'.

Bearing this cautionary note in mind, Table 2 reveals that the number of road deaths has fallen in both countries between 1970 and 1980. If the National Safety Council (NSC) figures (those in parentheses) are adopted, then there has been a fall in the United States from 54 633 fatalities to 52 600, a reduction of 3.72 per cent. Official British figures indicate a reduction in annual fatalities from 7 499 in 1970 to 6 010 in 1980, a 19.85 per cent fall. A comparison between 1975 and 1980 for the two nations indicates that deaths have actually increased over that period in the USA (by 14.7 per cent) whereas deaths in Britain have been reduced (by 5.59 per cent). However, the choice of years for comparison can be misleading because of annual fluctuations. Both Britain and the USA have achieved a fall in road deaths per 10 000 vehicles and per 100 000 population. There has also been a fall per car-kilometre travelled. Put differently, it is possible to conclude that the two nations have reduced the number of road deaths despite the increasing number of vehicles on the roads.

Table 2 Road death statistics, 1970–80

Year		Number of road deaths	Vehicles per 100 population	Road deaths per 100 000 population	Car user deaths per 100 million car kilometres (prior to 1973 – car miles)	Pedestrian Road deaths per 10 000 vehicles	deaths per 100 000 population
1970	USA	(54 633) 54 800	53	(26.8) 25	—	(4.92) 5	5
	GB	7 499	28	14	2.9	5	5.4
1971	USA	(54 381) 51 965	55	(26.4) 25	—	(4.68) 5	5
	GB	7 699	29	14	2.8	5	5.4
1972	USA	(56 278) 56 300	56	(27) 26	—	(4.60) 5	5
	GB	7 763	30	14	2.7	4.8	5.7
1973	USA	(55 511) 55 800	57	(26.5) 25	3	(4.28) 4	5
	GB	7 406	31	14	3	4	5
1974	USA	(46 402) 46 200	61	(22) 21	2	(3.44) 3	4
	GB	6 883	32	13	1	4	5
1975	USA	(45 853) 46 550	65	(21.5) 21	2	(3.33) 3	4
	GB	6 366	32	12	1	4	4
1976	USA	(47 038) 45 422	66	(21.9) 21	2	(3.28) 3	3
	GB	6 570	32	12	1	4	4
1977	USA	(49 510) 45 422	66	(22.9) 21	2	(3.33) 3	3
	GB	6 614	32	12	1	4	4
1978	USA	(52 411) 50 331	70	(24) 23	1.5	(3.41) 3.3	4.7
	GB	6 831	32	13	1.2	3.8	4.5
1979	USA	(52 800) 51 088	70	(24) 23	1.5	(3.31) 3.3	3.7
	GB	6 352	34	12	1.1	3.4	3.9
1980	USA	(52 600) 51 088	70	(23.2) 23	1.5	(3.19) 3.1	3.7
	GB	6 010	35	11	1.0	3.1	3.6

Sources: Government Statistical Office. *Road Accidents, Great Britain* (HMSO, London; 1971–81). Figures in brackets are taken from National Safety Council *Accident Facts* (NSC, Chicago; 1981).

Table 3   Statistics for persons injured, 1970–80

	USA				Great Britain		
	Injury accidents	*Rate*[a]	*Injuries*	*Rate*[a]	*Injury accidents*	*Rate*[a]	*Injuries*	*Rate*[a]
1970	1 346 800	72.1	2 000 000	110.9	267 457	130	355 869	172
1971	1 346 800	70.5	2 000 000	104.8	258 727	118	344 390	156
1972	1 815 400	90.0	2 794 600	138.0	265 105	115	351 964	153
1973	1 874 400	88.0	2 841 500	135.0	262 392	110	346 290	145
1974	1 768 800	85.0	2 653 000	128.0	244 042	102	317 726	132
1975	1 861 131	87.0	2 808 323	131.0	246 286	101	318 584	130
1976	1 926 350	83.0	2 913 066	125.0	253.000	101	331 600	130
1977	2 004 481	84.0	3 016 259	127.0	265 861	99	341 447	128
1978	2 156 000	87.0	3 166 700	127.0	264 769	95	342 964	123
1979	2 155 200	87.0	3 150 000	128.0	254 967	91	328 161	117
1980	2 053 000	82.0	3 010 000	120.0	252 300	87	322 150	111

Source: International Road Federation *World Road Statistics* (IRF, Geneva and Washington, DC; 1974–82).
[a]Rate per 100 million vehicle-kilometres.

Table 3 presents data for injury accidents and injuries for the two countries. The problems of comparison based on such evidence have been noted above but a general reduction in the number of injury accidents and injuries (and also their rates of occurrence) can be noted in Britain. An increase in the US rates and raw injury data can be detected.

International comparisons of accident data can be confused not just by matters of statistical technique and classification but also by a number of intervening variables which are not directly related to safety policy, e.g. the effects of the mid-1970s 'oil crisis' and its consequences for lower speed limits and changed driving habits. Evidence is also emerging in the United States to suggest that the move towards 'subcompact' vehicles has had an adverse effect on accident statistics.[11] It has been claimed, for example, that the occupants of small cars have a much greater likelihood of sustaining serious or fatal injuries than occupants of larger cars. The switch to smaller cars in the USA has been taking place during the period analysed in Table 2 (and, more particularly, from 1975 onwards) and this may have had the effect of increasing the number of road deaths between 1975 and 1980. Groups like the Insurance Institute for Highway Safety have argued that stricter passive restraint standards for smaller cars are needed if fatalities are not to increase substantially over the next two years.

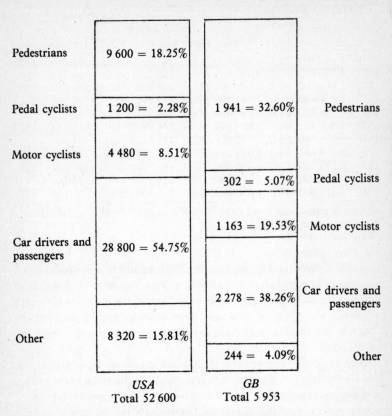

Fig. 5   Road deaths in Britain and the USA (1980). Sources: National Safety Council *Accident Facts* (NSC, Chicago; 1981), British Road Federation *Basic Road Statistics* (BRF, London; 1983).

The significance of occupant protection in small cars can be understood more clearly by reference to Fig. 5 which presents an 'accident profile' for US and British fatalities in 1980. Certain immediate differences are clear: the fact that over half of US road deaths affect car occupants whereas the British proportion is just below 40 per cent. Pedestrians account for 32 per cent of British deaths but only 18 per cent of US fatalities. Concealed within the 'other' category of Fig. 5 is the fact that in 1980 there were 210 deaths among drivers and passengers of goods vehicles; truck occupants in the United States account for 6800 deaths in the same year. Expressed as a proportion of road deaths as a whole in each country the figure for Britain is 3.52 per cent and for the USA it is 12.92 per cent. Overall, therefore, there are some considerable differences in the 'accident profile' for each nation although of course the much greater number of fatalities in the USA makes direct comparisons once again more complex than they may appear. The relative proportions within each profile have remained relatively constant over the last decade with the significant exception of motor-cycle riders. Deaths among this latter category have increased between 1970 and 1980 from 761 to 1163 in Britain (a rise of 52.8 per cent) and from 2330 to 4480 in the United States (+ 92.27 per cent). This rise reflects, of course, the growth in popularity of this mode of transport from the mid-1970s onwards.

As a final point of international comparison, Table 4 presents the mortality statistics and deaths per 100 000 population for a number of different countries in different years. This information suggests the place of Britain and the USA in the 'international road safety league table'. The comparisons made in Table 4 are intended to be merely suggestive and such broad-ranging international comparisons are certainly open to criticism of the type discussed above.

The question that must now be considered concerns the actual contribution that national safety policies have made to a reduction in road traffic casualties. More particularly, there is a special need to analyse the consequences of the radical burst of policy making in the USA during the 1960s. The problem which one immediately encounters here is that of disentangling the effect of safety standards from other variables such as changing vehicle population (especially as regards subcompact automobiles or motor cycles), changing driving behaviour (following the rise in gasoline prices) and the effects of an economic downturn (which is often linked to a fall in the number of road traffic accidents). The question of effectiveness becomes, therefore, a fiercely contested issue and the subject of the same type of technical disagreement which we have found elsewhere in this book. In 1982 the NHTSA estimated that the new policy direction had saved at least 83 000 lives since 1966 and that as new cars replace older, less safe models, about 10000 additional lives would be saved annually.[12] The basis of these figures is the general claim that a 1982 model-year car is 25 per cent safer (in protecting occupants from injury) than a model-year-1965 equivalent. The NHTSA has also conducted a number of studies into the effectiveness

Table 4   Motor-vehicle deaths by nation

Nation	Year	Deaths	Rate[a]	Nation	Year	Deaths	Rate[a]
Syrian Arab Rep.	1981	177	1.7	Puerto Rico	1979	505	14.8
Egypt	1978	854	2.1	Greece	1981	1 482	15.2
Peru	1978	889	5.0	Hungary	1980	1 731	16.2
Paraguay	1978	188	6.2	East Germany	1976	2 746	16.4
Nicaragua	1978	168	7.0	Spain	1979	6 562[b]	17.7
Uruguay	1978	207	7.2	West Germany	1981	11 255	18.2
Dominican Rep.	1978	398	7.8	Italy	1978	10 354[c]	18.3
England, Wales	1981	4,045	8.2	Ireland	1978	627	18.9
Hong Kong	1981	478	9.3	New Zealand	1980	599	19.1
Norway	1981	390	9.5	Panama	1980	351	19.1
Japan	1980	11 555	9.9	Switzerland	1980	1 210	19.2
Israel	1980	404	10.4	Costa Rica	1979	434	20.0
Sweden	1980	910	11.0	France	1978	10 910[d]	20.3
Singapore	1981	281	11.5	Canada	1978	5 170[e]	21.7
Chile	1979	1 266	11.6	Ecuador	1979	1 817	21.8
Netherlands	1981	1 738	12.2	N. Ireland	1978	345	22.4
Bulgaria	1981	1 157	13.0	Australia	1980	3 478	23.8
Denmark	1981	679	13.3	United States	1979	53 524[e]	23.8
Finland	1979	658	13.8	Austria	1981	1 834	24.4
Thailand	1981	6 567	13.8	Belgium	1976	2 463[c]	25.1
Scotland	1981	718	13.9	Portugal	1979	2 948	29.9
Argentina	1978	3 853	14.6	Kuwait	1979	477	35.6
Cuba	1977	1 484	14.7	Venezuela	1978	4 822	36.7

[a] Deaths per 100 000 population.

Source: World Health Organization.
DEATH DEFINITION: In general, deaths are included if they occur within thirty days after the accident, but other time periods are used as follows: [b] twenty-four hours, [c] at accident scene only, [d] three days, [e] one year.
Taken from: National Safety Council, *Accident Facts 1983*, p. 49.

of existing standards[13] and these have generally identified large improvements in safety as an outcome of federal regulation.

Claims of this sort from the agency have been supported by the work of Leon Robertson of Yale University, who has argued that some 37 000 lives were saved between 1975 and 1978 by federal safety standards.[14] Robertson's claim is based on a statistical analysis of 263 025 vehicles over the four-year period. Following this analysis he was able to identify a substantial reduction in car occupant deaths per 100 million vehicle-miles travelled and some reduction in the rates of vehicle collision with pedestrians, motor cyclists and pedal cyclists. Robertson's work can also be seen as a response to the work of economists such as Peltzman who have claimed that the effects of regulation on occupant fatalities are offset by increased non-occupant deaths.[15] In a critical analysis[16] of Peltzman's key paper on this subject, Robertson has argued strongly that once certain justifiable modifications are made to Peltzman's data – such as separating deaths related to 'non-regulated' vehicles from those involving vehicles subject to the new set of FMVSSs – the evidence points firmly to the conclusion that automobile safety regulation has substantially reduced occupant deaths.

The technical and political arguments over road traffic statistics cannot be separated from a related debate over the cost and cost-effectiveness of safety standards in the USA. Certainly, the motor manufacturers have continued to assert that the NHTSA has imposed a massive financial burden on the consumer with consequences both in terms of price inflation and the financial stability of the US motor industry. General Motors have estimated that the cost of government regulation in 1974 was $1.3 thousand million.[17] Chrysler have calculated that the total burden of regulation would add $1000 to the price of each automobile by 1985.[18] In opposition to these claims, the agency's own assessment of the overall cost of safety features on 1978 models was $300 – substantially less than the figure quoted by many motor manufacturers. In 1982, the NHTSA estimated that federal safety regulations add an average of $370 to the price of a new car.[19] However, the NHTSA asserts that these costs – and also that of a slight loss in fuel economy owing to the weight of improved bumpers, brakes and side doors – are offset by reduced insurance premiums and a saving in medical, funeral and post-accident rehabilitation expenses.

In Britain, arguments over the effectiveness of legislation have been less heated than in the USA. This much is, of course, entirely predictable from the discussion in Parts II and III. It might be added that the general downturn in British accident statistics over the last decade has also encouraged a lack of controversy. A relatively steady fall can be discerned in British road deaths and there is also a prevalent mood of optimism that compulsory seat-belt wear will reduce occupant casualties further. It needs to be said, however, that road accidents are still a major cause of death and serious injury; in the years 1970–80 some 75 993 people were killed on the roads in Britain (the equivalent figure for the USA is 567 417 deaths). The scale of hazard is made even clearer if one remembers that road traffic accidents kill people at an earlier age than other causes such as cancer or heart disease. It is for this reason that 'as a perpetrator of premature death the motor vehicle has no equal'.[20]

Reaching conclusions about the effectiveness of British and US policies depends upon a whole series of inevitably contentious arguments and assumptions. The experience of federal safety standards suggests that they have made a significant contribution to the saving of human life. At the same time there are many groups in the USA who would argue that this contribution could be made even greater by increased regulatory activity, with FMVSS 208 being a particularly crucial case in point. Criticism of Britain for not implementing such standards must be tempered in at least two ways: first, in that compulsory seat-belt legislation provides an alternative method of increasing occupant restraint but without the need for a relatively complex 'technical fix'; secondly, in that European nations have often adopted US standards as a means of avoiding barriers to trade. Despite this, it remains true that occupant protection standards offer considerable potential for fatality reduction and, as such, deserve to be the attention of far greater political debate in Britain.

The case for regulation may be even stronger in the area of pedestrian, as opposed to occupant, protection. As Fig. 5 reveals, pedestrians are second only to car occupants as victims in both countries and the proportion of deaths in this category is particularly large in Britain. One could add that this group has not chosen to travel by motor vehicle and yet must suffer the consequences of the driving behaviour and mode of transport adopted by others. The effectiveness of engineering measures for reducing pedestrian casualties surely deserves to be a major area of discussion within both countries in future.

Finally, the more fundamental criticisms of transport systems need to be considered, the argument being that the present scale of trauma can only be substantially reduced by a structural move towards alternative transport technologies such as railways and buses and certainly away from the present emphasis on the private car. It is beyond the scope of this book to assess the practicality and economic feasibility of such a move, but accident statistics do imply that there are important safety arguments which need to be taken seriously into account when considering the provision of public transport in any local or national context. What these arguments highlight once again is the fact that apparently narrow issues of technological risk cannot be separated from wider matters of social policy and of the type of society that is to be built for the future.

Notes and references

1   Mackay, G. M. Reducing car crash injuries: folklore, science and promise. *The First Foley Memorial Lecture, 29 September 1982*, p.13. Available from Pedestrians' Association, 1 Wandsworth Road, London SW8 1LJ.
2   National Safety Council. *Accident Facts. 1981* (NSC, Chicago; 1981), p.71.
3   Habermas, J. *Towards a Rational Society* (Heinemann, London; 1971).
4   See Wynne, B. *Rationality and Ritual: the Windscale Inquiry and Nuclear Decisions in Britain*. British Society for the History of Science, Chalfont St. Giles 1982.
5   Since 1966 federal controls have also been established over fuel economy, emissions and damage resistance.
6   Smith, T. Death on the road. *New Scientist* 22 October 1981, pp. 260–1. See also Adams, J. *Transport Planning; Vision and Practice*. (Routledge & Kegan Paul, London; 1981).
7   Ashton, S. J. A preliminary assessment of the potential for pedestrian injury reduction through vehicle design. *Proc. 24th Stapp Car Crash Conference* (Society of Automotive Engineers, Warrendale, PA; 1980). Ashton, S. J. and Mackay, G. M. Benefits from changes in vehicle exterior design – field accident and experimental work in Europe, in *Pedestrian Impact Injury and Assessment, P-121* (Society of Automotive Engineers, Warrendale, PA; February 1983), pp.255–63.
8   Ashton, S. J. and Mackay, G. M. Benefits from changes in vehicle exterior design – field accident and experimental work in Europe. (See reference 7.)
9   See Ashton, S. A bibliography of pedestrian accident references with emphasis on vehicle design and pedestrian injuries, in *Pedestrian Impact Injury and Assessment, P-121*, pp.265–75. (See reference 7.) Taylor, H.

Pedestrian safety: the role of research. *TRRL Supplementary Report 319*, 1977.

10 Mackay, G. M. Reducing car crash injuries: folklore, science and promise. *The First Foley Memorial Lecture*, p.5. (See reference 1.)

11 *Status Report*, Vol. 17, No. 20, 30 December 1982.

12 NHTSA, *Cost of Automobile Safety Regulations: Preliminary Report*, 1982. See also: *Status Report*. Vol. 17, No. 6, 27 April 1982.

13 Four cost–benefit analyses of existing FMVSSs have been conducted. These relate to FMVSS 214 (Side door strength), FMVSS 202 (Head restraints), FMVSS 203 and 204 (Steering columns).

14 Robertson, L. S. Automobile safety regulations and death reductions in the United States. *Am J. Public Health*, **71** (8) August 1981, pp. 818–22.

15 Peltzman, S. The effects of automobile safety regulation. *J. Political Economy*, **83**, August 1975, pp. 677–725.

16 Robertson, L. S. A critical analysis of Peltzman's 'The effects of automobile safety regulation'. *J. Economic Issues*, XI (3), September 1977, pp. 587–600.

17 Thayer, H. E. Business in an era of legislation and regulation. *Chemistry and Industry*, 19 March 1977, p. 226.

18 *The Economist*, 12 August 1978, p.60.

19 NHTSA, *Cost of Automobile Safety Regulations: Preliminary Report*, 1982.

20 Smith, T. Death on the road. *New Scientist*, 22 October 1981, p.260. In Britain, road accidents account for approximately 47 per cent of deaths in the 15- to 19-year-old age group.

Chapter 11

Risk and public policy

Throughout this book two related themes have underpinned the analysis of policies for road traffic safety. The first of these concerns the notion of technological risk and the role it can play in interpreting present public policies and, all-importantly, in planning future regulatory strategies. The second theme was initially raised in Chapter 1: 'How can technological hazards be controlled in a manner which is both effective and equitable?' This final chapter will consider these two issues with a view to establishing the significance of 'risk assessment' as an area of political and technical analysis.

One of the principal objectives of the previous chapters has been to present a framework within which the specific case of road traffic safety policies can be located. This framework was discussed at length in Chapters 2 and 10 but basically it consists of four analytical components: technical expertise, the role of the state, pressure group organisations, and the social assessment of risk. What is important about this framework is that it appears equally applicable to a variety of other examples within the control of risk-related technologies and to a range of national and local settings. Furthermore, the interconnections between these components imply a series of questions and topics for investigation which are fundamental not only to an analysis of road traffic safety policies but also to other cases involving a risk component, such as the control of carcinogenic chemicals or the civil development of nuclear power. The framework outlined here – together with the theoretical approaches on which it draws – suggests, therefore, a linkage between different forms of technological risk. This linkage is partly inherent in the risks themselves, through the common elements of 'probability' and 'consequences', but also, and perhaps more crucially, in their *social treatment*. It is the social treatment of technological hazards which has formed the basis for discussion in the previous chapters.

The type of question raised by the specific approach to technological risk adopted here has a clear relevance to the development of public policies. What political role has been assumed by technical experts in any individual case? Related to this there is the possible existence of separate branches of expertise, each of which may point to rather different policy conclusions and serve specific social interests. The relationship of the state to pressure groups can be crucial for the control of technological risk. Have manufacturing organisations 'captured' the state regulatory mechanisms or is there a greater pluralism in the distribution of political power? Technical expertise can, of course, play a part in these relationships through the scientisation of debate. The changing social assessment of risk can also be important in influencing state activities. Furthermore, such assessments are dependent upon the knowledge of a hazard which is available to the general public and upon the degree of 'social powerlessness' which is felt in any situation. Very often the task of social assessment becomes tacitly delegated to self-styled public interest groups; how in specific cases do these relate to public anxieties and what access do they have to technical expertise or key regulatory authorities?

Although topics such as these flow easily from the basic analytical framework, the specific questions raised call for the study of individual cases in the control of technological risk and not for glib assertions or easy generalisations. This tension between the interconnectedness of many issues and the need to examine individual cases separately is inherent to the analysis of technological risk. Although imbalances in this tension are inevitable – and may well be visible in this book – the alternatives are either to lose sight of the overall challenge posed by technological hazards within modern societies or to retreat into a sterile debate over 'acceptable risks' which disregards the individual characteristics of the hazard and its social control. The challenge for both academic investigations and public policies in this area is to appreciate the general framework within which specific examples can be located but to deal also with the everyday realities according to which matters of risk are perceived and acted upon.

Any discussion of public policies for the control of technological risks inevitably raises the question of how we are to evaluate those policies. In Chapter 1 it was suggested that there are at least two criteria according to which these are to be judged:

(1) *Effectiveness*: defined in terms of achieving an 'optimal balance' between costs and benefits so as to protect the maximum number of lives at the minimum cost.
(2) *Equity*: in terms of stimulating rather than stifling public debate in order to ensure that the potential victims of any decision have a powerful voice in its resolution.

However, there is also a third criterion which may be applied by concerned parties to state decision-making procedures:

(3) *Legitimation*: the success of any political process in presenting the appearance rather than the substance of democratic accountability.

We need to be aware of the existence of the third criterion and mindful of its consequences for criteria 1 and 2. Equally important is that the second criterion should not be overlooked in the customary focus on the first. The approach to technological risk adopted here has given emphasis to both equity and effectiveness but it is important to grasp that these concepts only take on their true significance when the wider social and technological context is taken into account. A narrow focus on specific decisions – should the NHTSA adopt a passive restraint ruling?, is a ban on the pesticide 2,4,5–T justified in Britain?, are pressurised water reactors a 'safe' energy source? – ignores the broader technological and social alternatives which are available. Within these alternatives concerning national transportation systems, methods of agriculture or energy systems, risk is only one factor for consideration. What an analysis of technological risk will often necessitate is a disinterring of the choices so that discussion is not limited to an artificially narrow (and frequently 'scientised') focus but instead opened up to broader scrutiny. The major example here concerns the assumptions about the future role of the motor car which underlie debates over road traffic safety. An examination of these debates simply within the terms of reference provided by the major participants is to overlook the point that what is *not* under discussion can often be even more significant than what actually *is*: hence the importance of the concept of 'un-politics'.

Perhaps paradoxically the best role for future studies of technological risk is not just to consider the particular debates over a hazard and its consequences but rather to take a larger view of the technological and social systems within which a specific risk has emerged. Certainly, no conclusions can ever be reached about 'acceptable' levels of risk until the technological choices have been considered and the crucial effects of political power in structuring debate have been fully taken into account. It is for this reason that the present study has attempted to unravel the policy processes in Britain and the United States over a single issue. Such an approach is not without its difficulties – as can be judged here – but it does represent a move forward from an approach to risk acceptability which deems a risk 'acceptable' simply because it has been 'accepted' in the past. What is also clear is that the study of technological risks leads into an examination of the division of power in a society and, in particular, into a questioning of its regulatory procedures and institutions. It may well be that present public concerns over technological hazards are not so much a matter of the risks themselves but rather of the social acceptability of decision-making bodies and their operating principles. Demands for increased participation by 'public interest' groups come to be seen in this light as a challenge to the legitimacy of present institutions. The long-term consequences of ignoring these demands would be a 'legitimation crisis' which would emcompass far more than risk alone. This suggests yet another reason for both the effectiveness *and* equity of present regulatory procedures being seriously debated.

In conclusion, what final comments can be offered concerning the twin themes of this book? It has been argued here that the concept of technological risk can play a useful role in the development and interpretation of public policies. However, this role will only be successfully performed if it is recognised that issues of risk need to be seen in their full social context. Quite simply, hazards are inseparable from the circumstances in which they occur, the technological alternatives which are available and the political and economic processes which have led to their occurrence. A shortsighted focus on 'risk management' is misleading and will ultimately prove worthless for policy making. Equally, studies of risk that ignore the specifics of context so as to reach sweeping generalisations about risk acceptability will produce empty abstractions and fail to grasp that the assessment of risk involves far more than an understanding of probabilities and consequences.

The second theme – of effectiveness and equity – can be considered in terms very similar to those in the previous paragraph. Effectiveness and equity depend upon full knowledge of the available social and technological alternatives, hence the value of risk studies in 'disinterring the choices'. Equally, it is important that the social and political dimensions of regulatory decisions do not become concealed under the cover of 'scientisation' which has so frequently presented itself in this book. Here again, studies of technological risk have an important part to play. Decisions about risk are essentially decisions about social priorities and the values by which our societies wish to be guided. To exclude the bulk of the population from these fundamental choices would be to ensure *neither* the equity *nor* the effectiveness of regulatory policies.

Index